COMPLIANT STRUCTURES
IN
NATURE AND ENGINEERING

WIT*PRESS*

WIT Press publishes leading books in Science and Technology.
Visit our website for the current list of titles.
www.witpress.com

WITeLibrary

Home of the Transactions of the Wessex Institute, the WIT electronic-library provides the international
scientific community with immediate and permanent access to individual papers presented at WIT
conferences. Visit the WIT eLibrary at www.witpress.com.

Design and Nature

Objectives

Our understanding of the modern world is largely based on an ever increasing volume of scientific knowledge. Engineering designers have at their disposal a vast array of relationships for materials, mechanisms and control, and these laws have been painstakingly assembled by observation of nature. As space activity accustoms us to cosmic scales, and as medicine and biology to the molecular scale of genetics, we have also become more aware of the rich diversity of the structural world around us.

The parallels between human design and nature has inspired many geniuses through history, in engineering, mathematics and other subjects. Much more recently there has been significant research related to design and invention. Even so, current developments in design engineering, and the huge increase in biological knowledge, together with the virtual revolution in computer power and numerical modelling, have all made possible more comprehensive studies of nature. It is these developments which have led to the establishment of this international book series.

Its rationale rests upon the universality of scientific laws in both nature and human design, and on their common material basis. Our organic and inorganic worlds have common energy requirements, which are of great theoretical significance in interpreting our environment.

Individual books in the series cover topics in depth such as mathematics in nature, evolution, natural selection, vision and acoustic systems, robotics, shape in nature, biomimetics, creativity and others. While being rigorous in their approach, the books are structured to appeal to specialist and non-specialist alike.

Series Editor

M.W. Collins
School of Engineering Systems and Design
South Bank University
London, SE1 0AA
UK

J.A. Bryant
Dept. of Biological Sciences
University of Exeter
Exeter, EX4 4QG
UK

M.A. Atherton
School of Engineering and Design
South Bank University
London, SE1 0AA
UK

COMPLIANT STRUCTURES
IN
NATURE AND ENGINEERING

Edited by

C.H.M. Jenkins
South Dakota School of Mines and Technology, USA

WITPRESS Southampton, Boston

Compliant Structures in Nature and Engineering

Edited by

C.H.M. Jenkins
South Dakota School of Mines and Technology, USA

Published by

WIT Press
Ashurst Lodge, Ashurst, Southampton, SO40 7AA, UK
Tel: 44 (0) 238 029 3223; Fax: 44 (0) 238 029 2853
E-Mail: witpress@witpress.com
http://www.witpress.com

For USA, Canada and Mexico

WIT Press
25 Bridge Street, Billerica, MA 01821, USA
Tel: 978 667 5841; Fax: 978 667 7582
E-Mail: infousa@witpress.com
http://www.witpress.com

British Library Cataloguing-in-Publication Data

A Catalogue record for this book is available
from the British Library

ISBN: 1-85312-941-0
ISSN: 1478-0585

Library of Congress Catalog Card Number: 2004101300

Contents

SECTION V – COMPLIANT STRUCTURE DESIGN

Preface

Nature is the grand designer. Human engineers have taken great motivation from nature since the earliest of times. Natural shelter of the forest canopy or mountain cave likely led early humans to begin replicating their own versions. Early water containers may well have been designed after the flower holding morning dew or the internal bladder of animals.

Biological systems are driven to reduce energy cost both in fabrication and maintenance. The spider must make up the energy and time lost in web building as quickly as possible through prey capture. Additionally, the web must continue to perform even in the presence of significant degradation, else building begins all over again. Over eons, nature has converged on *structural compliance* or flexibility as a key component of energy efficiency. Often, the compliant solution is a less costly alternative to the stiff solution; for example, stiffness requires additional mass in most cases. Moreover, enabling increased intelligence goes hand-in-hand with increased compliance – intelligence would be of little use to a rock!

This present work celebrates structural compliance in nature and human technology. Examples of compliant structures in nature abound, from the walls of the smallest cell, to the wings of the condor, to the tail of the gray whale. The subject of compliant structures in nature and engineering is timely and important, albeit quite broad and challenging. This volume seeks to provide, in one place, a concise summary of the important features of these interesting structures. Wherever possible, we show a mapping between naturally compliant structures, and the promise and opportunity commensurate in human engineering.

We begin with two chapters that describe in detail the wonders of natural compliance. Professor Vincent introduces us first to fundamentals of compliance in animals, while Professor Ennos provides a similar discussion of compliance in plants. Then follows two chapters that provide insight into engineered compliant materials. Professor Khanna and colleague describe polymeric foams and Dr. Bar-Cohen discusses electro-active polymers, both of which have direct analogs in naturally compliant systems.

We then turn our attention to the "language" that is found so useful in describing the mechanics of highly compliant structural systems, namely nonlinear continue mechanics. Drs. Jenkins, Schur, and Greschik attempt to make this difficult subject as tractable and concise as possible for the interested reader.

The later portion of the book attempts to give the reader an introduction to human engineered applications of compliant structures. Dr. Schur considers pressurized membranes, and provides numerous linkages between natural and engineered inflatables. Rope and rope-like structures in nature and engineering are presented by Drs. Evans and Ridge. Compliance in habitats, both natural and engineered, is discussed by Drs. Kimpian and Jenkins, while Professor Ifju describes compliant aerospace vehicles. A final application chapter by Chmielewski and Jenkins provides a glimpse into the future of compliant space structures. Lastly, we leave the reader with a chapter that provides some guidance for the design and engineering of compliant structures.

The editor wishes to first thank the distinguished group of authors for their outstanding contributions to this volume, without which it would not exist. Gratitude is also expressed to the WIT Press staff for their patience and assistance in assembling this work. Credit must also be given to the editor's students and colleagues, who contributed in numerous ways to this project. Lastly, the editor expresses deepest gratitude to his family for their continued support of his work.

May we find continued inspiration from the grand designer.

C. H. M. Jenkins
2005

Design in nature – introduction to the series

Michael W. Collins
London South Bank University, UK.

Prologue

> *almost a miracle* [Cecil Lewis, 1, p. 126]
>
> *almost miraculously* [Stuart Kauffman, 2, p. 25]

'It was a beautiful evening' wrote Cecil Lewis [1] of the day in 1917 when he took a new SE5 on a test flight. 'At ten thousand feet the view immense, England quartered on its northern perimeter at twenty two thousand feet, Kent was below me …… for a second the amazing adventure of flight overwhelmed me. Nothing between me and oblivion but a pair of light linen-covered wings and the roar of a 200-hp engine! …… It was a triumph of human intelligence and skill – almost a miracle' (SEE Plate 1).

Cecil Lewis was only 19 years old at the time, having left the English public school Oundle, in order to join the Royal Flying Corps in the First World War.

Almost 40 years later, in happier times than those of Cecil Lewis, as another ex-schoolboy I was 'filling in time' with a Student Apprenticeship before going to University. My very first job was as 'D.O. Librarian' in an aeronautical engineering drawing office. The circumstances may have been prosaic, but one feature always intrigued me. At the apex of the very large pyramid, at the top of every document distribution list, was the Chief Designer. Of course, I never met him or even saw him, but to me his title expressed the fount of authority, intelligence and creativity, the *producer* of 'almost miracles' for the 1950's.

'Almost miracles' mean different things to different people. Another 40 years brings us to a new millennium, to Stuart Kauffman [2] writing in 2000. Kauffman, a highly regarded American biologist 'is a founding member of the Santa Fe Institute, the leading centre for the emerging sciences of complexity' [2, cover blurb]. In discussing DNA symmetry and replication, he says [2, page 25]: "It seems to most biologists that this beautiful double helix aperiodic structure is almost miraculously pre-fitted by chemistry and God for the task of being the master molecule of life. If so, then the origin of life must be based on some form of a double-stranded aperiodic solid" (see Plate II). Yes, Kauffman is in the heady business of studying life starting 'from non-life here, or on Mars'.

We have reflected Cecil Lewis's and Kauffman's near miracles in Plates I and II. In the case of Cecil Lewis he was till in the first flush of man's ability to fly. Not for him the necessity of filing a flight plan. Like the *natural* fliers, the birds, he could move at will in three-dimensional space.

However, even then, he could far out-fly them, whether in speed or in height. Stuart Kauffman, however, moves about in multi-dimensional space. *His* is a 'fitness landscape in … thirteen-dimensional parameter space' [2, p. 70].

We do need, at the same time, our sense of wonder to be well informed. Of course, Cecil Lewis's near miracle has been totally replaced, by Concorde, by travel to the moon, and now by planetary exploration. In the same way, while the thirteen-dimensional space of Kauffman may well impress many of his readers, and the eleven-dimensional space of Stephen Hawking [3] was obviously expected to impress the average UK Daily Telegraph readers, in engineering terms this is a standard practice. Two of the Series Editors {MAA and MWC] started to consider [4] the problem of *visualisation* of complex data. This included reference to the optimisation of nuclear power station design [the UK Magnox system], which used a contour-tracking procedure focusing on 30 major parameters out of about 100 parameters in total [Russ Lewis, 5].

We conclude this prologue with the realisation that nature, nature's laws and the use of nature's laws in human design all have the capacity to enlighten, inform and inspire us. This series will have achieved its end if it demonstrates only a small part of that capacity.

Plate I: 'It was a triumph of human intelligence and skill - almost a miracle'. 'View from an aeroplane' [1, p182-183] (Reproduced by permission of the Victoria and Albert Museum Picture Library).

(a)

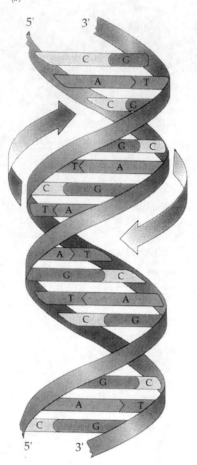

Plate II: 'This beautiful double helix.....structure is almost miraculously pre-fitted....'

DNA is a double helix

Plate II: Watson and Crick proposed that DNA is a double-helical molecule. The helical bands represent the two sugar-phosphate chains, with pairs of bases forming horizontal connections between the chains. The two chains run in opposite directions; biochemists can now pinpoint the position of every atom in a DNA macromolecule.

(Reproduced by permission from *Life. Volume 1 the Cell and Heredity*. 4th Edition by W.K. Purves, G.H. Orians and H.C. Heller, p246, Sinauer Associates, W.H. Freeman & Co.)

Research Field of John Bryant, Series Co-Editor

John Bryant's research is mainly concerned with the initiation of DNA replication - the very start of the process of copying the genome. It is far more complicated than we envisaged even ten years ago.....indeed it has a beautiful and almost awe-inspiring complexity. Each stage is tightly regulated so as to ensure that the cell only duplicates its genome at appropriate times. As we understand more about these control mechanisms we can only wonder at, and about, the evolutionary processes through which they developed.

Nature and engineering

The beavers have practised civil engineering since they became a species
[Eric Laithwaite, 6, p. 231]

Intellectually, the engineer and the artist are not far apart [Michael French, 7, p. 179]

The subject area of our series has great public interest and popularity, if we take the increasing number of publications as evidence. But this needs clarifying. Like Eric Laithwaite having to make a choice at Grammar School [6, p. xi] we might be forgiven for supposing that *our* subject is either biology or physics. On thinking more carefully, we could define our subject as the commonality of the laws of physics, in the natural [biological] and man-made [engineered] worlds. This is nearer the truth.

In the event, Eric Laithwaite chose physics. He went on to become a noted engineer and inventor, being awarded, in 1966, the Royal Society S.G. Brown Medal for Invention. So, for *him*, the beavers were engineers, not scientists.

In the same way, Michael French compares biologists, not with physicists, but with engineers and architects [7, pp. 1–2]. His book, like Laithwaites', is engineering-oriented – 'about design for function, and invention' [7, p. xvii].

So, despite so many of the recent publications being by biologists and physicists, we have chosen two engineers to start our Introduction. In fact, their approach represents a relatively new exploitation of the laws of physics, and materials science, as used in the biological design of living organisms. This points us in the direction of 'biomimetics' which is a recent concept involving the application of biological materials in engineered systems [p. xvii, Vol. 4 of this Series].

Laithwaite and French raise other issues. The first is noticeable by its absence. Those readers whose discipline is chemistry or chemical engineering might wonder if the subject has been 'air-brushed out'. Of course not – if no chemistry, then there is no DNS, no design in nature. We have already quoted Kauffman in this regard.

The next, lightly touched on by French [7, p. 235], as also by Kauffman [2, p. 24], is the question of what is meant by 'beauty'. While French strictly connects it to function in design, we will connect it to art in general, and find it is an integral part of our overall study. As French implies, the engineer and the artist are good friends.

The final issue is the question of mathematics. Whereas French [7, p. 291] rather pejoratively quotes from Bondi that 'mathematicians are not particularly good at thinking … good rather at avoiding thought', Laithwaite is obviously fascinated by the whole thing. For instance, he, like me, is highly intrigued [who isn't] by the identity.

$$e^{i\pi} = -1$$

In the same vein, he deals in some detail with the topics of 'ideal shape' in the form of the golden section [6, pp. 199–202] of Fibonacci numbers, and of helices in plants. He points out that the logarithmic spiral [6, pp. 201–202] retains its shape with growth, coinciding with French's reference to gnomonic shell growth [7, p. 273].

So then, two engineers have introduced our discussion. We now have to explain what *we* mean by the word '*design*'.

Design in the mainstream

The buttercups and the locomotive show evidence of design
[Michael French, 7, p. 1]

I am, in fact, not so much concerned with origins or reasons as with relations or resemblances

[Theodore Cook, 8, p. 4]

We can best describe our use of the word 'design' by the acronym *wysiwyg* – what you see is what you get. Our ambition is to explore fully the richness of the 'design of the buttercup' and the comparison of the designs of nature and engineering, all in the same spirit of Michael French. We shall avoid all issues like 'despite there being 'evidence of design' we do not believe ...' on the one hand, or 'because there is evidence of design, we therefore believe ...' on the other. The point has been put more elegantly by Theodore Cook, as long ago as 1914 [8, above].

So, we do not, as does Richard Dawkins, use the expression *designoid*, in 'Climbing Mount Improbable' [9, p. 4], he addresses this very point. 'Designoidal objects look designed, so much so that some people – probably, alas, most people – think that they are designed'. So he uses designoid because of his antipathy to theism – 'no sane creator ... would have conceived on his drawing board' he says on p. 121 [9]. In our use of the word design, however, we retain Richard Dawkins' friendship, with his pitcher plant giving 'every appearance of being excellently well designed' [9, p. 9], and his approbation of engineers – 'often the people best qualified to analyse how animal and plant bodies work' [9, p. 16].

However, in using the word design, neither do we mean *conscious design, intelligent design, [intelligent] design or [   ] design* ... merely design.

Typical use of these explanations is given as follows, with the understanding that 'conscious design' is rather an archaic description:

i.	Conscious design	[Cook, 8, p. 4]	[Ruse, 10, p. 44]
ii.	Intelligent design	[Miller, 11, p. 93]	
iii.	Intelligent – design	[Ruse, 10, p. 120]	
iv.	design	[Miller, 11, pp. 92, 126]	[Ruse, 10, p. 121]

[Behe, 12, p. 209]   [Dembski, 13, Title]

The last-mentioned author, William Dembski has, sadly, suffered for his beliefs, as explained in 'The Lynching of Bill Dembski' [14]. Nevertheless, in fairness, Dembski separates out the ideas of 'design' and 'designer', as this extended quote makes clear:

'Thus, in practice, to infer design is typically to end up with a 'designer' in the classical sense. *Nevertheless, it is useful to separate* [MWC's italics] design from the theories of intelligence and intelligent agency' [13, p. 36].

While the use of the word 'design' here may not be coincidental with that of Dembski, yet the act of separation is crucial, and consistent with the rationale for this Series. By using *wysiwyg* we are trying to retain the friendship of both Dawkins and Dembski and, further, to retain and parallel their common enthusiasm and commitment. In the Series, then, we seek to stay in the mainstream of all aspects of design in the natural world and man-made worlds, stressing commonality rather than controversy and reconciliation of differences rather than their sharpening. In that spirit, where necessary, current controversies will be openly discussed and separate issues carefully identified.

Even this brief discussion has shown that the concept of 'design' is both subtle and wide-ranging in its connotations. We now address three specific aspects which are sometimes ignored or even avoided, namely, *mathematics*, *thermodynamics* and *history*.

Mathematics

We like to think mathematics was discovered, not invented
Prof. Tim Pedley, verbal, Salford, 1998

The universe appears to have been designed by a pure mathematician
[James Jeans, 15, p. 137]
quoted in   [Paul Davies, 16, p. 202]

Now while the commonality of scientific laws in the natural world is generally accepted, the fact that the world is also mathematically *oriented* is less well understood. Of course, the concept of mathematics being somehow 'built in' to nature's structure is highly significant in terms of our rationale – nature's designs being parallel to man-made designs. Paul Davies expressed this concept in various telling phrases. In 'The Mind of God' we read '… all known fundamental laws are found to be mathematical in form' [16, p. 84]. 'To the scientist, mathematics … is also, astonishingly, the language of nature itself' [p. 16, 93], and as the heading for Figure 10 [p. 109] 'The laws of physics and computable mathematics may form a unique closed cycle of existence'.

In fairness, it should be added, as does Davies, that this approach is not universally accepted, and mathematicians have 'two broadly opposed schools of thought' [16, p. 141]. In the chapter on mathematics in nature' in *this* Volume the issue is dealt with more fully. However, the point we make here is that the overall detailed study of mathematics is essential for our rationale, which cannot be done in more general single-authored books. Paul Davies himself [16, p. 16] starts the reader with 'no previous knowledge of mathematics of physics is necessary'. Philip Ball, in his beautiful exposition of pattern formation in nature, likewise, restricts the mathematical treatment – 'I will not need to use in this book' (he says [17, p. 14]) 'any more mathematics than can be expressed in words rather than in abstruse equations'. Despite this restriction, however, Ball eulogizes mathematics – 'the natural language of pattern and form is mathematics … mathematics has its own very profound beauty … mathematics is perfectly able to produce and describe structures of immense complexity and subtlety ' [17, pp. 10–11].

The conclusion is straightforward – mathematics is an essential part of the design 'spectrum'.

Thermodynamics

The second law, like the first, is an expression of the observed behaviour of finite systems
[Gordon Rogers and Yon Mayhew, 18, p. 809]

Thus the second law is a statistical law in statistical mechanics
[Stuart Kauffman, 2, p. 86]

In seeking to understand thermodynamics there is not so much an obstacle to be surmounted, as ditches to be avoided. This is because thermodynamics uses concepts in common English use like 'energy', 'work', 'heat' and 'temperature', and because the First Law is an expression of the well-accepted 'conservation of energy' principle. However, these concepts are very closely defined in thermodynamics, and it is essential to understand their definitions. When we reach the Second Law, the problem is all too clear. What does entropy *really* mean? Why do different statements of the Law look completely different? So an 'amateur' understanding of thermodynamics can lead to an absence of appreciation of the Zeroth Law [to do with equilibrium and temperature] an erroneous confidence in First Law issues, and greater or lesser confusion regarding the Second Law! These are ditches indeed.

The other key aspect of thermodynamics is that it is part of the warp and weft of our industrial society. It was through the French engineer Carnot's brilliant perceptions, leading to the Second Law, the procedures for optimising work-producing heat engine design became clear. The same Law, with its stated necessity for heat rejection and reversibility, was the explanation of what otherwise looked like rather low heat engine efficiencies. In fact, essentially, as a consequence of the Second Law, best practice power station efficiencies were of the order 30% over a long period of time. As a major consequence of the enormous consumption of fossil fuels [coal and oil for example] in those power stations, and including internal combustion engines, carbon dioxide concentration in the atmosphere has increased dramatically. Over the two centuries 1800–2000 the increase has been some 28%, with approximately half that figure occurring since 1960. This is shown by Fig. 3.3 of John Houghton [19, p. 31]. Such is a major part of the background to the Greenhouse effect.

Carnot perceived that a crucial factor in achieving higher efficiencies was for the heating source to be at the *highest possible temperature*, which led in its turn to the definition of the Absolute Temperature Scale by the British engineer, Lord Kelvin.

It was then the German physicist Clausius who defined entropy – 'a new physical quantity as fundamental and universal as energy' [Kondepudi and Prigogine, 20, p. 78]. It was not just the heat that was important, but the *heat modified by the absolute temperature*, the entropy, that was needed. As a consequence, quantitatively low values of entropy are 'good', and perhaps this has lead to conceptual difficulties. Similarly, entropy increases are caused by the individual processes in the heat engine operation [irreversibilities]. Finally, the Austrian physicist Boltzmann developed a theory of molecular statistics and entropy, leading to the association of entropy with *disorder* [20, p. xii]. Altogether then non-scientific [and even scientific and engineering] readers might be forgiven for viewing entropy as a sort of 'spanner in the thermodynamic works' – to be kept as low as possible.

Now it is not fully appreciated that the Laws of Thermodynamics are *empirical* – so [write Rogers and Mayhew] 'the Second Law, like the First, is an expression of … observed behaviour'. That empirical prevalence extends to the statistical mechanics interpretation – 'the macro state is a collection of microstates … the Second Law can be reformulated in its famous statistical mechanics incarnation' [Kauffman, 2, p. 86]. Post World War II, Shannon's information theory, has caused entropy to be associated formally with information. 'The conclusion we are led to' [Paul Davies, 21, p. 39] 'is that the universe came stocked with information, or negative entropy, from the word go'. Incidentally, our 'forgiven' readers might feel well justified by the expression negative entropy!

So much for the classical past of thermodynamics. Davies's quote points us to a new look at the subject. *What we are now seeing is an almost overwhelming desire to systematise the application of thermodynamics to biology.*

… vast amounts of entropy can be gained through the gravitational contraction of diffuse gas into stars … we are still living of this store of low entropy [Roger Penrose, 22, p. 417].

… far from equilibrium states can lose their stability and evolve to one of the many states available to the system … we see a probabilistic Nature that generates new organised structure, a Nature that can create life itself [Dilip Kondepudi and Ilya Prigogine, 20, p. 409].

The sequence of the application of thermodynamics to biology can be traced back to Erwin Schrödinger's lectures given at Trinity College, Dublin, Ireland, at the height of the Second World

War, currently published as 'What is Life?' [23a, 23b]. In the chapter 'Order, Disorder and Entropy' Schrödinger postulates the following sequence: that living matter avoids the decay to equilibrium [or maximum entropy] by feeding on negative entropy from the environment, that is by 'continually sucking orderliness from its environment', and that the plants which form the ultimate source of this orderliness, themselves 'have the most powerful supply of negative entropy in the sunlight' [23a, pp. 67–75].

To take things further, we turn from the more readily available Reference 23a, to 23b, where Roger Penrose's original Foreword has evolved into a substantial Introduction. This latter Introduction is an important source in itself as it takes up Schrodinger's postulation of the sun's negentropic effect. Using Penrose's own words, [23b, p. xx]: the Sun is not just an energy source, but … a very hot spot in an otherwise dark sky … the energy comes to us in a low-entropy form … and we return it all in a high entropy form to the cold background sky. Where does this entropy imbalance come from? … the Sun has condensed from a previous uniform distribution of materials by gravitational contraction. We trace this uniformity … to the Big Bang … the extraordinary uniformity of the Big Bang … is ultimately responsible for the entropy imbalance that gives us our Second Law of Thermodynamics and upon which all life depends. So, too, we repeat Davies [21, p. 39] as 'a kind of converse to chaos theory'.

I regard the concept of 'gnergy' as one of the most important results of my theoretical investigations in biology over the past two decades
[Sungchal Ji, 25, p. 152]

Such a law could be my hoped-for fourth law of thermodynamics for open self-constructing systems
[Stuart Kauffman, 2, p. 84]

We pass rapidly on to Sungchal Ji, with the proposed concept of 'gnergy' encompassing both energy and information, and to Kauffman with his hoped-for Fourth Law of Thermodynamics. At least they cannot be accused of lack of ambition! Ji's rather beautiful graphical interpretation of the evolutions of density and information since the Big Bang [25, p. 156] is reproduced here, as Plate III. [In doing so, however, it may be noticed that Ji's zero initial information density is hardly consistent with Davies' initial stock of information. This point will be addressed in the chapter on thermodynamics in Volume 2 of the Series]. Eric Chaisson's more concise research paper approach [26] should be noted, as it elegantly combines and quantifies some of the key issues raised by both Ji and Kauffman. It forms a nice introduction to the subject area.

We are about to bury our thermodynamics 'bone'. However, it must be appreciated that other 'dogs' still prefer non-thermodynamics 'bones', for example Stephen Boyden [27] and Ken Wilber [28]. The latter's ambitious 'A Theory of Everything' is sub-titled 'An Integral Vision for Business, Politics and Spirituality'. In his Note to the Reader he makes what to him is a conclusive remark about the 'second law of thermodynamics telling us that in the real world disorder always increases. Yet simple observation tells us that in the real world, life creates order everywhere: the universe is winding up, not down' [28, p. x]. For readers who, like me, cannot put their 'bones' down, this statement cannot be allowed to rest, and represents another issue for Thermodynamics in Volume 2. However, my comment is not meant to be pejorative. Ken Wilber seeks, as do so many writing in this subject area, a mastery almost painful to appreciate!

The final point here is the most interesting of all, namely that the origin of life remains a question. 'How this happened we don't know' said Stephen Hawking recently [29, p. 161]. Somewhat differently, Ilya Prigogine some ten years ago [30, p. 24] – 'we are still far from a detailed explanation of the origins of life, notwithstanding we begin to see the type of science which is necessary ... mechanisms which lead from the laws of chemistry to "information". However, where there's a bone there's a dog, [if the reader will forgive this final use of the metaphor] and in this case our dog is Michael Conrad. Conrad's essential thesis contrasts with that of Schrödinger [31, p. 178], and is rather that – to quote the Abstract [31, p. 177] – 'the non-linear self-organising dynamics of biological systems are *inherent* [my italics] in any ... theory ... requirements of both quantum mechanics and general relativity'. Conrad's line [ten of the twenty four references in 31 are by himself as sole author] is termed the fluctuon model, and is particularly interesting in relating to 'nanobiological phenomena and that might be detected through nanobiological techniques'. Stuart Kauffman [2, Chapter 10] similarly surveys quantum mechanics and general relativity, but more in the nature of questioning than Conrad's tighter theorising ....

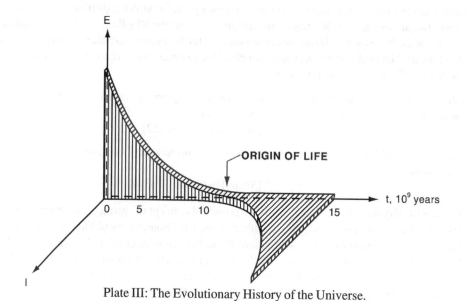

Plate III: The Evolutionary History of the Universe.

In this graph, E and I represent energy and information densities. t is time, on an approximately logarithmic scale, with the origin an estimated 15 billion years ago at the Big Bang. The substantial increase in I occurs following biological 'emergence of the first self-replicating systems ... about 3 billion years ago' [after Sungchal Ji].

History

'This concept of an ideal, perfect form behind the messy particulars of reality is one that is generally attributed to Plato'

[Philip Ball, 17, p. 11]

'Leonardo da Vinci was my childhood hero, and he remains one of the few great geniuses of history'

[Michael White, 32, p. xi]

*'The only scientific book I read that summer was Charles Darwin's 'The Origin of Species'
... but we do still read Darwin'*
[Kenneth Miller, 11, p. 6]

Having sought to show that a fuller understanding of 'Design in Nature' needs to be both mathematically and thermodynamically oriented, we will now point out its historical aspects. We will focus on thee principal characters – Plato, Leonardo da Vinci and Darwin. It is not so easy to give reasons for the choice of these three, but I believe that they represent timeless flashes of genius. Somewhat unexpectedly, they can be viewed in the context of *engineering design.*

So, Plato is associated with one of the key aspects of design, namely form [cf quote by Ball above]. Leonardo epitomizes the ideal of the engineering designer, namely a 'universal man' at home in any branch of knowledge and able to conceptualise almost limitlessly. So we read [33, p. 488] ... 'Italian painter, sculptor, architect, engineer and scientist ... of immensely inventive and enquiring mind, studying aspects of the natural world from anatomy to aerodynamics'. Finally, Darwin can be associated with the idea of progress and adaptation with time [namely, evolution]. It is difficult to overemphasise this, the point being made explicitly in the *titles* of two recent books. Michael French's [7] title is 'Invention and Evolution'. Design in Nature and Engineering'. Similarly, Norman Crowe on architecture [34] 'Nature and the idea of a man-made world. An Investigation into the Evolutionary Roots of Form and Order in the Built Environment'. These are but two examples. We mentioned flashes of genius. These flashes also possess mathematical connotations. ... *Plato esteemed the science of numbers highly* ... [David Smith, 35, p. 89].

In that Plato postulated transcendent [non-earthly] form, he must have been close in approach to the multi-dimensional character of the studies we have already discussed in out Prologue. Platonism *per se* is dealt with at some length by Roger Penrose [22, pp. 146–151] whose 'sympathies lie strongly with Platonistic view that mathematics truth is absolute, external and eternal ...'. Paul Davies [16, p. 145] carries Penrose's sympathies forward as ... 'Many physicists share his Platonic vision of mathematics'.

'Norway builds Da Vinci's 500 year-old bridge ... it conformed with the laws of mathematics'
[Roger Boyes, 36]

Turning to Leonardo, Michael White freely admits his hero's deficiency in this area. And yet, despite Leonardo's being 'barely competent' [32, p. 152] in mathematics and reliant on Pacioli ['he gained a good deal from Pacioli [32, p. 153]], he designed better than he knew. So we have the Norwegian artist Veljorn Sand, who was the persistent catalyst [it took him 5 years] to secure funding for Leonardo's design, paying Leonardo two compliments, firstly to do with his genius ['when you work with geniuses, you work with eternal forms that never go out of fashion'] and secondly his *implicit* mathematical ability [... 'the design was of lasting beauty because it conformed with the laws of mathematics and geometry ... the Mona Lisa of bridges']. To round off Leonardo's relationship with mathematics, he was nothing if not ambitious, and is on record himself as having a very deep commitment. Is it a case of an initial shortcoming being more than subsequently compensated for? So Sherwin Nuland [a surgeon] gives this different picture of Leonardo ... 'for Leonardo, mathematics was the ultimate key to the understanding of the nature he scrutinised so carefully ... to all of science, including the biology of man' [37, p. 53]. Nuland quotes Leonardo as 'no human investigation can be termed true knowledge if it does not proceed to mathematical demonstration'.

Darwin and Mathematics

Inside the sanctum sanctorum they got things done ... to Stokes this was 'flimsy to the last degree' ... But Huxley pulled off the coup ... It was published intact'
[Adrian Desmond, 38, p. 42]

'... Kelvin got very few calculations wrong ... here he understandably failed to include the contribution of the heat of radioactivity'
[Dennis Weaire, 39, p. 61]

'Darwin's view of persistent co-evolution remains by and large unconnected without fundamental physics, even though the evolution of the biosphere is manifestly a physical process. Physicists cannot escape the problem ... We will search for constructive laws true of any biosphere. We will found a general biology. And we will be spellbound'
[Stuart Kauffman, 2, pp. 245, 269]

Finally, Darwin and mathematics. 'The Origin of Species' [41] is essentially, in engineering terms, and experimental report writ large, unaccompanied by mathematical theory. So we have an amusing account as to why Eric Laithwaite chose physics rather than biology. 'Physics seems to be mostly sums, biology mostly essays ... my best friend is going to do biology, so I can keep asking him about it and keep in touch that way. That does it ... I'll do physics' [6, pp. xi–xii]. Eric Laithwaite's schoolboy choice was a personal reflection of an extremely sharp division in the Royal Society regarding the application of Darwin's work. In fact, Desmond's quote above relates not to a publication of Darwin himself, but an ms submitted on Huxley's suggestion by Kovaleski. The real point here is that the Royal Society's conservative Physical Secretary, George Gabriel Stokes' [38, p. 41] opposed the Kovaleski acceptance because it would make 'speculative Darwinism as axiomatic as Newton's laws' and compromise the rock-like status of knowledge' [38, p. 42]. Now GGS lost, and if Desmond's comment is fair, GGS was spectacularly wrong since Darwin *is* roughly on a par of acceptance with Newton's laws. Not only so, but GGS's close friend Kelvin managed to miscalculate the age of the Earth [second quote above], a scientific *cause celebre* of the time.

GGS is given 'a bad book' by Desmond. In fact, he was an extraordinarily talented and productive physical mathematician and Stokes Summer Schools are run in Ireland, organised by Alastair Wood of Dublin City University [who wrote the parallel section on GGS [39] to that of Kelvin]. I declare a personal interest here. I have an immense regard and affection for Stokes, having worked for decades on numerical studies of convective heat transfer using the Navier-Stokes equations. In fact, Stokes spoke better than he knew, in making an outright comparison [having renamed the word 'speculative'] of Darwinistic [biology] with Newtonian [Physics]. That 1873 assessment was repeated in out anecdotal comment of Laithwaite around 1940, and repeated more tellingly by Kauffman in 2000. Here we remind ourselves that Kauffman is a biologist himself.

Digressing, Darwin was not the only experimentalist to have problems with the Royal Society. Joule [James Prescott Joule 1818–1889] the near-genius who worked assiduously on the equivalence of various forms of energy – notable heat and work – suffered the indignity of having only abstracts of submitted papers published by the Royal Society, on two occasions [J.G. Crowther, 41, pp. 189, 204]. He was young, very young, so despite the setbacks he was still only 32 years old when finally elected to the RS [41, p. 214].

Our final Darwin-related character is Kelvin who, despite the age-of-the-earth *faux pas*, has almost ethereal status of having proposed the Absolute Temperature Scale. In a subsequent volume in this series it is intended to focus on the contributions of [the two Scotsmen] James Clerk Maxwell and Kelvin to thermodynamics, and how this now relates to present day biology –

information, complexity and the genome for example. The latter is epitomised by the recent work of Jeffrey Wicken, the full title of a major publication speaking for itself – 'Evolution, Thermodynamics and Information. Extending the Darwinian programme' [43]. So do the titles of some 17 Journal publications that he references [44, p. 233] for example 'A thermodynamic theory of evolution' in 1980 [43a].

In all this, out quiet participant is Darwin himself. Part of his genius, I believe, was his caution, and he let his data collection speak for itself. No mathematics *there*, but an immense sub-surface, iceberg-like, volume of mathematics *underneath*, shown for its worth, as the genome unfolds, and interpreted in terms of information, complexity and Shannon entropy by those such as Kauffman and Wicken.

History summarised

So our three examples of Plato, Leonardo da Vinci and Darwin, have been given a brief introduction. Rather improbably, their genius has been introduced in terms of *engineering design* and *mathematical significance*. Above all, their genius was, and is, timeless. How else could Plato's views on form and mathematics be regarded as relevant two and a half *millennia* later? How else could Leonardo's bridge design be accepted half a millennium later? How else could Darwin's conclusions stand the test of exhaustive and sometimes hostile assessment, lasting for almost a century and a half?

A further aspect of this timelessness, which will be merely stated rather than discussed, is that the Renaissance [epitomised by Leonardo] had as one of its sources the rediscovery of the Greek texts ... 'the finding of ancient manuscripts that gave the intellectuals of the Renaissance direct access to classical thought ...' [32, p. 39]. So Michael White gives as Appendix 11: 'Leonardo and his place in the History of Science' [32, pp. 339–342], a chronological sequence running from Pythagoras through to Newton ....

Epilogue

Miraculous harmony at Epidaurus   [Henri Stierlin, 45, p. 168]

At the commencement of the Prologue to this Introduction, two 'almost miracles' were described. We conclude with a final example going back to 330 BC – to the absolute end of Greek classicism [45, p. 227]. 'Miraculous harmony at Epidaurus' is how Henri Stierlin describes the wonderfully preserved Greek 'theatre set into the hill of Epidaurus' [44, pp. 168–169] – see Plate IV. There are three distinct aspects to this piece of architecture by Polyclitus the Younger. The design has a mathematical basis – including what is now termed the Golden Section and the Fibonacci sequence. Secondly, the harmony spoken of by Stierlin is a consequence of the theatre's 'symmetry' – a subtle technical quality originating in Greek ideas of form. Lastly, the combination of what we now call 'the built environment' with its natural environment has a timeless aesthetic attractiveness. In fact, Plate IV is reproduced not from the reference we have discussed, but a Greek Tourist Organisation advertisement.

In concluding, our introduction has covered an almost impossible range of disciplines, but it is only such a range that can possible do justice to the theme of design in nature. If 'we' is broadened to comprise editors, contributors and publishers, we want to share our sense of inspiration of design in the natural world and man-made worlds that our three authors of near miracles, Cecil Lewis, Stuart Kauffman and Henri Stierlin have epitomised.

Plate IV: 'Miraculous harmony at Epidaurus'.

(See page xiv of Optimisation Mechanics in Nature): 'Around the orchestra, the shell-like theatre set into the hill fans out like a radial structure, whose concentric rows of seating are all focused on the stage where the dramitic action would unfold. With its diameter of 120m., the theatre of Epidaurus is one of the finest semi-circular buildings of Antiquity. Its design, the work of Polyclitus the Younger, according to Pausanias, dates from the end of the fourth century B.C. It is based on a series of mathematical principles and proportions, such as the Golden Section and the so-called Fibonacci Sequence. Its harmony is thus the result of a symmetria in the real sense of the term' [45, p168].
(Reproduced by permission of the Greek National Tourism Organisation).

References

[1]   Lewis, C., *Sagittarius Rising*, 3rd Edition, The Folio Society: London, 1998.

[2]   Kauffman, S.A., *Investigations*, Oxford, 2000.

[3]   Hawking, S., *Why we need 11 dimensions*. Highlighted paragraph in 'I believe in a 'brane' new world', extract from Ref. 29. Daily Telegraph, p. 20, 31st October 2000.

[4]   Atherton, M.A., Piva, S., Barrozi, G.S. & Collins, M.W., Enhanced visualization of complex thermo fluid data: horizontal combined convection cases. *Proc. 18th National Conference on Heat Transfer*, Eds. A. Nero, G. Dubini & F. Ingoli, UIT [Italian Union of Thermo fluid dynamics], pp. 243–257, 2000.

[5]   Lewis, R.T.V., *Reactor Performance and Optimization*. English Electric Company [now Marconi] Internal Document, 1960.

[6]   Laithwaite, E., *An Inventor in the Garden of Eden*. Cambridge, 1994.

[7]   French, M., *Invention and Evolution. Design in Nature and Engineering*. 2nd Edition, Cambridge, 1994.

[8]   Cook, T.A., *The Curves of Life*. Reproduced from original Constable edition, 1914, Dover, 1979.

[9]   Dawkins, R., *Climbing Mount Improbable*. Penguin, 1996.

[10]   Ruse, M., *Can a Darwinian be a Christian*. Cambridge, 2001.

[11]   Miller, K.R., *Finding Darwin's God*. Cliff Street Books [Harper Collins], 1999.

[12]   Behe, M.J., *Darwin's Black Box*. Touchstone [Simon & Schuster], 1998.

[13]   Dembski, W.A., *The Design Inference*. Cambridge, 1998.

[14]   Heeren, F., *The Lynching of Bill Dembski*, The American Spectator, November 2000.

[15]   Jeans, J., *The Mysterious Universe*, Cambridge, 1931.

[16]   Davies, P., *The Mind of God*, Penguin, 1993.

[17]   Ball, P., *The Self-Made Tapestry*, Oxford, 1999.

[18]   Rogers, G. & Mayhew, Y., *Engineering Thermodynamics, Work and Heat Transfer*, 4th Edition, Prentice Hall, 1992.

[19]   Houghton, J., *Global Warming*, Lion, 1994.

[20]   Kondepudi, D. & Prigogine, I., *Modern Thermodynamics*, Wiley, 1998.

[21]   Davies, P., *The Fifth Miracle*, Penguin, 1999.

[22]   Penrose, R., *The Emperor's New Mind*, Oxford, 1989/1999.

[23a] Schrödinger, E., *What is Life?* with *Mind and Matter and Autobiographic Sketches*, and a Foreword by R. Penrose, Canto Edition, Cambridge, 1992.

[23b] Schrödinger, E., *What is Life?* and an Introduction by R. Penrose, The Folio Society: London, 2000.
       [Note: these are quite distinct publications. The key section *What is Life?* is type-set differently and the page numbers do not correspond.]

[24]   Stewart, I., *Does God Play Dice?* 2nd Edition, Penguin, 1997.

[25]   Ji, S., *Biocybernetics: A Machine Theory of Biology*, Chapter 1 in: *Molecular Theories of Cell Life and Death*, Ed. S. Ji, Rutgers, 1991.

[26]   Chaisson, E., The cosmic environment for the growth of complexity, *Biosystems*, **46**, pp. 13–19, 1998.

[27]   Boyden, S., *Western civilization in biological perspective*, Oxford, 1987.

[28]   Wilber, K., *A Theory of Everything*, Gateway: Dublin, 2001.

[29]   Hawking, S., *The Universe in a Nutshell*, Bantam Press, 2001.

[30] Prigogine, I., *Schrödinger and the Riddle of Life*, Chapter 2 in: *Molecular Theories of Cell Life and Death*, Ed. S. Ji, Rutgers, 1991.

[31] Conrad, M., Origin of life and the underlying physics of the universe, *Biosystems*, **42**, pp. 117–190, 1997.

[32] White, M., *Leonardo*, Little Brown & Co.: London, 2000.

[33] *The Complete Family Encyclopaedia*, Fraser Stewart Book Wholesale Ltd., Helicon Publishing: London, 1992.

[34] Crowe, N., *Nature and the Idea of a Man-Made World*, MIT Press: Cambridge MA, USA & London, UK, 1995.

[35] Smith, D., *History of Mathematics*, Volume 1, First published 1923, Dover Edition, New York, 1958.

[36] Boyes, R., *Norway builds Da Vinci's 500-year-old bridge*, The Times [UK Newspaper], London, 1November 2001.

[37] Nuland, S., *Leonardo da Vinci*, Weidenfield & Nicolson, London, 2000.

[38] Desmond, A., *Huxley Evolution's High Priest*, Michael Joseph: London, 200.

[39] Weaire, D., *William Thomson [Lord Kelvin] 1824–1907*, Chapter 8 in: *Creators of Mathematics: the Irish Connection*, Ed. K. Houston, University College, Dublin Press: Ireland, 2000.

[40] Darwin, C., *The Origin of Species*, Wordsworth Classics Edition, Ware, Herefordshire, UK, 2000.

[41] Crowther, J.G., *The British Scientists of the Nineteenth Century*, Volume 1, Allen Lane/ Penguin, Pelican Books, 1940.

[42] Wood, A., *George Gabriel Stokes 1819–1903*, Chapter 5 in: *Creators of Mathematics: the Irish Connection*, Ed. K. Houston, University College, Dublin Press: Ireland, 2000.

[43] Wicken, J.S., *Evolution, Thermodynamics and Information*, Oxford University Press 1987.

[43a] Wicken, J.S., A thermodynamic theory of evolution, *J. Theor. Biol.*, **87**, pp. 9–23, 1980.

[45] Stierlin, H., *Greece from Mycenae to the Parthenon*, Series on Architecture and Design by TASCHEN, Editor-in-Chief A. Taschen, Taschen: Cologne, Germany, 2001.

Section I

Compliant Structures
in Nature

CHAPTER 1

Compliant structures and materials in animals

J.F.V. Vincent

Centre for Biomimetic and Natural Technologies, University of Bath, UK

Abstract

The ability of plants and animals to run away from loads by being compliant saves much energy because the structures consume less energy in their production and require less energy for maintenance. However, as a model for engineering structures there are difficulties since compliant structures are commonly less stable, have less linear properties and are therefore more difficult to control and handle.

1 Introduction

The materials from which the structures of animals are made have a gigantic range of stiffness. Ceramics (shell and bone) can be as stiff as 60 or 70 GPa [1] while gel-like materials, such as the extensible intersegmental membrane of many female locust species, can have a Young's modulus as low as 1 kPa [2]. Obviously ceramics cannot be classed as compliant materials, so where is the line to be drawn between "stiff" and "compliant"? In engineering terms compliance is more a term of function, indicating a material that is an effective shock absorber, has the equivalence of zero stiffness (by comparison with the other materials in the structure) or can extend so much that its properties cannot be modelled adequately by a normal linear model. So the functional definition is as much to do with context (and therefore comparative properties) as with mechanical properties. And the important mechanical property is probably ultimate strain rather than stiffness (table or food jellies are very soft but cannot be stretched very far before they fracture). Such soft tissues are remarkably widespread in the animal world and represent a useful, safe, cheap and efficient way of containing and organising other materials. Jim Gordon (author of the seminal *The New Science of Strong Materials*) once calculated that when one yawns, the strain energy density in the skin covering the cheek is about the same as that in a piece of mild steel just before fracture!

The most commonly encountered compliant, high strain, material is the polyisoprenoid natural rubber, which is made from latex from the tree *Hevea*. Here, the resistance to deformation is provided by the tendency of the chain to revert to a random configuration whose driver is Brownian motion. The degree of randomness (or the number of allowed conformations of the molecule) is related to the freedom of rotation about the bonds along the main chain (double bonds provide stiffness), to the degree to which the side groups along the chain interfere with each other as they thresh around (steric hindrance) and to the lack of stabilising secondary structure. Natural rubber has both the freedom and the low degree of steric hindrance. However, single-phase elastomers such as natural rubber are rare, probably absent from living organisms. The side chains of proteins are frequently quite large and the rotation about the backbone bonds is not particularly free, so the number of conformations is limited, giving rise to a few repeating structures (alpha- and collagen-helices, beta sheet, etc.) most of which are intrinsically stable and therefore stiff. In hydrated conditions, water is attracted to charged sites and separates them. Since the water molecules bind and unbind at high speed (residency time of about 10^{-26} s) they also lubricate the movement of the polymer molecules and provide spatial freedom, so plasticising the material. This tendency is opposed by interactions between hydrophobic side groups that tend to associate in the presence of water. If the water content is reduced by the co-operative effect of these hydrophobic interactions, the charged side groups will also interact, further stabilising the polymer. Therefore materials with low stiffness and high extensibility are not inevitable in organisms; they are the result of specific chemistry and molecular structures.

2 Compliant molecules

2.1 Proteins and polysaccharides

There are several materials found in animals that can extend by more than 10% (which is rather more than the breaking strain of collagens), even up to 100% (e.g. elastin, found in vertebrate animals). By analogy with rubbers derived from plants and polymer chemistry, these are often classed as rubbery materials even though a piece of *Hevea* rubber can extend to 5 or 6 times its original length. However, this is an oversimplification, since it implies that high extensibility is due to a single mechanism. The commonality is that a polymeric molecule whose normal state is to be folded back on itself, whether the folding is orderly or random, will be capable of high extensions if the chains do not link together and are free to move and straighten out. The mechanisms by which they can return to their unextended length (i.e. recover elastically) can in principle be various. In fact it is likely that purely rubbery elasticity is rare in nature. We are becoming more aware that the mechanism of elastic recoil suggested by Urry for elastin (see below) is general [3]; it has been found in gluten, a plant protein, and probably occurs in resilin and abductin, rubbery proteins found in bivalve molluscs and insects, respectively.

However, there are other components. The skin of the sea cucumber (an animal related to sea urchins and starfish), a material that can change from stiff to nearly liquid as part of the animal's defence-and-escape behaviour, has a network of "microfibrils" which may provide a link between the collagen fibrils, causing them to form more stable bundles with fixed topological relationships. The problem then is how can a highly extensible material of very low stiffness (implying only weak crosslinks) return to its original shape after such extreme deformation? The microfibrils in the sea cucumber are chemically very similar to the mammalian protein fibrillin (a protein rich in cysteine), which serves as a scaffolding for the deposition of elastin; similar filaments are found in sea anemones and jelly-fish. So perhaps microfibrils are a common feature in connective tissues, forming a more structured matrix. They were isolated [4] by dissolving unbonded protein and polysaccharides in guanidine hydrochloride (which breaks H bonds) and then dissolving the collagen with a collagenase. In the electron microscope the microfibrils, from which the collagen had been removed, were still clumped together with spaces between which corresponded to the size of the collagen fibrils;

so presumably they were not much changed. Breaking the sulfur bonds and then adding NH_2 groups allowed the skin to swell and the microfibrils were seen to be more widely spaced. They are 10–14 nm in diameter with 13-nm diameter beads spaced about 45 nm apart along their length (Fig. 1). Mechanical testing of the extracted skin (in sea water) showed the feltwork of microfibrils to be able to stretch to a strain of 2.75 (engineering strain) before breaking (Fig. 2). By comparison with titin (q.v.) the beads might be areas of hydrophobicity that unravel when the molecule is stretched.

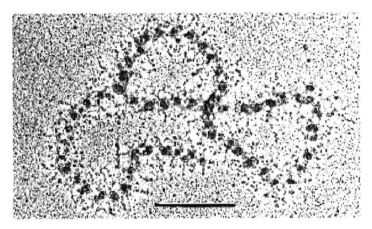

Figure 1: Microfibres from the skin of a sea cucumber, isolated using guanidine-HCl, a breaker of H bonds.

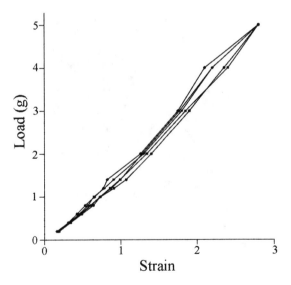

Figure 2: Stress–strain curve of microfibrils form skin of a sea cucumber, extracted with guanidine-HCl and collagenase, then tested in sea water.

The fibrillin microfibrils in the filaments of the bovine ocular zonule (a network of fibres that suspends the lens from the ciliary body in the eye) are more orientated than those in the skin of the sea cucumber, and typically show a maximum strain of about 75%, nearer 25% *in vivo*, where they are permanently prestrained [5].

2.2 High strain

2.2.1 Titin

Titin (also known as connectin) is a giant filamentous protein that stretches between the Z- and M-lines of the vertebrate muscle sarcomere. It probably maintains the structural integrity of the sarcomere and generates the passive force of muscle. The molecule is an entropic (rubbery) spring that unfolds as it is stretched (> 400 pN) and refolds upon release. Unfolding of the molecule is characterized by the disappearance of mechanical hysteresis at high forces; refolding results in hysteresis at low forces. The various globular domains in titin require different unfolding forces due to differences in the activation energies for their unfolding [6]. The resulting force–deflection curve is an elaborate and lengthy saw-tooth profile.

2.2.2 Nacre matrix

When mother-of-pearl fractures, the matrix is spun into fibres or ligaments across the gaps between the platelets (Fig. 3). Their action contributes at least half of the toughness of nacre [7], a mechanism that can be mimicked, to a limited extent, by low modulus non-setting glue between the platelets of a model material [8]. These ligaments have been stretched in an atomic force microscope, when they elongate in a stepwise manner suggesting that the process involves folded domains or loops being pulled open.

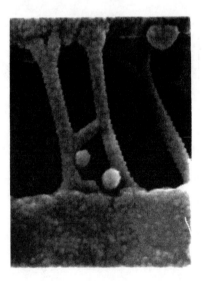

Figure 3: Ligaments (silk-like) bridging the gap between layers of nacre as part of the fracture process.

The steps occur with forces of a few hundred pN, smaller than the force (more than a nanonewton) that would be required to break the main chain peptide bonds [9]. This behaviour is similar both to some dragline silks and to titin [6]. This mechanism has been modelled (unpublished at the time of writing) by George Mayer at the University of Washington. Using a specially formulated glue designed by a colleague in Case Western Reserve University, he showed that the formation of the ligaments could both absorb large amounts of energy and make the material self-healing, so that it could at least partially repair itself after damage. There is a whole topic area of compliant or plastic matrices that is unexplored in the development of composite materials. Usually they are seen as insufficient to maintain a stiff structure. But this is largely due to our inability to make composites with a high proportion of the stiff (ceramic, glass) phase. Nacre has only 5% of the soft matrix, at which proportion it has very little influence on the overall stiffness [7]. Yet it dominates the energy-absorption properties.

2.3 Strain energy storage

2.3.1 Elastin
This is the soft yellow material found stretched between the bones of the skeleton, forming ligaments such as the *ligamentum nuchae*, which acts as a counterbalance spring for the head and neck in hoofed animals (figure 4). Elastin of one sort or another is also found in the aorta and arteries of vertebrates where it provides elastic recoil that evens out the pulses of the blood and reduces the load on the heart. Chemically elastin is very stable, having a half-life in the human body of around 50 years. This is attributable to the covalent cross-links (desmosine and isodesmosine, each derived from four lysine groups on the newly-synthesised protein) which will resist very high temperatures. Hence elastin is commonly prepared by superheating ligament to 110°C. The collagen and other tissues all melt and dissolve, leaving elastin untouched.

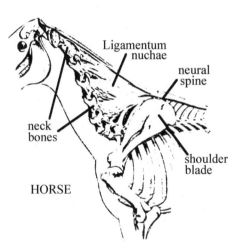

Figure 4: *Ligamentum nuchae* in a horse.

It is instructive to see how ideas on elastin evolved and what part ideas of rubber elasticity played in the overall concepts. Elastin was recognised to have a high content of nonpolar amino acids by 1938, and was shown to swell, like nylon, in organic solvents. The nonpolar side chains would also account for their rubbery behaviour, since they would not readily participate in cross links. Further similarity with rubber was the absence of molecular orientation shown by X-ray diffraction. An important difference is that elastin, but not rubber, has oxygen and nitrogen in the backbone and therefore has the potential for forming hydrogen bonds that would stiffen the network. Water is an essential plasticiser even though mature elastin is highly insoluble. The discovery of the soluble precursor of elastin – about 850 residues long and named tropoelastin – allowed the determination of amino-acid sequences and conformational possibilities of the molecule.

Several models for elastin's elasticity have been mooted in the last half-century. The random chain model, the most likely starting point, had support from a number of investigators [10–12] using the techniques of thermodynamics that showed the production of excess heat when elastin was stretched. This was attributable to the water adsorbed into the protein on elongation and indicated a network of random chains within the elastin fibres, like that in a typical rubber.

Better understanding of the protein chemistry led to the idea that the rubbery mechanism was locked away inside globules of elastin with the hydrophobic residues tucked away in the centre of an oily droplet [13]. This model supposed the elastic mechanism to reside in the exchange of surface or wetting energy on exposing the interior of this droplet to the surrounding aqueous medium when it was stretched and deformed. The difference between this and the random coil model was in the availability of water. The random coil model required water to enter from outside the network, whereas the droplet model allowed sufficient space between the droplets for the necessary water. When elastin is prevented from exchanging water with its environment by isolating it in a bath of mineral oil the excess heat is zero, suggesting that the random network model is correct, or that the volume of water retained between the droplets is insufficient [14]. At about the same time, the repeating amino-acid sequences, with their strong suggestion of specific molecular conformations, led to the "oiled coil" model [15]. They proposed that the movement of parts of the molecule between watery and oily environments is controlled by these defined conformations of the protein, rather than a random chain. The main shape is the β-turn, made of sequences of (VPGGV) or (VPGVGV) where V is valine, P is proline, and G is glycine. In this the exterior positions are exposed to solvent whilst the hydrophobic residues are buried; most of the peptide backbone is hydrated. A larger structure made from these units, which have been found to repeat 5 to 10 times in various lengths of the molecule, is a broad left-handed helix, about 1.3 nm in diameter, with hydrophobic interior and no hydrogen bonding along the length of the helix. These oiled coils were then to be linked together at their ends to form a space-filling network. We now have a picture of a fibrous material that nonetheless can show both the elastic and thermodynamic characteristics of rubber.

This model was further refined by Urry (reviewed by Urry [16] who modelled the protein physically), producing polymers of the (VPGVG) and related sequences, cross-linking them chemically and using γ-irradiation. He showed that elastin fibres, visible in the electron microscope, are relatively large helices with a watery core in which the β-turns function as spacers. The (VGV) segments therefore have a large amount of space around them and can rotate about the protein backbone in a relatively random manner, characterised by Urry as a librational entropy mechanism. The helix has such a large diameter that it gives the appearance of long-range randomness in the X-ray diffraction patterns. In action it is a stretchable spiral.

2.3.2 Resilin

Probably because it is easily solvated and therefore difficult to retain within the structure of insect cuticle, resilin is covalently crosslinked with di- and ter-tyrosine residues immediately it is secreted [17]. It is thus impossible to extract and separate in the usual way with proteins, and for a long time all the information that was available was the amino-acid composition. The main amino acid is glycine (40%) whose presence supports a rubber elasticity model since the single hydrogen side-group of this amino acid will limit the movement of the peptide chain as little as possible. This, plus the low stiffness and high extensibility of resilin, led Weis-Fogh to propose that resilin is a random-coil rubber, an idea which he supported with elegant experiments on the thermodynamics of its elasticity. These showed clearly that the elastic restoring force is provided by entropy. But with elastin and wheat gluten, two very extensible, elastic, proteins, being shown to be non-rubbery, Weis-Fogh's ideas appear increasingly isolated. Two other amino acids with small side-groups, alanine and serine, are also prevalent in resilin, contributing a further 20% of the protein and suggesting the presence of silk-like structures. There are also significant amounts (7–10%) of proline that is involved in very consistent patterns suggestive of the beta-structures that are found in elastin [18]. So Urry's mechanism for elasticity of elastin is probably general and is found in other proteins.

2.3.3 Abductin

This protein forms the bulk of the hinge between the shells of bivalve molluscs, providing the force to cause the shells to open or gape, reacting to the force generated by the adductor muscle. It is also used in swimming [19], where it needs to be highly resilient. It does not seem to do this too well, returning only 80% of its strain energy at 10°C, rising to 90% at 35°C [20]. This low resilience may be associated with the presence of $CaCO_3$ crystal in its bulk, which may be there to increase its fracture resistance. Its amino acid sequence suggests that its elastic mechanism may be similar to that of elastin [21].

2.3.4 Collagen

"Collagen" is a generic term for 15–20 different structures based on the aggregation of triple-helical tropocollagen molecules. Collagen type I is probably the most-studied, being responsible for the stiffness of tendons. It seems that several different processes dominate its mechanical properties depending on the strain. At strains up to 3% the stiffness is tens of MPa, like a rubber, and kinks in the collagen structure are straightening, first at the fibrillar and then at the molecular level. At higher strains where the stiffness increases to 2–5 GPa the tropocollagen molecules glide within the fibrils before the fibril ultimately breaks [22, 23]. Tendon is nearly all collagen, and provides significant savings in energy for locomotion by storing strain energy from one locomotory cycle to the next [24]. This occurs in animals that swim [25–27] and run [28, 29]. Tendons store strain energy in tension rather than compression or bending (the preferred mode for resilin and abductin) but are relatively safe from fracture since the individual fibre bundles are not well connected laterally. This makes the tendon insensitive to notches and other damage, and therefore relatively safe. Dry tendon has extremely high specific energy storage of about 10 J/g. However, in this state it is relatively inextensible.

3 Compliant composites

To a first approximation, the modulus of a composite can be given by the following formulae:

$$\text{Equal strain (Voigt, parallel) model -} \quad E_c = E_f V_f + E_m (1 - V_f) \qquad \text{(1, figure 5)}$$

$$\text{Equal stress (Reuss, series) model -} \quad \frac{1}{E_c} = \frac{1}{E_f} V_f + \frac{1}{E_m} (1 - V_f) \qquad \text{(2, figure 5)}$$

where E and V are the stiffness and volume fraction of the composite (c), fibre (f), and matrix (m) components.

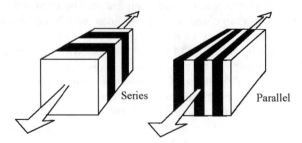

Figure 5: Limit models for composite materials.

Thus in a composite material, in which the components are arranged in parallel to the applied load, the stiffness can be dominated by a relatively small proportion of high modulus fibres, whereas when the components are arranged in series the low modulus components will dominate. In reality, most materials fall into the zone between these two limiting cases. A low modulus is then commonly attained by a combination of a high volume fraction of an effective plasticiser, the abundance of a molecule with some form of long-range elasticity and only a small volume fraction of any fibres that might stiffen the material.

Connective tissues in general (including many skins) are hierarchical composites of a number of fibrous and non-fibrous components whose mechanical properties are governed by the proportions and orientations of the different components and their interactions. (Rather a vague statement, but the plethora of non-functioning mathematical and mechanical models for skin makes it seem unlikely that the mechanical properties of collagenous tissues are simply derived or can be readily understood.)

3.1 Skin

All multicellular animals have some sort of basement membrane system, which holds the cells together, and many (arthropods are a notable exception) have an outer covering that is essentially collagenous. In earthworms, sharks, and nematodes the collagen is very highly and very precisely orientated, which can be directly related to the transmission of force by the skin, although imperfect knowledge of the three-dimensional effects on such a material (e.g., the amount by which it gets thinner as it stretches) must inevitably limit our understanding of its function and the resulting implications for the animal. Other animals such as coelenterates (both sessile and mobile) have a complex system of fibres in the body wall (Fig. 6) [30]. In all these skins the collagen fibres are wound around the body in a double-helical pattern so that it is obvious that the mechanical properties depend strongly on orientation effects.

The geometry and mechanics of the fibre-wound pressure vessel has been explored a number of times, independently, by biologists and engineers, and summarised by Clarke [30]. However, this model is very simple, with all fibres changing their orientation uniformly and simultaneously. Most soft tissues are much more complex, with semi-randomly orientated fibres arranged in a three-dimensional network. Human (for that matter, mammalian) skin has the collagen fibres more like a feltwork so that there is mainly only a limited net orientation of the collagen that is expressed as local differences in extensibility. Whereas it is obviously adaptive in a human for the skin over the lower abdomen to be able to stretch in all directions, it is not so obvious that skin elsewhere can be more adaptive in its response if it stretches less in one direction than another. This was investigated by Langer who mapped the extensibility of skin over the entire human body. He summarised his finding as lines (now known as Langer's lines) drawn on the skin that indicate the direction and relative magnitude of extensibility [31].

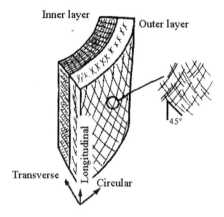

Figure 6: Main fibre orientations in the body wall of a sea anemone.

The reorientation of collagen in skin when it is stretched can be greatly affected by the introduction of a short split or notch [32]. A notch induces a zone of concentrated stress at its tip that decreases very quickly with increasing distance ahead of the tip [33]. The effect of this stress (detected as reorientated collagen fibres) disappears only 0.5 mm ahead of a 5-mm crack in aortic media of the pig (a model for skin) that is stretched biaxially (Fig. 7) by about a third of its original length.

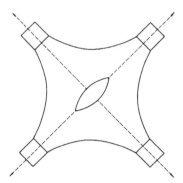

Figure 7: Notch in a piece of tissue under two-dimensional strain.

The stress concentration has its maximum local stresses perpendicular to the long axis of the crack, so that the collagen fibres align in a direction perpendicular to the crack tip. If the crack is to advance it now has to cross many more fibres and will require much more energy to do so. With a random arrangement of fibres, the material is therefore initially isotropic so that initiation and propagation of the crack will be equally difficult in all directions. This is probably the best way of stopping the progress of an imperfection, and we should be pleased that our outer covering is so effectively puncture-proof. This trick places skin firmly in the category of a responsive material.

The important characteristics of skins leading to this type of property are heterogeneity (stiff fibres in a softer matrix) and a degree of mobility of the fibres. Depending on the resistance to crack propagation and degree of initial orientation of the fibres, skins can be stretched to high (10 to 50%) strains that are associated with an elastic modulus increasing with deformation, giving a J-shaped stress–strain curve. This curve has many interesting characteristics, and seems independently to be associated with high toughness [34], perhaps an underlying reason for using such an arrangement of fibres in an outer covering. This was first pointed out by Jim Gordon who argued that materials showing low stiffness at low extensions would not be able to transfer the necessary energy to the tip of a crack to enable it to grow further, despite the relatively low work of fracture that has been measured for such materials.

Purslow [35] used a simple model, based on a power law, which can generate a variety of shapes of stress–strain curve. The basic formula relates stress to strain as $\sigma = k.e^n$, where k is a constant and n affects the shape of the curve such that it is straight when $n = 1$, rubber-like when n < 1 and skin-like when n > 1. As his criterion of toughness he used the concept of notch-sensitivity – the tendency for damage, once inflicted, to spread. He then separated stress and strain as driving agents in fracture, so that he could decide under what circumstances a non-linear material with either a higher fracture stress, or a higher fracture strain, might be more "difficult" to break. Starting with a sample whose stress–strain behaviour was described by the power-law he established, mathematically, how the elastic strain energy in the sample would vary with notch length and notch-sensitivity, producing some predictions based on straight-line graphs (a straight ruler is one of science's most potent analytical tools!). In mechanical tests, butyl and silicone rubbers conformed well, latex rubber less well (possibly because it crystallises as it is stretched and the rubber molecules lay against each other with greater regularity).

The effect of increasing the length of the initial notch decreases fracture stress more than fracture strain for a skin-like material, and decreases fracture strain more than fracture stress for a rubber-like material. These two responses can be shown to work best under two different sets of conditions. The skin-like material will be best able to resist fracture under service conditions of high displacement – Purslow uses the example of skin stretched over a knee joint and the high strains experienced in the skin when the knee is bent. The rubber-like curve is probably best suited to applications where the load is the defining parameter. Examples of this type are rare in biology.

3.2 Auxetic membranes

Most materials when they are deformed in one direction respond by opposite deformation in the orthogonal directions: if you stretch a rubber band it gets narrower and thinner. This is one expression of its keeping a constant volume and is expressed in the tensile Poisson ratio:

$$v = \frac{-\varepsilon_t}{\varepsilon_l} \qquad (3)$$

where ε_t is the transverse strain and ε_l is the longitudinal strain. Since there are three directions for deformation (x, y and z) there are 6 Poisson ratios. For most materials these ratios average

0.5, indicating a constant volume. However, some materials (called "auxetic" by Ken Evans of Exeter University, UK) have a negative Poisson ratio: they get wider and thicker as they are extended. Conversely they get narrower and thinner as they are longitudinally compressed. This also implies that their volume changes. This type of behaviour can happen in the plane due to unfolding structures such as leaves (Fig. 8) [36] and skin [37] and in three dimensions due to the arrangement of fibres or particles forming an interconnected structure with re-entrant structures [38]. Since the volume is changing so markedly, auxetic materials commonly show high strains and low stiffness, although stiff materials such as cancellous bone are also auxetic. Surprisingly few biological materials have been reported as auxetic.

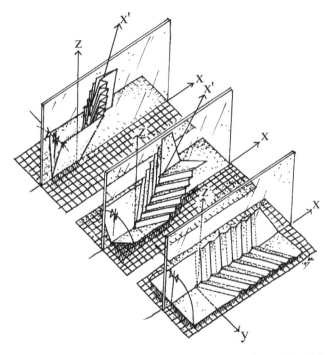

Figure 8: Deployment of an auxetic structure based on a beech leaf.

3.3 Feathers and wings of birds

Feathers are highly compliant in bending at the tip [39]. This not only contributes to their longevity (they bend out of the way when loaded, rather than getting damaged), but contributes significantly to the flight performance. When a bird is coming in to land and is effectively stalling (the angle of attack of the wing is greater than about 15 degrees) the feathers on the upper surface of the trailing edge of the wing bend upwards. This is in direct response to the circulation of air around the trailing edge from beneath and forwards along the upper surface. The feathers form a barrier that stops this air from travelling further forwards, thus destroying the circulation of air that provides the lift, hence allowing the wing to generate lift at higher angles of attack and at lower air speeds.

3.4 Insect cuticle

The exoskeleton of arthropods contains as its fibre the polysaccharide, chitin, in a complex matrix mainly composed of proteins. In most instances the matrix is rendered hydrophobic by phenolic tanning or a similar mechanism, but some protein matrices can change their degree of hydration. The most studied example is the larva of *Rhodnius prolixus*, a blood-sucking bug, which has the chance of feeding only irregularly (perhaps only once every 3 months) and so has to be sure of taking in as much nourishment as possible when that chance arises. In order to do this it softens its abdominal cuticle so that the strain at maximum load increases from 0.25 to 0.7 [40]. Associated with this, the water content increases from 25.8% to 31.3% and the stiffness drops from 62 to 2.5 MPa. This is associated with a drop in the pH of the cuticular protein, thus increasing the charge density and the propensity of the cuticular proteins to bind water. However, this is not an elastic mechanism; the cuticle shows a greatly increased rate of creep.

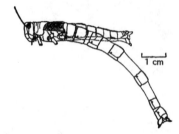

Figure 9: Extensible cuticle in the abdomen of a locust. Legs and wings have been omitted for clarity.

A highly compliant elastic material is found in the abdominal intersegmental membrane of the locust (Fig. 9). Chitin is present, but orientated orthogonally to the direction of extension of the membrane [41] and so has little effect on the stiffness, which is about 1 kPa. The proteins are not only very soft but are highly hydrated, containing about 70% of water [2]. The effects of denaturants on these proteins suggest that they do not have a precisely folded and densely packed hydrophobic core comparable to that in globular proteins such as egg albumen, and so they do not denature in the same way. Instead, they resemble unordered, randomly coiled, thermally agitated polymer chains, whose hydrodynamic volumes depend upon the composition of the medium. The major part of the cuticular proteins is therefore probably unordered and random, both in solution and in the intact cuticle [42].

3.5 Insect wings

When an insect sheds its old cuticle as part of its growth cycle, the new cuticle is soft and folded before it expands. During expansion (Fig. 10) it softens and then stiffens again when expansion is completed, thus providing a new and larger skeleton for the insect. These processes can be most readily followed in the wing [43, 44].

The unexpanded wing is like a bag that has been crumpled – the walls are highly folded so that most of the extension can come from flattening out the folds. The folded cuticle is initially relatively stiff and elastic with 30% breaking strain. Within 10 minutes of emerging the locust has softened the folded cuticle by a factor of at least 10, giving it a two-phase force–strain curve. The folds allow it to be stretched plastically by a factor of about 2.5, after which the folds are flattened and resistance to extension increases. This degree of folding accounts for practically all the extension. Once flattened, the cuticle changes rapidly, becoming 10 times stiffer and twice as strong. These changes in stiffness are under the control of the cells that secrete the cuticle since the process of expansion can be halted by treatment with cyanide. This can all happen with the wing removed from the insect, but only if the cut end is sealed so that the blood cannot leak out. So the mechanism is hydraulic and the pressure for expansion is generated by the reduction in volume of the part of the wing that has already expanded and flattened. The neatest way of putting these observations together is to think of a zone of expansion travelling along the wing. Ahead of this zone the epidermal cells soften the cuticle, probably by changing its pH [40] and hence the water content. This part of the process is probably under hormonal control, most probably bursicon [44]. Once the cuticle has been softened, the blood pressure in the wing veins is sufficient to straighten them out, stretching the folded bag of the upper and lower wing membranes and reducing the volume of the bag as it does so. The cells then tan, dehydrate and stiffen the expanded cuticle, confirming the reduction in volume. The overall process is analogous to zone melting, where the properties of a metal strip are changed by passing it through a small zone where it is partially melted and then annealed, changing the crystalline structure.

Figure 10: Stages in the expansion of a locust forewing. The main vein is drawn to emphasise the expansion process. Scale line is 5 mm.

4 Compliant structures

4.1 Hydraulic structures

All skeletons are compliant in that they have to be jointed and flexible in order to provide movement as well as support. The hydraulic skeleton is probably the most flexible, both as a highly hydrated contained solid such as the jelly of jelly fish [45] and the water-supported shape of the sea anemone [46] that is generated by the anisotropic properties of the body wall: it is 3.2 times as stiff circumferentially as longitudinally due to differential orientations of collagen, and so will extend above the substrate when the internal pressure is raised, despite the fact that a pressurised tube generates a hoop stress that is twice the longitudinal stress as a simple matter of its geometry [47]

The control of compliance as a function of the volume of a worm, and other cylindrical or sub-cylindrical animals, and the angle at which the collagen fibrils are arranged in the skin has been rehearsed many times [30]. This model also works for fish such as sharks that do not rely on a swim bladder for neutral bouyancy and so can change their internal pressure and the state of extension of the skin collagen, which then serves both as an exotendon for transmitting force and an elastic energy store.

4.2 Skeletal structures

Stiff skeletons, whether calcified (vertebrates, molluscs, crustacea) or made of tanned protein (insects, spiders) are rendered compliant by the presence of joints. This much is common knowledge and trivial. However, there is some evidence of compliance due to tensegrity structures [48] in which stiff struts are held apart in a web of tensile compliant ropes or tendons (Fig. 11). An example may be the way ribs are held apart rather like a boat is kept away from the edge of the dock using "springs"; another example is the structure of the flexible lumbar spine in mammals such as carnivores and rodents. The role of tensegrity in the internal structure of cells has excited more interest, though with less proof.

An animal cell that, unlike a plant cell, has no cell wall to give it skeletal integrity, is commonly modelled as a compliant bag full of protoplasm that is organised only by membranes, which form partitions within the cell. However, many cells are capable of movement, indicating that there are internal structures capable of generating tension (actin microfibrils) and resisting compression (microtubules). Do they interact in a patterned manner? The architecture of tensegrity displays some essential qualitative features of cytoskeletal shape change in adherent cells [49].

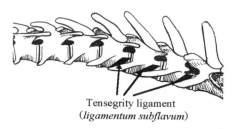

Tensegrity ligament
(*ligamentum subflavum*)

Figure 11: Part of the lumbar region of a rabbit's vertebral column showing the tensegrity ligaments, arranged such that they stretch when the spine is compressed longitudinally. The head end is to the left.

In a simple model of a tensegrity structure comprising six rigid struts interconnected by 24 linearly elastic cables, the cables were prestressed in tension which was counterbalanced by the compression of struts. The system was then stretched uniaxially. The calculated stiffness increases with increasing prestress, increasing approximately linearly with increasing stretching force. This is consistent with observations in living endothelial cells exposed to shear stresses [49]. The similarities continue in that the stiffness of a tensegrity structure is different for extension, compression and shear under large deformations even though the stifnesses of the cables and struts may be constant. The structural stiffness increases as the structure gets smaller and the internal tension thus increases.

At a more macro level, the mantle of cuttlefish *Sepia officinalis* expands to be filled with water in preparation for its jet-propelled escape behaviour. The elastic mechanism is supplied by collagen fibrils that are arranged as a type of 3D tensegrity structure, so that as the mantle contracts, the fibrils are stretched [50]. The mantle is very compliant up to a circumferential strains of 0.45. Beyond this the mantle is much stiffer, both circumferentially (0.542 ± 0.025 MPa) and through its thickness (0.152 ± 0.041 MPa). Almost 80% of the work done on the tissue during circumferential compression is recovered during elastic recoil of the tissue, probably sufficient to power refilling of the mantle.

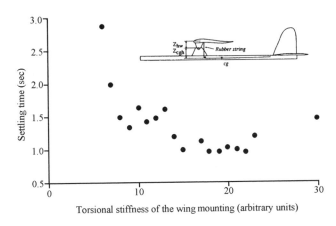

Figure 12: Freewing model (inset) showing compliant mounting and the speed with which it can recover from a burst of vorticity. There is a minimum time at a stiffness of 20 (1 unit is equivalent to 1 rubber band on the mounting!).

Many skeletons have highly compliant joints, especially fish in which the mass of the fish is supported by water. There are some interesting compliant mechanisms such as the actuation mechanism of teleost fins. The wings of birds are compliantly "mounted" – they are allowed to rotate along the span. This gives much greater stability in turbulent air: the wing can move much more freely in response to the air around it and thus not only generate lift over a wider variety of air flows [51], but can recover much more quickly from turbulence. Mathematical modelling and experimental studies on a wind-tunnel model (Fig. 12) show that this is probably a scaling effect that works well for small aircraft but not large (Sandiford, unpublished report).

References

[1] Currey, J.D., The design of mineralised hard tissues for their mechanical functions. *Journal of Experimental Biology*, **202**, pp. 3285–3294, 1999.

[2] Vincent, J.F.V., Locust oviposition: stress softening of the extensible intersegmental membranes. *Proceedings of the Royal Society, London, Series B*, **188**, pp. 189–201, 1975.

[3] Urry, D.W., Elastic biomolecular machines. *Scientific American*, pp. 44–49, January 1995.

[4] Thurmond, F.A. & Trotter, J.A. Morphology and biomechanics of the microfibrillar network of sea cucumber dermis. *Journal of Experimental Biology*, **199**, pp. 1817–1828, 1996.

[5] Wright, D.M., Duance, V.C., Wess, T.J., Kielty, C.M. & Purslow, P.P., The supramolecular organisation of fibrillin-rich microfibrils determines the mechanical

properties of bovine zonular filaments. *Journal of Experimental Biology*, **202**, pp. 3011–3020, 1999.

[6]   Kellermayer, M.S.Z., Smith, S.B., Bustamante, C. & Granzier, H.L., Complete unfolding of the titin molecule under external force. *Journal of Structural Biology*, **122**, pp. 197–205, 1998.

[7]   Jackson, A.P., Vincent, J.F.V. & Turner, R.M., The mechanical design of nacre. *Proceedings of the Royal Society, London, Series B*, **234**, pp. 415–440, 1998.

[8]   Jackson, A.P., Vincent, J.F.V. & Turner, R.M. A physical model of nacre. *Composites Science and Technology*, **36**, pp. 255–266 1998.

[9]   Smith, B.L., Schaffer, T.E., Viani, M., Thompson, J.B., Frederick, N.A., Kindt, J., Belcher, A., Stucky, G.D., Morse, D.E. & Hansma, P.K., Molecular mechanistic origin of the toughness of natural adhesives, fibres and composites. *Nature, London*, **399**, pp. 761–763, 1999.

[10] Volpin, D. & Ciferri, A., Thermoelasticity of elastin. *Nature, London*, **225**, p. 382, 1970

[11] Hoeve, C.A.J. & Flory, P.J., The elastic properties of elastin. *Biopolymers*, **13,** pp. 677–686 1974.

[12] Dorrington, K.L. & McCrum, N.G., Elastin as a rubber. *Biopolymers*, **16** pp. 1201–1222 1977.

[13] Weis-Fogh, T. & Andersen, S.O., New molecular model for the long-range elasticity of elastin. *Nature, London* **227**, 718–721, 1970.

[14] Gosline, J.M., The elastic properties of rubber-like proteins and highly extensible tissues. In: *The Mechanical Properties of Biological Materials*, eds. J.F.V. Vincent & J.D. Currey, The University Press: Cambridge, pp. 331–357, 1980.

[15] Gray, W.R., Sandberg, L.B. & Foster, J.A., Molecular model for elastic structure and function. *Nature, London*, **240**, pp. 461–466, 1973.

[16] Urry, D.W., What is elastin; what is not. *Ultrastructural Pathology*, **4**, pp. 227–251, 1983.

[17] Andersen, S.O. & Weis-Fogh, T., Resilin, a rubber-like protein in arthropod cuticle. *Advances in Insect Physiology*, **2**, pp. 1–65, 1964.

[18] Ardell, D.H. & Andersen, S.O., Tentative identification of a resilin gene in *Drosophila melanogaster*. *Insect Biochemistry and Molecular Biology*, **31**, pp. 965–970, 2001.

[19] Alexander, R.McN., Rubber-like properties of the inner hinge-ligament of Pectinidae. *Journal of Experimental Biology*, **44**, pp. 119–130, 1966.

[20] Bowie, M.A., Layes, J.D. & Demont, M.E., Damping in the hinge of the scallop *Placopecten magellanicus*. *Journal of Experimental Biology*, **175**, pp. 311–315, 1993.

[21] Martino, M., Coviello, A. & Tamburro, A.M., Synthesis and structural characterization of poly(LGGVG), an elastin-like polypeptide. *International Journal of Biological Macromolecules*, **27**, pp. 59–64, 2000.

[22] Diamant, J., Keller, A., Baer, E., Litt, M. & Arridge, R.G.C., Collagen: Ultrastructure and its relation to mechanical properties as a function of ageing. *Proceedings of the Royal Society, London, Series B*, **180**, pp. 293–315, 1972.

[23] Fratzl, P., Misof, K., Zizak, I., Rapp, G., Amenitsch, H. & Bernstorff, S., Fibrillar structure and mechanical properties of collagen. *Journal of Structural Biology*, **122**, pp. 119–122, 1997.

[24] Farley, C.T., Glasheen, J. & McMahon, T.A., Running springs: speed and animal size. *Journal of Experimental Biology*, **185**, pp. 71–86, 1993.

[25] Gosline, J.M. & Shadwick, R.E., Molluscan collagen and its mechanical organisation in squid mantle. In: *The Mollusca*, eds. V. Fretter & A. Graham, pp. 371–398, 1983.

[26] Macgillivray, P.S., Anderson, E.J., Wright, G.M. & Demont, M.E., Structure and mechanics of the squid mantle. *Journal of Experimental Biology*, **202**, pp. 683–695, 1999.

[27] Pabst, D.A., Springs in swimming animals. *American Zoologist*, **36**, pp. 723–735, 1996.

[28] Alexander, R.McN. & Ker, R.F., Locomotion – running is priced by the step. *Nature, London*, **346**, pp. 220–221, 1990.

[29] Ker, R.F., Dynamic tensile properties of the plantaris tendon of sheep (*Ovis aries*). *Journal of Experimental Biology* , **93**, pp. 283–302, 1981.

[30] Clark, R.B., *The Dynamics of Metazoan Evolution.* Clarendon Press: Oxford, 1964.

[31] Gibson, T., Stark, H. & Kenedi, R.M., The significance of Langer's lines. In: Hueston, J.T., (Ed.) *Trans 5th Int Congr Plastic & Reconstruct Surgery*, Butterworth: Australia, 1971.

[32] Purslow, P.P., Bigi, A., Ripamonte, A. & Roveri, N., Collagen fibre reorientation around a crack in biaxially stretched aortic media. *International Journal of Biological Macromolecules*, **6**, pp. 21–25, 1984.

[33] Cook, J. & Gordon, J.E., A mechanism for the control of crack propagation in all-brittle systems. *Proceedings of the Royal Society, London, Series A*, **282**, pp. 508–520, 1964.

[34] Mai, Y.-M. & Atkins, A.G., Further comments on J-shaped stress-strain curves and the crack resistance of biological materials. *Journal of Physics D: Applied Physics*, **22**, pp. 48–54, 1989.

[35] Purslow, P.P., Notch-sensitivity of non-linear materials. *Journal of. Materials Science*, **26**, pp. 4468–4476, 1991.

[36] Kobayashi, H., Kresling, B. & Vincent, J.F.V., The geometry of unfolding tree leaves. *Proceedings of the Royal Society, London, Series B*, **265**, pp. 147–154, 1998.

[37] Lees, C., Vincent, J.F.V. & Hillerton, J.E., Poisson's ratio in skin. *Journal of Bio-medical-mechanical Behaviour and Materials Engineering*, **1**, pp. 19–23, 1991.

[38] Lakes, R.S., Deformation mechanisms of negative Poisson's ratio materials: structural aspects. *Journal of Materials Science*, **26**, pp. 2287–2292, 1991.

[39] Purslow, P.P. & Vincent, J.F.V., Mechanical properties of primary feathers from the pigeon. *Journal of Experimental Biology* , **72**, pp. 251–260, 1978.

[40] Reynolds, S.E., The mechanical properties of the abdominal cuticle of *Rhodnius* larvae. *Journal of Experimental Biology*, **62**, pp. 69–80, 1975.

[41] Vincent, J.F.V., The morphology and ultrastructure of the intersegmental membrane of the female locust. *Tissue and Cell*, **13**, pp. 831–852, 1981.

[42] Andersen, S.O., Matrix proteins from insect pliable cuticles: are they flexible and easily deformed? *Insect Biochemistry and Molecular Biology*, **31**, pp. 445–452, 2001.

[43] Glaser, A.E. & Vincent, J.F.V., The autonomous inflation of insect wings. *Journal of Insect Physiology*, **25**, pp. 315–318, 1979.

[44] Reynolds, S.E., Control of cuticle extensibility in the wings of adult *Manduca* at the time of eclosion: effects of eclosion hormone and bursicon. *Journal of Experimental Biology*, **70**, pp. 27–39, 1977.

[45] Alexander, R.McN., Viscoelastic properties of jellyfish. *Journal of Experimental Biology*, **41**, pp. 363–369, 1964.

[46] Koehl, M.A.R., Mechanical diversity of connective tissue of the body wall of sea anemones. *Journal of Experimental Biology*, **69**, pp. 107–125, 1977.

[47] Gosline, J.M., Connective tissue mechanics of *Metridium senile* II Viscoelastic properties and a macromolecular model. *Journal of Experimental Biology*, **55**, pp. 775–795, 1971.

[48] Calladine, C.R., Buckminster Fuller's "Tensegrity" structures and Clerk Maxwell's rules for the construction of stiff frames. *International Journal of Solidsand Structures*, **14**, pp. 161–172, 1978.

[49] Wang, N. & Ingber, D.E., Control of cytoskeletal mechanics by extracellular-matrix, cell-shape, and mechanical tension. *Biophysical Journal*, **66**, pp. 2181–2189, 1994.

[50] Curtin, A., Woledge, R.C. & Bone, Q., Energy storage by passive elastic structures in the mantle of *Sepia officinalis*. *Journal of Experimental Biology*, **203**, pp. 869–878, 2000.

[51] Krus, P., Natural methods for flight stability in birds. *World Aviation Congress and exposition, SAE AIAA*, 1997.

CHAPTER 2

Compliance in plants

A.R. Ennos
School of Biological Sciences, University of Manchester, UK.

Abstract

The stems and branches of plants appear to be well designed to support the leaves because they arrange their tissues so that they are rigid in bending; stiff fibres are located towards the perimeter and they are held in tension, like the reinforcing rods of prestressed concrete beams, by turgor pressure within central parenchyma cells. However, plants are not fully rigid structures and their compliant design also allows them to grow, reconfigure and even move. Growth results from cell division and cell expansion, which is powered by internal turgor pressure within the cells. This stretches the temporarily compliant cell wall, expansion being controlled by varying the orientation of the helical cellulose microfibrils that give the cell wall its strength. The unfolding of some tree leaves is powered by expansion of the midrib.

The branched design of trees gives them far more compliance than conventional engineering structures and helps them avoid damage. Their crowns reconfigure in high winds, reducing drag by over two thirds, and the complex movements of the different branches prevents damaging resonance from building up. Fine control of the compliance of stems is achieved by altering the arrangement of fibrous tissue within plant organs and their cross-sectional shape. Torsional compliance is increased by having isolated reinforcing fibres and a non-circular shape, whereas flexural compliance is increased either by winding reinforcing tissue in a helix, or locating it centrally. Petioles and the stems of water plants and climbers exhibit even more extreme designs to allow reconfiguration, allowing themselves to stretch, bend, and twist easily, while leaves are so compliant that they roll up into a streamlined tube when subjected to strong winds. Some plants, in contrast, actually use compliance to allow wind-induced movements to disperse their propagules, while others have specially weakened "hinge" regions that allow them to move. Many of the techniques used by plants and described here could be mimicked to make engineering structures that are more durable.

1 Introduction

If animals are nature's equivalent of vehicles and machines, plants are surely the equivalent of civil-engineering structures like electricity pylons, wind turbines and flag poles. In all of them, the main structure holds another part clear of the ground. In a plant it is the stem, branches and roots that have the job of raising the leaves above those of other, competing plants. The leaves harvest light by the process of photosynthesis and so power the plant's growth and reproduction.

In such situations most man-made structures are made as rigid as possible so that they can withstand their own weight and the force of the wind without being deflected. As we shall see in this chapter, however, plants use quite a different strategy, using controlled compliance to reduce their support costs. They can change shape to make themselves more streamlined while preventing potentially dangerous resonance from developing; they can hang onto other plants for support; and some can even move about to a certain extent. But plants have a challenge that is not shared by engineering structures. They have to grow, maintaining their mechanical integrity throughout their lives, yet without being overdesigned at the start, and some even need to move. These requirements demand a further level of controlled compliance. This chapter shows how plants manage to overcome all their problems and produce structures that can withstand external forces, and yet still grow and even move when they need to. However, before we can understand how plants develop and use compliance, we must first examine how their basic mechanical design allows them to provide support.

2 The basic structural design of plants

Unlike animals or engineers, plants do not produce solid lumps of structural material. Instead, plants could be described as true cellular solids, since their skeleton is composed of the walls that surround all of their cells [1, 2]. The plant cell wall is actually a fibrous composite, composed of microfibrils of the sugar cellulose held within a matrix that is made up largely of hemicellulose and often stiffened by incorporation of lignin. The cell wall is braced against collapse by the liquid contents of the cell, which push outwards with turgor pressures of up to 2 MPa, just as footballs are kept inflated by pressurized air. Each cell is therefore supported by its own hydrostatic skeleton. Cells with thick or lignified walls have no need for turgor, however, and can provide support even when they are dead and their cell contents have disappeared.

The long organs of plants – the stems, branches and roots – are usually cylindrical and are far more complex in structure than merely being large numbers of cells stuck together. Even the most simple and primitive plants, such as mosses, have stems that are supported by two different types of cells. Most of the stem is composed of large thin-walled nearly spherical cells that are packed so closely together that the gaps between them are more-or-less closed up. This **parenchyma** tissue is held in place by being surrounded by a strong outer skin that is made up of a single flat layer of **epidermis** cells. The epidermis thus acts as the skin of a much larger hydrostatic skeleton, greatly increasing the rigidity of the stem. Water is supplied to the top of many primitive plants through the centre of the stem, flowing up tubes made of rows of dead cells each of which has a rigid lignified cell wall. This tissue is called **xylem**.

In more advanced plants, support is improved by incorporating other types of cells within the stem and arranging the different cell types in particular ways. In a typical flowering plant, or angiosperm, the rigid xylem tissue is moved towards the perimeter of the stem, where it is arranged in a ring of so-called **vascular bundles** (Fig. 1). Some of the xylem cells are thin-walled **vessels** that have a wide lumen that pipes water efficiently to the leaves. The rest are long narrow **fibres** whose thick walls have a mechanical function, acting like the reinforcing rods of a pre-stressed concrete girder. Because they are so resistant to stretching they help the stem resist bending forces, and they are protected from being compressed because they are held in pretension by the turgor pressure within the parenchyma cells. Rods of another type of cell,

collenchyma, may also be present around the outside of the stem. These are fibrous cells with non-lignified walls that also resist stretching well and provide additional support to the stem. Collenchyma is found in the stalks of celery (these are the bits that get stuck in your teeth!), in flax, where they make up the useful fibres, and in many other non-woody plants.

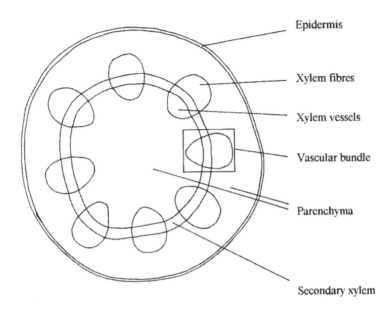

Figure 1: Transverse section of the stem of a typical flowering plant. The parenchyma tissue provides turgor that helps to keep the more rigid, xylem fibres in the vascular bundles in tension. Extra support is first given by the epidermis, and later in life by fibres in the secondary xylem that is formed by a ring of cambial tissue.

These herbaceous plant stems all require living cells to provide the turgor, which is both expensive metabolically and impossible to maintain in freezing conditions. For this reason trees and shrubs, which have permanent above-ground structures, replace this form of support by laying down large amounts of woody tissue. This **secondary xylem** is produced by cells that are arranged in a ring between the vascular bundles, and that divide to form the successive growth rings of wood, both vessels and fibres, that are familiar in tree trunks. These soon provide far more support than the original primary tissue of the stem that dies to leave a narrow "pith" in the centre of the trunk.

3 Compliance and plant growth

3.1 How plant cells expand

Plants produce all their new cells by the process of cell division, and at specialized sites called **meristems** [1]. Two types of meristem are responsible for extension growth. Most plants grow at the tip of the shoot and root at so-called **apical meristems,** whereas some such as grasses and horsetails also grow from points arranged along the stems or leaves called **intercalary**

meristems. Wherever they produce the cells, however, cell division just produces large numbers of tiny cells, each of which is already surrounded by a thin primary cell wall. How can such cells expand to allow the plant to get longer, especially those that have later to provide support for the plant? The answer is that the cell walls are briefly made more compliant, allowing the turgor pressure within the cells to power their expansion [3,4]. The final shape of the cell and the extent of the expansion are controlled by the orientation of the cellulose microfibrils.

The principles involved in cell expansion are, in fact, well known to engineers, since plant cells can be thought of as fibre-wound cylindrical pressure vessels [5]. The stresses set up in the walls of such vessels can be readily calculated by analysis and are given by Laplace's equations. The circumferential stress, σ_C, is given by the equation

$$\sigma_C = PR/t \tag{1}$$

where P is the internal pressure, R is the radius of the vessel and t is the thickness of its walls. This is precisely double the longitudinal stress, σ_L, which is given by the expression

$$\sigma_L = PR/2t. \tag{2}$$

The walls of man-made pressure vessels such as pressurized gas holders or rocket-fuel holders are often strengthened by helically wound fibres, and it is well known that the strength is optimized if they are wound at an angle of just under 55° to the long axis of the cylinder.

In primary plant cell walls, in contrast, the cellulose microfibrils are usually arranged at a much larger angle to the longitudinal axis of the cell (Fig. 2a), so they are far more resistant to circumferential stresses than longitudinal ones. When the matrix of the cell is softened, therefore, by lowering its pH, the turgor pressure within the cell causes it to extend, a process that continues until the mean fibre angle finally reaches 55°. The cell can then lay down a further, secondary cell wall within the primary wall to produce the final, stronger cell.

One advantage of this mechanism is that plants can control how much they extend merely by altering the initial angle of the cellulose microfibrils [6–8]; plants growing in sheltered environments, lay down the fibrils at a large angle and so the plant extends rapidly, whereas in windier conditions they lay them down at a lower angle, so producing shorter, stouter stems. The change in fibre orientation can be even more pronounced in roots. If a root is mechanically impeded by being grown in very hard soil the microfibrils are briefly laid down at less that 55° (Fig. 2b), so that the cells get thicker rather than longer. This produces a wider root that can then act as a more powerful hydraulic ram to force the tapered root cap through the soil [9].

The cells that have the greatest problem with extending are the primary xylem cells. They lose their cell contents as soon as they have finished extending, and so cannot produce a secondary cell wall. This is potentially disastrous for the plant as xylem has to have thick, lignified cell walls to prevent the cells from collapsing inwards as water is sucked up through them to the leaves The solution they adopt is to incorporate thickened rings or helices of lignified tissue into the wall [1]. These designs, strikingly similar to those developed for the hoses of vacuum cleaners, allow the primary xylem cells to extend while reinforcing it sufficiently when it starts to conduct water.

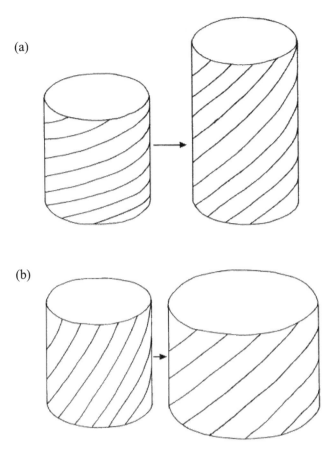

Figure 2: The control of cell growth by fibre angle. In most plant cells (a) the cellulose fibres are laid down at a large angle to the longitudinal axis. Hence when the cell wall is softened and the cell expands it only extends. In cells of roots that have been severely impeded the fibres are laid down at a low angle to the longitudinal axis (b) and so expand the cells outwards.

3.2 How leaves unfold

In parts of the world that have a seasonally dry or cold climate plants cannot grow all year round, and many drop their leaves. They then have to protect their delicate meristems within perennating buds throughout the period of dormancy. As better weather returns, the plants start growing again and produce a new canopy, and there is strong selection pressure to do this as rapidly as possible. To speed up the process, many bulb plants and trees carry out all the necessary cell division at the end of the previous growing season so that the cells need merely expand to their full size to produce the new canopy. There is just one problem; large numbers of flat leaves have to be packed into a small bud. In trees such as hornbeam and beech, this problem is overcome by folding the preformed leaves. It has been suggested [10] that the midrib is folded up within the bud, but it is far too thick to do this. What actually happens is that the opening of the leaf is powered by simple extension of the midrib as its cells expand

(Figure 3). The shear resistance of the tissue between the secondary veins consequently causes them to swing outwards until the leaf blade is flattened. The angle, α, to which the outer veins are swung can be readily calculated by trigonometry and depends entirely on the extent to which the midrib expands. It is given by the equation

$$\cos \alpha = X_0/X \qquad (3)$$

where X_0 is the initial distance between adjacent veins on the midrib and X is its final length. Further expansion of the leaf then follows as the cells all over the leaf surface, as well as those in the veins, expand further.

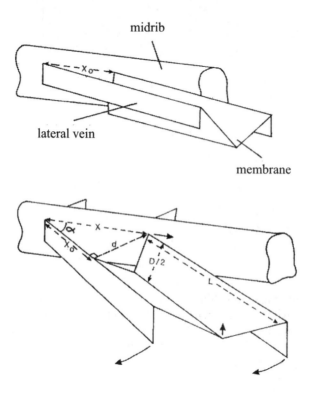

Figure 3: The geometry of leaf unfolding in hornbeams and hazels. As the midrib extends, the folded lateral veins are pushed outwards because of the resistance of the membrane between them to shear. They stop only when constrained by the membrane becoming flat.

4 Compliance in self-supporting plants

4.1 The effect of branching

One of the main ways in which plants differ from engineering structures is in their extremely branched form; the single stem or trunk splits into branches that further split into smaller branches and twigs that hold the leaves. This branching growth form first evolved because it was a better way of holding a given surface area of tissue clear of the ground than using a single unbranched stem [11]. Leaves evolved later to further increase the area exposed for photosynthesis.

The structural implications of this design are profound, as each twig and each branch acts as a separate structural element, totally free to move at its tip and subjected overwhelmingly to bending forces. This is totally different from a typical space-frame engineering structure such as a truss bridge or electricity pylon, which are made up of large numbers of interlocking elements. These constrain each others movements, so that the structure behaves as a single unit, while the individual elements tend to be subjected to either tension or compression. The most immediate consequence of these differences is that branched structures such as trees are far more compliant than engineering structures and deform much more when loaded, especially at the tips of the branches. The behaviour of the structure is also almost impossible to predict since each branch acts separately, though affected by more basal regions, so that the whole structure acts as an horrendously complex coupled oscillator. The whole thing looks from an engineer's point of view very poorly designed, yet trees can stand up to hurricanes that destroy most rigid man-made structures.

The compliant branched structure gives trees two major advantages over rigid ones in withstanding high winds. First, the free and separate movement of each branch and twig allows the crown of a tree to reconfigure efficiently in high winds, reducing the mean drag on the tree. In high winds, branches are bent together downwind to form a more streamlined shape [12,13]; any branch that sticks out from the general shape will be subjected to higher winds that bend it into the crown, whereas inner branches will be sheltered and will be deflected less. The effectiveness of this process has been shown by experiments in which 5-m pine trees were placed in wind tunnels [13]. As the wind speed increased from 9 to 38 m s^{-1} the windward branches were bent back, the crown was displaced downwind, and the drag coefficient fell from 0.43 to 0.15. Unfortunately, no similar measurements have been made on broadleaved trees, due mainly to the difficulty in getting large enough trees into a wind tunnel or measuring forces and windspeeds on mature trees in the field, but it is likely that they perform at least as well as conifers in this respect.

A second advantage is that the compliant branching system acts as an efficient shock absorber that protects the tree from sudden gusts of wind [14]. In a traditional rigid engineering structure, suddenly applying a force induces momentary stresses that are double those produced by a constant force. In a tree, on the other hand, the complex branched system will cushion the blow, delaying the time at which the trunk actually experiences the force. Because the branches are all different, moreover, they will delay the force by a different amount so that the trunk is further protected. This shock-absorbing system also helps trees cope with variable winds and turbulent airflows [15]. Because the twigs, branches and branch systems sway at a whole range of frequencies, many of them far lower than the resonant frequency of the trunk, they act to shield the tree from dangerous resonance. The system is not totally successful; trees still do exhibit resonant behaviour, with a primary resonant frequency, and conifers in particular do fail at wind speeds that are far lower than they should be able to withstand simply because their swaying can double or treble the peak forces [16]. However, this may be because these trees, having been grown in plantations, tend to have a single straight trunk and a small little-branched crown. Broadleaved trees, with their greater branching should perform better in this respect. It may even be that these trees can keep the energy largely within ends of the branches, so that it is used up breaking these expendable areas off the tree rather than causing it to fail as a whole. Certainly after a storm the ground tends to be littered with leaves, twigs and small branches. Unfortunately the branching systems of trees are so immensely complex that no biologist has managed to analyse them as coupled oscillators, or even make computer simulations of how they should behave in the wind. If that was done we might get a better idea of how they worked or how an engineer could design an optimized structure of this type.

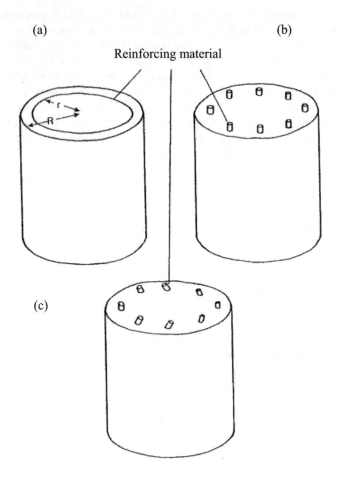

Figure 4: Three contrasting ways of arranging rigid material in the shoots of plants. Shoots reinforced by an outer ring of rigid material (a) are rigid in both flexure and torsion. Shoots reinforced by isolated axially oriented fibres (b) are rigid in flexure but compliant in torsion, while (c) reinforcement by helically wound fibres gives a shoot that is compliant in both flexure and torsion.

4.2 Compliant designs of shoots

Whatever the merits of their branching pattern, the ability of plants to stand up depends on their stems, branches and petioles having two conflicting properties: they must be rigid enough to stand up, and compliant enough to deflect away from the wind. Plants have developed many ways of doing this.

4.2.1 Stems

As we saw in the first section, stems and branches are composed of turgid water-filled tissue reinforced, and sometimes replaced later in life, by rigid lignified tissue. However, their precise mechanical properties depend greatly on the exact pattern of the reinforcement and their cross-sectional shape. Tree trunks and branches, for which rigidity is at a premium, are reinforced by a solid ring of woody tissue (Fig. 4a), which almost becomes a solid cylinder as secondary growth proceeds. This gives them both high flexural rigidity and high torsional rigidity. The young stems of herbs such as sunflowers *Helianthus annuus*, however, are reinforced by isolated fibres arranged near the periphery (Fig. 4b). This gives them similar high flexural rigidity but much higher torsional compliance, allowing them to twist their heads during the day to keep them facing the sun. Daffodils also have isolated fibres running within their flower stalks, and they improve their ability to allow their horizontal flowers to deflect away from the wind by a further adaptation [17]. They are not circular but elliptical in cross section, a fact that further increases their torsional compliance, so that the ratio between the two, the so-called twist-to-bend ratio, *EI/GK*, is around 13 (for cylinders of isotropic incompressible material this ratio is 1.5), where E is the elastic moduls, G is the shear modulus, I is the bending moment of inertia and K the polar moment of inertia. As the wind catches the trumpet heads, the stems can therefore twist as well as bend allowing them to be deflected downwind. Sedges have an even more extreme design. Their stems are triangular in cross section and contain many narrow isolated fibres of lignified tissue (Fig. 5), making them around 100 times easier to twist than to bend [18]. Because the stems are also curved downwards towards their tip, the wind therefore deflects them downwind solely by twisting them (Fig. 5), reducing their drag and reducing the chances of self-pollination.

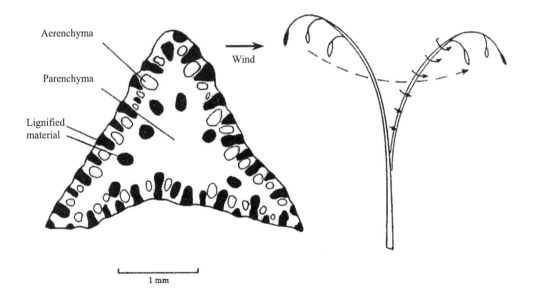

Figure 5: The mechanical design of the stem of the sedge *Carex acutiformis*. The transverse section (left) shows the triangular shape and isolated fibres that allow it to twist extremely easily, so that the sagging flower head twists away from the wind (right).

A third way of arranging reinforcing tissue in a stem is for them to be wound as a helix (Fig. 4c). This arrangement also allows high torsional compliance but it also greatly increases the flexural compliance, because bending such a stem merely rearranges the fibres within it rather than stretching or compressing them. Self-supporting herbs rarely arrange their fibres in this way because it would make their stems too flexible, but trees growing in windy areas often respond by producing wood in which the fibres wind up the trunk in this way [19, 20]. The development of this so-called **spiral grain** reduces the rigidity of the trunk [21, 22] and allows it to bend further away from the wind without being damaged. The cellulose microfibrils within the wood fibres themselves are also wound at a higher angle to the long axis of the cell than in normal wood, giving this "flexure wood" even higher compliance and breaking strain.

4.2.2 Petioles

The **petioles** or leaf stalks of plants have even more complex mechanical demands on them than stems. Because they cantilever out more-or-less horizontally from their base they have to resist the vertical forces imposed by the weight of the leaf yet be compliant to horizontal wind forces so that the leaves can flag downwind, reducing drag. There are two main ways in which petioles achieve this.

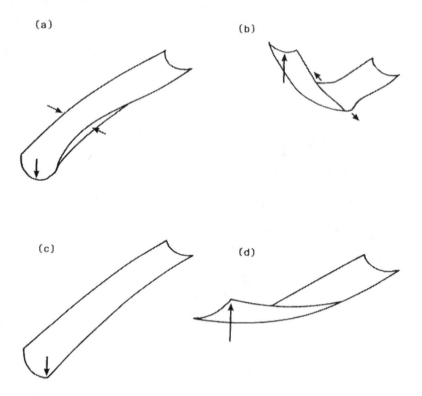

Figure 6: Mechanical behaviour of cambered beams. A beam is more resistant to forces on its concave surface (a) than on its convex surface (b) because in the first case the camber increases whereas in the latter it is flattened out. The same happens when the load is off-centre, so torsion is also more strongly resisted against forces on the concave surface (c) than on the convex one (d).

The petioles of poplar trees are elliptical in cross-section, their long axis being vertical [23]. This gives adequate rigidity to support the leaves against gravity but allows them to bend easily downwind. They also have rather high torsional compliance as a result, however, so even in light winds the leaves are continually being tilted about, giving rise to the name of one species the "quaking aspen".

A much more common design is for the petiole to be channel shaped [23, 24]. This structure, like that of a flexible measuring tape, gives excellent resistance to downward forces but is much more compliant to upward flexing and to torsion (Fig. 6). As a consequence, channel-shaped petioles readily deflect downwind by a combination of bending and twisting [24]. The channel shape is also adopted by the narrow leaves of plants such as grasses and bluebells, and as these curve downwards along their length, like the stems of sedges, they also twist readily away from the wind.

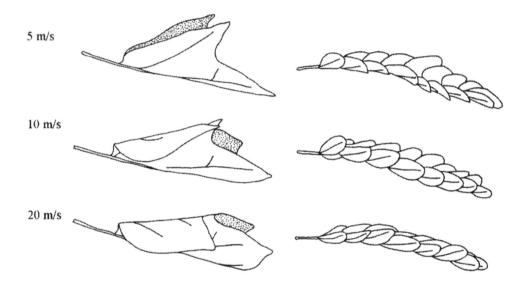

Figure 7: The behaviour of the lobed leaves of the tulip tree *Liriodendron tulipifera* (left) and the pinnate leaves of black walnut *Juglans nigra* (right). Redrawn after [25]. They both curl up into tubes as winds increase, reducing drag.

4.2.3 Leaves

However the stems and petioles behave, it is the leaves of plants that make up the majority of its surface area and are therefore likely to be subjected to the greatest aerodynamic forces by the wind. This force can to some extent be reduced by the compliance of their petioles that can allow the leaves to fold back and overlap each other when the wind blows, but further reduction in drag can be effected by the compliance of the leaves themselves. Vogel [25] has shown that in wind speeds of 5 to 20 ms^{-1}, lobed leaves progressively roll up into streamlined tubes, while the leaflets of pinnate leaves flex downwind and wrap around each other to form a similarly streamlined structure (Fig. 7). In both cases the drag coefficient can be reduced by around 70%. Unfortunately, no study has investigated how the venation of the leaves allows this to happen while being rigid enough to support the leaves. It may well involve similar use of channel-shaped structures as we saw in petioles and is used in insect wings [26].

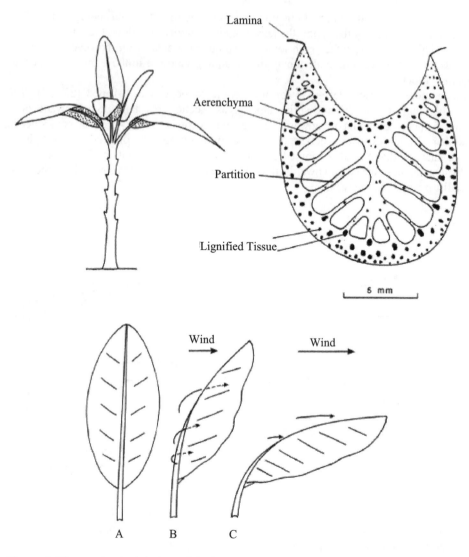

Figure 8: The mechanical design of the banana. A view of the whole plant (top left) shows how the petioles curve off the stem, bending downward towards their tips, and the huge leaf lamina. A transverse section of the semi-hollow petiole reveals its U shape and isolated fibres which makes it easy to twist. A top view of a petiole and leaf (bottom, A) show how in increasing wind it first twists away from the wind (B) and then bends further away and allows the lamina to fold up (C).

4.2.4 The design of banana shoots

Perhaps the most spectacular of all designs that combine rigidity and compliance is seen in the huge petioles and leaves of bananas [27]. The petiole is superbly designed to be rigid in bending; it is hollow, with the outer wall reinforced by large numbers of fibres, and braced against buckling by longitudinal stringers and bulkheads make of lightweight sheets of stellate parenchyma (Fig. 8). At the same time it is extremely easy to twist because of its channel-shaped cross section and isolated fibres, and like the sedge stem its downward curvature allows it to twist rather than bend away from the wind. The downward curvature also supports the leaf lamina, which is held against gravity by its own domed shape. This enables the lamina to do without rigid lateral veins, and so in strong winds the two sides can fold readily backwards to meet each other and flag downwind (Fig. 8). Therefore, although extremely light and cheap to construct, the whole structure can withstand hurricanes.

5 Compliance in water plants

Plants living in water, such as seaweeds, sea grasses and aquatic water weeds have much less of a problem with support than land plants because they are more-or-less neutrally buoyant. Many indeed hold themselves up to the light merely by trapping air within their leaves or fronds. However, the horizontal drag forces imposed on them (by water currents or waves) can be much greater than those on land plants. As a consequence they tend to exhibit even more extreme compliance to prevent damage, and reconfigure even more with the flow.

Both seaweeds and aquatic angiosperms [28–30] concentrate their rigid material towards the centre of their stipes or stems, where it is well placed to resist tension but readily flexes, allowing the plants to follow the current. But even this rigid tissue is more compliant than in land plants; the cellulose microfibrils in the cell wall tend to be arranged at a much higher angle to the long axis and are embedded in a more compliant, usually unlignified, matrix. The result is that they have much higher breaking strains than land plants: around 15% in the water crowfoot *Ranunculus fluitans* [28] and 40% in the seaweed *Nereocystis lutkeana* [29]. This allows the stem to act as a suspension system, stretching to absorb sudden shocks, just like a climbing rope. The resilience that results from having such compliant tissue is even seen in the sea palm *Postelsia palmaeformis*, a seaweed that is adapted to stand up out of the water at low tide, by having a thick, tubular stipe [31]. If a wave hits it, the stipe simply buckles, allowing the sea palm to flop over onto its side, but when the force subsides the stipe straightens again and the palm flips back up undamaged.

The leaves and fronds of plants that are growing in faster-moving water tend to be narrower and more rope-like than those in still water [32]. They readily reconfigure downstream, and they flutter less in fast-moving water and overlap more with each other, so producing less drag than wider, more strap-like leaves.

6 Compliance in climbing plants

One way in which land plants can reduce their support costs is to climb up other, self-supporting plants and so parasitise their investment in support [33]. Climbing plants therefore do not need such thick stems, or strong anchorage systems. However, because they need to grow upwards to find their supports in the first place, and because their supports will probably sway about or even fall over, climbing plants have had to develop structures that combine rigidity and compliance.

One functional group of climbing plants are the twiners, such as runner beans and bindweed, which wind their way up the trunks of the hosts. Apart from being narrow, the stems of these plants are better adapted for rigidity than compliance. They tend to be reinforced by rings of rigid lignified tissue that help them resist being unwound from their support.

A second group of climbers, scrambling plants such as cleavers and hops, grow through the branches and foliage of their hosts, holding themselves up using downward pointing hairs or spines to increase the friction with their supports. Though they have narrow stems, the young shoots still have to hold themselves up to try and find new foliage to grow up, and so like twiners they tend to be sheathed with a ring of rigid tissue. However, near the base of the plant the stem is capable of being stretched by up to 25% of its original length [34]. This helps prevent the plant from being pulled out of the ground if its support moves, acting just like the compliant stems of water plants to reduce the peak loads that are transmitted to the root system.

The most evolutionarily advanced form of climbers are the tendril climbers that grip their supports actively (see the next section) using modified petioles, branches or flower stalks. Like scramblers, the young shoot has to be able to support itself until its tendrils take a grip, but then it needs to be able to be moved towards that support as the tendril pulls it up. Tendril plants such as vetches and peas manage this by having stems with isolated strands of woody tissue at their corners or wing-like flanges, which increase the flexural rigidity but readily allow the stem to *twist* towards the support. Older stem regions are adapted mainly for compliance. Woody climbers or lianas lay down their woody tissue (needed to supply water to the leaves) in isolated strands that are wound around each other in a helix [33]. This gives lianas the look and properties of ropes, making them flexible enough to cope even if their supporting tree falls over, and suitable for using to make suspension bridges or even as a means of transport for jungle-bound hominids. Many herbaceous climbers use their tendrils themselves as a suspension system. In bryony and passion flowers, for instance, the tendrils throw themselves into spring-like coils once they have gripped a branch. This pulls the plant upwards and acts like the springs of a car to reduce peak forces. Just like the stems of twining plants, these tendrils develop an outer ring of rigid tissue, which give them the torsional rigidity that they require; stretching helical springs, after all, twists the wire from which they are made [35].

7 Compliance in roots

Most roots are rigid structures that transmit the loads on plants into the soil and so help anchor them [36]. Basal roots are often reinforced by a solid mass of lignified tissue or even a ring, giving them flexural rigidity that allows them to transfer bending forces into the soil. More distal roots, meanwhile, are subjected to mostly tensile forces and are reinforced by a rigid central stele. Some climbing plants, though, have fairly compliant basal roots that act like shock absorbers, just like their stem base. Those of cleavers have a breaking strain of around 28% [34]. Many arctic plants also exhibit a strange pattern of root growth that helps them cope with frost-heave events. In freeze-thaw cycles, arctic soils expand and contract, a process that would jack a plant with conventional roots out of the ground. The arctic plants counter this by developing roots that grow like helical springs [37]; in frost-heave events they simply uncoil without being damaged.

8 Compliance and seed dispersal

We have seen that usually plants try to avoid potentially catastrophic resonance to build up, but some plants actually use wind-induced resonance to help disperse their seeds. The seed-capsules of the liana *Alsomitra macrocarpa* are football-like structures held onto the stem by a short, rubbery stalk [38]. The gentle convection breezes that pass the seed capsule generate a string of von Karman vortices, which detach at the "vortex shedding" frequency, causing the seed capsule to sway from side to side at the end of its stalk. The gliding seeds for which the plant is famous are thereby flung out and glide long distances downwind. Similar movements are induced in the spore cases of mosses [39]. Unfortunately the morphology of the stalks of neither plant has been investigated.

Pine cones are far less flexible but compliance still pays some part in their opening. The scales of a cone are composed mainly of corky tissue, which is reinforced near its abaxial surface by a line of woody fibres. These two tissues exhibit different responses to humidity. When the scales are wet the cone is held firmly shut, but when it dries out the corky tissue contracts more than the fibres pulling the scales out and down, opening the cone and releasing the winged seeds.

9 Compliance and plant movement

Though they are basically sedentary, plants can and do move, and they power their movement by the same mechanism by which they grow; they use turgor. Movement is generated by blocks of large, thin-walled cells whose compliance is momentarily increased by lowering its pH, allowing them to expand. Plants then have to organize other tissue cleverly to produce compliant hinges.

In many cases, structures need to be able to bend in all sorts of directions: tendrils have to be able to grip onto supports whichever side they touch them on; leaves must be able to tilt in all sorts of directions to point to the sun; and roots must be able to deflect away from soil particles. As a result, tendrils, roots and **pulvini** (structures at the base of some leaves that orientate the leaf blade) all have similar structures. Rigid material is localized to a narrow rod in the centre and is surrounded on all sides with large movement-generating cells [2]. Asymmetrical expansion of these causes the structures to bend. In the venus fly trap *Dionea*, the large cells are arranged along the outside of the hinge between the two jaws, so expanding the cells closes the jaws [40]. Julian Vincent has suggested, however, that this process is speeded up because the two jaws of the trap are bistable plates and flip from one state to the other as the trap closes [41].

10 Conclusion: the potential for biomimetics

At first glance plants do not appear to be ideal candidates to mimic for structural engineers. The design of their shoot systems, consisting as it does of branched systems of relatively narrow, and usually solid rods, seems mechanically inefficient, certainly compared with efficient man-made space frame and monocoque structures. Yet as we have seen, closer examination reveals hidden sophistication in their designs, which can repay further investigation. For a start, branched structures have compliant properties that help them reduce aerodynamic loads, both statically, by reconfiguration and dynamically, by reduction in resonance. Secondly, compared with the case in composite materials and pre-stressed concrete, plants arrange the reinforcing material in their limbs in a wide variety of ways that confer contrasting levels of flexural and torsional compliance. The use of torsion, in particular, by plants might profitably be mimicked by engineers. Thirdly the methods by which they control their growth and even move might be a useful model for the design of flexible inflatable structures.

Much remains to be discovered about compliance in plants, particularly about the dynamic properties of branched structures and the structural engineering of leaves. Nevertheless, we know enough to see that their designs have much to teach us. Joseph Paxton, the designer of London's Crystal Palace is famously said to have learnt about how to design for rigidity by considering the leaf of the giant water lily *Victoria amazonica*. I believe that modern engineers could learn even more about design by looking at the compliance of plants.

References

[1] Rudall, P. *Anatomy of Flowering Plants.* Edward Arnold, London, 1987.

[2] Haberlandt, G. *Physiological Plant Anatomy.* Macmillan, London, 1914.

[3] Cosgrove, D.J. Biophysical control of plant cell growth. *Annual Review of Plant Phyiology* **37,** pp. 377–405, 1986.

[4] Cosgrove, D.J. How do plant cell walls expand? *Plant Physiology,***102,** pp. 1–6, 1993.

[5] Gordon, J.E. *Structures or Why Things Don't Fall Down* Penguin Books, London, 1978.

[6] Jaffe, M.J. Thigmomorphogenesis: the response of plant growth and development to mechanical stimulation. *Planta* **114,** pp. 143–157, 1973.

[7] Jaffe, M.J. Thigmomorphogenesis: a detailed characterisation of the response of beans (*Phaseolus vulgaris* L.) to mechanical stimulation. *Z. Pflanzenphysiology* **77,** pp. 437–453, 1976.

[8] Jaffe, M.J., Biro R.L. & Bridle, K. Thigmomorphogenesis: calibration of the parameters of the sensory function in beans *Physiologia Plantarum* **49,** pp. 410–416, 1980.

[9] Russell, R.S. *Plant Root Systems: their Function and Interaction with the Soil,* McGraw-Hill, London, 1977.

[10] Kobayashi, H, Kresling B. & Vincent J.F.V. The geometry of unfolding tree leaves *Proceedings of the Royal Society of London B,* **265,** pp. 147–154, 1998.

[11] Niklas, K.J. Morphological evolution through complex domains of fitness (Chapter 1) *Evolutionary Biology vol.12,* eds. M. Hecht, W. Strrer & B. Wallace, Plenum Press: New York, pp. 1–89, 1995.

[12] Bertram, J.E.A. Size-dependent differential scaling in branches: the mechanical design of trees revisited. *Trees* **4,** pp. 241–253, 1989.

[13] Mayhead G.J. Some drag coefficients for British trees derived from wind tunnel studies. *Agricultural Meteorology,* **12,** pp. 123–130, 1973.

[14] Wood,C.J.(1995) Understanding wind forces on trees (Chapter 7). *Wind and Trees,* eds. M.P. Coutts & J. Grace, Cambridge University Press: Cambridge, pp.133–164, 1995.

[15] Gardiner,B.A.(1995) The interactions of wind and tree movement in forest canopies trees (Chapter 2). *Wind and Trees,* eds. M.P. Coutts & J. Grace, Cambridge University Press: Cambridge, pp.41–59, 1995.

[16] Blackburn,P.,Petty,J.A.,Miller,K.F. An assessment of the static and dynamic factors involved in windthrow. *Forestry,* **61,** pp. 29–43, 1988.

[17] Etnier S.A, & Vogel, S. Reorientation of daffodil (*Narcissus* : Amaryllidaceae) flowers in wind: drag reduction and torsional flexibility. *American Journal of Botany* **87,** pp. 29–32, 2000.

[18] Ennos, A.R. The mechanics of the flower stem of the sedge *Carex acutiformis.* *Annals of Botany.* **72,** pp. 123–127, 1993.

[19] Telewski, F.W. Structure and function of flexure wood in *Abies fraseri. Tree Physiology* **5,** pp. 113–121, 1989.

[20] Telewski, F.W, & Jaffe, M.J. Thigmomorphogenesis: field and laboratory studies of *Abies fraseri* in response to wind or mechanical perturbation. *Physiologia Plantarum* **66,** pp. 211–218, 1986.

[21] Telewski,F.W.(1995) Wind-induced physiological and developmental responses in trees. (Chapter 14). *Wind and Trees,* eds. M.P. Coutts & J. Grace, Cambridge University Press: Cambridge, pp.237–263, 1995.

[22] Kubler, H. Function of spiral grain in trees. *Trees: Structure and Function,* **5,** pp. 125–135.

[23] Vogel, S. Twist-to-bend ratios and cross-sectional shapes of petioles and stems. *Journal of Experimental Botany* **43**, pp. 1527–1532, 1992.

[24] Ennos, A.R. Mechanical behaviour in torsion of insect wings, blades of grass and other cambered structures. *Proceedings of the Royal Society, B.* **259**, pp. 15–18,1995.

[25] Vogel,S. Drag and reconfiguration of broad leaves in high winds. *Journal of Experimental Botany,* **40**, pp. 941–948, 1989.

[26] Ennos, A.R. Flexible structures in biology. *Comments on Theoretical Biology.* **4**, pp. 133–149, 1997.

[27] Ennos, A.R., Spatz, H-CH. & Speck, T. The functional morphology of the petioles of the banana *Musa textilis. Journal of Experimental Botany.* **51**, pp. 2085–2093, 2000.

[28] Usherwood, J.R., Ennos, A.R. & Ball, D.J., Mechanical and anatomical adaptations in terrestrial and aquatic buttercups to their respective environments. *Journal of Experimental Botany*, **48**, pp. 1469–1475, 1997.

[29] Koehl, M.A.R. & Wainwright, S.A., Mechanical adaptations of a giant kelp. *Limnology and Oceanography*, **22**, pp. 1067–1071, 1977.

[30] Ennos, A.R., The aerodynamics and hydrodynamics of plants. *Journal of Experimental Biology*, **202**, pp. 3281–3284, 1999.

[31] Koehl, M.A.R. & Alberte, R.S., Flow, flapping and photosynthesis of *Nereocystis luetkeana*: a functional comparison of undulate and flat blade morphologies. *Marine Biology*, **99**, pp. 435–444, 1988.

[32] Holbrook, N.M., Denny, M.W. & Koehl, M.A.R., Intertidal trees: consequences of aggregation on the mechanical and photosynthetic properties of sea-palms *Postelsia palmaeformis* Ruprecht. *Journal of Experimental Marine Biology and Ecology*, **146**, pp. 39–67, 1991.

[33] Putz, F.E. & Holbrook, N.M., Biomechanical studies of vines (Chapter 3). *The Biology of Vines*, eds. F.E. Putz & H.A. Mooney, 65, Cambridge University Press, pp. 73–97, 1991.

[34] Goodman, A.M., Personal Communication.

[35] Spring Research Association, *Helical Springs.* Oxford University Press: Oxford, 1974.

[36] Ennos, A.R., The mechanics of root anchorage. *Advances in Botanical Research*, **33**, pp. 133–155, 2000.

[37] Callagham, T.V., Headley, A.D. & Lee, J.A., Root function in tundra plants (Chapter 22), *Plant Root Growth: an Ecological Perspective*, ed. D. Atkinson, Blackwell Scientific: Oxford, pp. 311–340, 1991.

[38] Azuma, A. & Okuno, Y., Flight of a samara *Alsomitra macrocarpa. Journal of Theoretical Biology*, **129**, pp. 263–274, 1987.

[39] Vogel, S., *Life in Moving Fluids*, Princeton University Press: Princeton, 1994.

[40] Fagerberg, W.R. & Allain, D., A quantitative study of tissue dynamics during closure in the traps of venus flytrap *Dionae -muscipula* Ellis. *American Journal of Botany*, **78**, pp. 647–657, 1991.

[41] Vincent, J.F.V., Personal Communication.

Section II

Compliant Materials

CHAPTER 3

Reinforced polyurethane flexible foams

S.K. Khanna & S. Gopalan
Mechanical and Aerospace Engineering Department, University of Missouri, USA

Abstract

Short glass-fibers, glass micro-spheres and chopped glass-fiber strands were used to reinforce polyurethane flexible foam, which is very widely used in a variety of applications, to determine its feasibility for improving the impact behavior of foam filled thin sheet metal structures. The reinforcements were added individually and in a hybrid combination. It has been observed that short glass fibers are more effective in improving the tensile and flexural deformation response of the foam compared to other reinforcing fillers. All types of reinforced foams show degradation in compressive strength compared to the unfilled polyurethane foam. The impact response of reinforced polyurethane flexible foam-filled aluminum tubes shows promise in improving energy absorption during impact.

1 Introduction

Cellular polymers or foams are multiphase materials systems that consist of a polymer matrix, a fluid phase, generally air or gas, and filler material (if used). Most polymers can be converted into a cellular material, but only a few polymers such as polyurethane, polystyrene and polyolefins have been widely used. Cellular or foam-like materials are also very common in nature. Some examples are wood, cork, leaves, sponge, proteins, bones, etc. Many foods such as bread, meringue, and chocolate, have foam like structure. Humans have tried to mimic their structure using both natural and simulated materials, and have used these new materials in many engineering and biological applications. The most common example is the white coffee cup used in fast food restaurants. However, lately more of these materials are being used for structural or load-bearing applications and energy-absorbing applications. Some examples are metal foams, ceramic foams (Reddy and Schultz [1]), foam in foam polyurethane foams (Yuan and Shutov [2]), and high porosity hydroxyapatite foam scaffolds for bone substitute (Ebaretonbofa and Evans [3]). Foams are ideal energy absorbers as they can undergo larger deformations at nearly constant stress. And if fillers, such as glass fibers or hollow microspheres of glass, are dispersed throughout the polymer matrix the specific energy of absorption in a composite structure can be increased.

Cellular polymers or polymer foams have a cellular structure produced by gas bubbles formed during the polymerization process. The properties of the foam depend on the size, shape and topology of the cells that constitute the foam. A variety of cell shapes, sizes and connectivity can be observed in both synthetic and natural foams, though the latter show more variety. Natural foams are observed in materials such as cork, wood, cancellous bone, iris leaf, stalks of various plants, coral, etc.

Foams are classified according to the nature of the cell structure (open, closed, or mixed) or according to their stiffness (rigid or flexible). Historically, rigid-type foam materials have been used to increase stiffness and provide extra energy absorption when applied, but their contribution diminishes with aging of the structure. Rigid polymer foams have found limited use in automobile bodies and aerospace structures for increased crash resistance. Semi-flexible and flexible foams have been used for cushioning and vibration damping, but not for improving crash resistance. Thus if flexible or semi-flexible foams having a relatively higher load bearing capacity with high recovery properties (similar to a coiled metal spring) can be fabricated, they could be used for energy absorption in lightweight structures.

Polymeric foams have many uses depending upon their physical characteristics. The most popular application of polymeric foams is for thermal insulation (Gibson and Ashby [4]). Polymeric foams are used as insulators because of their low thermal conductivity. Applications include things as simple as styrofoam coffee cups and refrigerated trucks, to complicated structures like the insulation for the booster rockets on the space shuttle (Gibson and Ashby [4]).

Polymeric foams have been found to be of good use in marine applications. Polymeric foams are non-corrosive in a salt-water sea environment. This is significant because most metals currently being used in marine applications are corrosive and start to deteriorate after time when exposed to the damp salt-water environment. Polymeric foams have also been found to have good buoyancy (Gibson and Ashby [4]). It has been found that some polymeric foams can make a structure float in water (Gibson and Ashby [4]). Usually, foams are used for rafts and floatation devices. The buoyancy comes from the closed cell structure of the foam. The closed cell structure of the foam traps air in the cell, giving the foam low density, which makes it able to float when placed in water (Gibson and Ashby [4]). It has also been noticed that foams, even when subjected to extreme damage from a collision, continue to float, which can be vital to the survival of a human trapped on a raft or flotation device on the sea. Foams also do not suffer from extended length of time in water (Gibson and Ashby [4]).

Polymeric foams have been found to be good filters (Gibson and Ashby [4]). Filters are able to sift through a liquid or gas and remove any larger particles in the liquid or gas. When a liquid or a gas is pushed through an open-cell polymeric foam, the larger particles are kept behind, trapped against cell walls as the rest of the liquid or gas passes through the open cell.

Polymeric foams are also used as water-repellent membranes that allow air to permeate whatever is underneath the membrane (Gibson and Ashby [4], [5], Szycher [6]). Often, as with burns on human skin, it is necessary to keep water out and allow air in, and polymer foam membranes can do that. These types of barriers also provide a hydrophobic barrier in some high-quality sporting and leisurewear (Gibson and Ashby [4]). Polymeric foams are also used to coat roofs of houses and other buildings because they are able to keep out the rain and moisture from the air, improving the life of the wood used to build the house or building ([5, 7–11]).

Since the surfaces of polymeric foams are often rough, they have a high coefficient of friction (Gibson and Ashby [4]). This high value makes the foam able to serve well as a non-slip surface. These types of surfaces are used on the soles of shoes, floors, mats, trays, and many other types of surfaces (Gibson and Ashby [4, 8–11]).

Polymeric foams have been found to have a great ability to damp sound and vibration (Gibson and Ashby [4], Titow and Lanhoam [12], Saha and Cahine [13], Ratcliffe and Crane [14], Wagner *et al.* [15]). This property of the foam, mixed with low weight of the foam and the easy moldability to a specified shape, allows the foam to be used in walls and ceilings of buildings. These types of foams are also used in automobiles and houses to absorb sound. Often times a layer of foam padding is applied to the floors before carpet is laid so that there is less noise heard on one side or the other of the floor ([9], Ratcliffe and Crane [14]).

Polymeric foams have been found to provide good lubrication. Because they are a rubber-like compound, they are able to deform around other working parts, which causes less wear to those parts. There are several companies that manufacture polymers, even polymeric foams, into bearings because of longer life for other mechanical parts that the bearings come into contact with ([9, 10, 12]). Also, if a polymer is used on another polymer, there is not as much wear as with a metal on metal, thus extending the life of the part(s) being used. (However, there may be high frictional forces between the parts because polymers have high coefficients of friction.)

Polymeric foams, especially polyurethane foams, are used in the medical industry as well ([10, 12]). In the area of medicine, polyurethane foams are used as cushioning in wheelchairs, splints, braces, and some types of bandaging. One of the features that make polyurethane foams appealing to the medical field is that the open cells in the foam allow the user a comfortable way to get better. The foam actually absorbs any impact that may occur and prevent another injury to an injured area. The foam also is a good material for use in this manner because the foam allows the skin to still be able to 'breathe', or be able to get some fresh air through the open cells that are in the foam [9]. Also, depending on the foam, it may also be used as a water-proof barrier, preventing the injured area from getting wet.

The second most popular use for polymeric foams is in packaging (Gibson and Ashby [4, 16, 17]). In packaging, especially of delicate materials, it is necessary to use a material that will absorb the energy if the package is dropped or falls. Polymeric foams have been found to be great at absorbing energy. Polymeric foams withstand large compressive strains, which allow more energy to be absorbed without injuring an item that might be on the other side of the foam (Gibson and Ashby [4]). Polymeric foams are important to packaging because they not only absorb the energy from an impact, they also have a low density, which makes the shipping cost less because it is lighter than if some other type of material was used (Gibson and Ashby [4, 16, 17]). Polymeric foams are also a favorite in packaging because they are easy to mold to a certain shape and they are also a cheap material to purchase. Polymeric foams are also used in the packaging of electronic components, because there is little or no static involved with the foam, so the electronic components do not get damaged from static discharge.

Polymeric foams also play an important role in structures. The most common uses for polymeric foams in a structural application are in sandwich panels. A sandwich panel is usually comprised of two plates, usually a metal (like aluminum), separated by a specific width (defined by the application) of polymeric foam or some other cellular solid (like wood). Some examples of sandwich structures include: the skin of airplanes, on and inside space vehicles, skis, boats (especially racing yachts), and buildings (Gibson and Ashby [4]). One of the most popular uses of sandwich panels is in manufacturing homes and buildings ([5, 7, 8]). There are several web sites that demonstrate the needs and uses of polyurethane foam sandwich panels ([5, 7, 8]). (Note that in sandwich panels of this kind, rigid polyurethane foam is used.) Some of the uses of sandwich panels include, but are not restricted to, use as an insulator and siding on houses ([5, 7, 8]), and use on or in walls and ceilings for noise insulation ([16]). Sandwich panels are used as siding partly because they offer more resistance and less damage from impact and weather damage ([7, 8, 11, 16]). The house would also be prevented from getting water damage to the wood of the house.

There are several authors who have researched the use of rigid polyurethane foam and its ability to absorb impact energy; however, there are very few resources for flexible polyurethane foams. Zhang *et al.* [18] discuss the temperature effects and strain rates on rigid polyurethane and compared those results with some other foams. Goods *et al.* [19] discuss the mechanical properties of rigid polyurethane foam. Shim *et al.* [20] discuss the response of rigid polyurethane foam when subjected to low-velocity impact. There are several other sources for rigid foam, some of them covering impact resistance in rigid polyurethane foam; however, there are no sources that examine the ability of a flexible polyurethane foam to absorb impact energy. Most of the resources for flexible polyurethane foams discuss its use as a damper or as a seat cushion, like in a chair or an automobile seat a few examples include (Saha and Cahine [13], Ratcliffe and Crane [14], Wagner *et al.* [15]).

Over the past few years engineering structural foams have been increasingly used for load-bearing applications. The polymers used are high-density polyethylene, polycarbonate, and polyurethane, among others (Gibson and Ashby [4], Hilyard [21], Chang, *et al.* [22], Zhang, *et al.* [18], Szycher [6], Klempner and Frisch [23], and Kumar and Weller [24]). Often additional solid phases are added to the cellular system in the form of fibers or particles. The addition of fibers, such as glass fibers or nylon fibers, results in materials called "fiber-reinforced foams". [Metheven and Shortall [25], Cotgreave and Shortall [26, 27]). A dispersion of particles, such as hollow glass or ceramic micro-spheres, in the polymer matrix results in a composite material called syntactic foams (Puterman and Narkis [28], Narkis and Puterman [29], Okuno and Woodhams [30], Thomas [31], Rizzi, *et al.* [32], Hostis and Devries [33], Goods *et al.* [34], and Titow and Lanham [35]). In the case of the fiber-reinforced foams, the fibers are added to the resin and the normal foaming process generates the random cellular structure, while in the case of syntactic foams the cellular structure is generated due to the addition of hollow micro-spheres into the polymer resin and not by the gas foaming process. Substantial research has been conducted on polymer foams and syntactic foams, however, much less effort has been spent on reinforced polymer foams. Some of the notable research effort in the area of reinforced polymer foams is briefly presented here.

Hornberger *et al.* [36] have evaluated the mechanical properties of glass-fiber reinforced polycarbonate structural foam. The glass fibers were used as reinforcements in the weight percentage varying from 5–30%. It was found that the tensile modulus of the structural foam increases with increase in glass-fiber content. Flexural modulus increases linearly with glass-fiber content. The flexural modulus of the composite in flow directions is higher than in cross-flow directions. The flow and cross-flow directions are defined based on fiber orientation.

The dynamic mechanical properties of natural-fiber-reinforced epoxy foam for the auto industry were evaluated by Bledzki *et al.* [37]. Dynamic mechanical analysis was carried out with the help of a torsion pendulum tester. To evaluate the effect of the change from the glass to the rubber-like state, differential scanning calorimetry (DSC) experiments were used. It was found that the increase of micro void content from 0–28% decreases the shear modulus. The frequency of the composite was found to increase with fiber content below a certain temperature

The mechanical behavior of reinforced polyurethane foams was investigated by Siegmann *et al.* [38]. Rigid polyurethane foams reinforced with e-glass chopped fibers, glass beads and graphite powders were used for testing. The chopped glass fibers do not increase the compressive strength and modulus of the foam. The glass beads and graphite powder improved the compressive modulus but does not cause any change in compressive strength. Optical and electron microscopy show that the reinforcements are located at the cell walls. They also developed a model for a mechanical behavior of three-phase systems based on the principle of superposition of a two-phase porous matrix and a third, rigid-filler phase.

Zhang *et al.* [39] were involved in the constitutive modeling and material characterization of polypropylene, polystyrene, and polyurethane foams. Their approach consisted of experimental investigations in which hydrostatic compression, axial compression and simple shear tests were conducted. These experimental results were used in the formulation of a phenomenological single-surface yield criterion. The resulting model was incorporated into the finite element program LS-DYNA3D.

The in-situ deformation of open-cell flexible polyurethane foam characterized by 3D computed microtomography was studied by Elliott and Windle [40]. They used X-ray tomography measurements of foam deformation to analyze the finite element models of foam deformation. They found that the images constructed using tomography of the undeformed foam were identical with its SEM micrographs.

The effect of particulate reinforcement on creep behavior of polyurethane foams was investigated by Alperstein *et al.* [41]. They found that the addition of beads as reinforcement to the system decreases the foam creep rate. It was found that foams reinforced with glass beads were better than the graphite reinforced foams, which is attributed to poor adhesion in the graphite-foam system.

The effect of nano and micro-silica fillers on polyurethane foam properties was studied by Javni *et al.* [42]. The fillers were micro-silica of 1.5 μm size and nano-silica of size 12 nm. The micro-silica fillers did not increase the density of either rigid or flexible foams, whereas the nano-fillers increased the density above 10% filler concentration in rigid foams. Nano-silica fillers lowered the compression strength of rigid foams. The hardness of flexible polyurethane foams with nano-silica increased and rebound resilience decreased whereas the micro-fillers had an opposite effect.

Petrovic *et al.* [43] investigated the behavior of glassy and elastomeric polyurethanes reinforced with nano-silica particles. The nano-silica-filled elastomers and glassy polyurethanes exhibited identical optical properties. It was evident from their experiments that tensile strength of the elastomeric polyurethanes increased threefold with the addition of 40% nano-silica, while the micro-silica caused an increase of about 50% in tensile strength. At the same time the tensile strength of the glassy polyurethanes did not change with either micro- or nano-fillers. The addition of these fillers showed a significant improvement of the elastomeric polyurethane foam properties in terms of elongation at break when compared with glassy polyurethanes.

The possibilities of using fiber-reinforced syntactic foams as a new lightweight structural three-phase composite was explored by Palumbo *et al.* [44]. They designed stiff lightweight hybrid composite beams and tested their mechanical properties. The reinforcement of the system with untreated glass microspheres caused a decrease of strength and increase of rigidity. The syntactic foam exhibited an elastic linear behavior in tension and compression. The hybrid structure collapses when the glass-fiber fabric reaches the tensile stress limit. The hollow cylindrical glass-fiber-reinforced plastic beam is not similar in the breaking aspect to that of the hybrid beam, as the absence of the syntactic foam core does not protect the glass-fiber-reinforced plastics from buckling, and leaves the composite susceptible to structural collapse.

The impact testing of long fiber-reinforced thermoplastic composites was studied by Jouri and Shortall [45]. Nylon 6 thermoplastic was reinforced with glass fibers. The glass reinforcement was carried out various proportions at varying temperatures ranging from –40°C to 150°C. Various techniques such as load-time trace analysis, scanning electron microscopy and high-speed photography were employed to derive information on the impact properties of the above systems. The fracture in the reinforced composite can be categorized into low-, intermediate- and high-temperature fractures. They observed that a low temperature test, yielded a definite peak in a load-time curve and the peak diffuses in high-temperature tests.

Kageoka *et al.* [46] studied the effects of melamine particle size on flexible polyurethane foam properties. Melamine particles of the order 5 microns to 60 microns were used. Optical microscopy was used to analyze the effect of melamine particles on foam properties. It was found that fine filler particles hardened the foam while the coarse filler particles softens the foam. The tensile tests showed that the tensile strength and the elongation at break decreased with both fine and coarse particles. The compression properties of the composite did not change much. They found that the oxygen index increased with melamine content. Fine melamine particles reduced the flammability of the foam more than the coarse ones.

The mechanical and the physical behavior of fiberglass reinforced polyester foams was studied by Mazzola *et al.* [47]. The fiber reinforcement causes a significant change in the temperature sensitivity of the foam's stiffness. The unreinforced foam's modulus and tensile strength decreases with temperature to a larger extent compared to reinforced foam. The presence of fibers in the polyester foams results in various crack-arresting mechanisms that causes improved impact resistance of fiber-reinforced foams. The author suggests the application of fiber-glass-reinforced polyester foams in van roofs.

The mechanical behavior of fiber-reinforced reaction injection-molded (RIM) polyurethane elastomers was studied by Brenner *et al.* [48]. The fibers used were either in the form of hammer-milled or chopped-strand fibers. The addition of glass fibers decreases the elongation to break; while at the same time increases the yield stress and modulus. In comparison to hammer-milled-fiber-reinforced foam, chopped-strand-fiber-reinforced foam show superior tensile and creep properties.

The influence of fillers on rubber-foam properties was analyzed by Hepburn and Alam [49]. In the closed-cell system, the ultimate tensile strength rises to a peak value and then falls as filler levels increases, whereas in the open-cell system there is no defined peak found. In a closed-cell system, the compression set properties improve with the presence of all fillers in but an opposite effect is seen in open-cell foams.

We now present an experimental investigation of the suitability of reinforced polyurethane flexible foam, which has a higher load-bearing capacity, but retains some of the features of unreinforced flexible foam, for energy absorption during impact. Such foam may provide good vibration damping, increase in stiffness, and higher energy absorption during impact of the structure modified with the reinforced flexible foam.

2 Experimental procedures

2.1 Foam fabrication

Polyurethane foam is made by mixing a polyol with a polyisocyanate. The polyol is usually either a polyether or polyesther and sometimes contains a catalyst to improve the reaction rate. The polyol hydrates when mixed with the isocyanate group, which is found in the polyisocyanate, creating a foaming action. The polyisocyanate used in the present application was methylene diphenylisocyanate (MDI). The polyisocyanate was responsible for creating the urethane structure (Salamone, [50]). However, the polyol was responsible for making the foam flexible, or rigid. If the polyol has a low molecular weight, it will create rigid foam, whereas a polyol with a high molecular weight will create a flexible foam, Szycher [6]. The reason for this drastic difference in foam after fabrication is due to the cross-linking that occurs during foam formation. In flexible foams, there is less cross-linking than in rigid foams [6]. So, the lower the molecular weight of the polyol, the more cross-linking occurs.

To make polyurethane foam, a combination of 22% MDI (Component A) and 78% polyol (Component B), were measured. These amounts are critical to ensure proper foam formation; changing the amount of either of these component percentages by just a mere 1% can drastically affect the foam and its physical properties. The filler material was mixed with component B. Component A was mixed with component B that also contains the filler and stirred together using a stir stick. The reaction is exothermic, so, when the components start to heat up, the foaming action is about to start. The hotter the mixture gets, the more foaming action will occur. Usually just as the mixture starts to get really warm to the touch, the mixture is ready to be placed in the mold. Putting the foam in the mold needs to be done quickly, prior to the mixture foaming, which will impede forming to the mold correctly. Thus the process of mixing components A and B and pouring the mixture into the mold where the foaming occurs has be done quickly and with care.

Once the foam is placed in the mold, it will usually continue to expand. Due to the presence of the fillers a large number of nucleation sites for gas-bubble formation are presented by the surfaces of the fillers. Thus a much larger number of bubbles are formed in filled foam as compared to unreinforced foam. When these bubbles grow and eventually form a cell structure in the reinforced polymer they achieve an equilibrium state with a smaller cell size but a larger number of cells per unit volume compared to monolithic foam. This is possibly due to the greater interaction between the bubbles as they grow and also the resistance to growth due to the presence of the fillers.

The foam is usually completely cured in three hours at room temperature or slightly above room temperature. Careful attention should be paid when letting the foam cure at a higher temperature because different physical properties can result. This is because the temperature affects the ability of the air to escape through the cell walls. For example, if the temperature is very warm, the reaction will occur faster and the mixture is better able to allow the air to escape. If the temperature is too low, the ability of the air to escape during foaming is decreased because the mixture is stiffer, requiring more pressure for the air in order for it to escape. In the present case, a temperature of 22.6°C (72.7°F) was the minimum target temperature. When the proper amounts of two components, polyisocyanate and polyol, and the reinforcement (such as glass fibers or glass micro-spheres) were mixed manually and poured into a mold, an exothermic reaction occurred and the foaming action took place. Once the foam was placed in the mold, it would expand and take the shape of the mold, which resulted in 0.5-inch thick plates.

2.2 Reinforcements Used

The following reinforcements were used (i) chopped glass-fiber strands of 6 mm length, (ii) milled E-glass fibers of 470 μm length and 16 μm diameter, (iii) hollow glass micro-spheres of an average diameter of 60 μm, density 0.2 g/cm^3, isostatic strength of 6.9 MPa, and (iv) hybrid milled glass-fibers and micro-spheres.

2.3 Physical Properties

Some of the polyurethane foam's physical properties were found in a rather simple fashion. Densities for each type of foam were found using a scale and a set of calipers in accordance with ASTM D3574-95, "Standard Test Methods for Flexible Cellular Materials – Slab, Bonded, and Molded Urethane Foams," Test A. There were three samples weighed and measured for each type of foam and an average density was determined. The density for each type of polyurethane foam tested is listed in Table I.

2.4 Microstructure Determination

The samples were cut gently into thin wafers using a fine blade. These wafers were later mounted on a stub and coated with silver paint at the edges. The silver paint is used to provide a conductive path from the surface of the coated sample to the stub, which then goes off to an electrical ground. Later the sample was placed in an oven at 150°F for 5–20 min for drying the paint. Since the samples are non-conductive, either sputter or carbon coating was employed. Then the samples were put under the scanning electron microscope for analysis. Two scanning electron microscopes were used: an AMRAY 1600 with an accelerating voltage of 20 kV and a Hitachi S-4700 FESEM with an accelerating voltage of 5 kV.

2.5 Tension Test

The purpose of conducting a tension test was to determine the tensile strength of each type of polyurethane foam. This test also gives an elastic modulus for the foam in tension. The procedure for tension testing was in accordance with ASTM D3574-95, "Standard Test Methods for Flexible Cellular Materials – Slab, Bonded, and Molded Urethane Foams," Test E. Test-specimen dimensions are shown in the ASTM standard. A special large extension clip gage of 25-mm gage length was used in the middle of the specimen to measure the elongation during the tension tests.

2.6 Compression Test

The purpose of conducting a compression test was to determine a compressive stress-strain relationship for the different types of reinforced polyurethane foam. Three samples of each type of foam were tested to give an average and to show the repeatability of data. This test also gives the compressive elastic modulus. The procedure for the compression test was in accordance with ASTM D3574-95, "Standard Test Methods for Flexible Cellular Materials – Slabs, Bonded, and Molded Urethane Foams," Test C. Pieces were cut from a polyurethane foam plate with a width and a length of 20.0-mm (0.787-inch). Two of the pieces were placed together to make a 25.4-mm (1.0 inch) thick specimen, and then tested as directed by the standard. There were three specimens tested. Each specimen was preflexed twice by compressing it 75 to 80% of its original thickness, in this case about 5 mm. The specimen was then relaxed for 6 min. Then the specimen was compressed to about 25% of its thickness at a rate of 0.83 mm/s (0.033 in/s).

2.7 Drop Weight Impact Tests

The impact behavior of 6061 aluminum tubes of thickness 1-mm and 50-mm diameter filled with chopped glass fiber strand reinforced foam was studied by using a MTS drop tower. Aluminum tubes of 250-mm length were filled with various fiber weight fraction reinforced foams and subjected to varying impact conditions in the three-point bend configuration with an instrumented drop weight of 80 Kg mass. Impact force and the acceleration were recorded as a function of time during the impact. The impact velocity was varied from 0.8–3.6 m/s. The impact energy varied from 40–460 J. Currently only chopped glass-fiber-strand-reinforced polyurethane-filled aluminum tubes have been tested under impact loading.

3 Results and Discussion

3.1 Foam Microstructure

(i) Chopped glass-fiber strands: It can be observed from Figure 1 that as the fiber weight fraction increases the cell size of the foam decreases. The fibers are typically located in the struts of the cells and do not bridge across the cells. The cells tend to line up along the fiber length and the cells become more irregular in shape for higher fiber fractions.

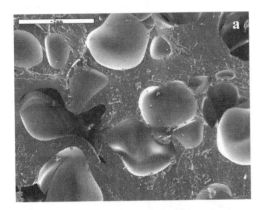
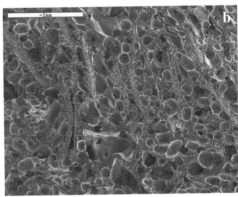

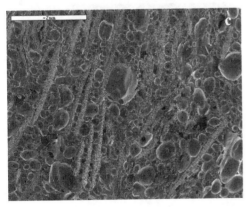

Figure 1: Effect of chopped glass-fiber strands (6-mm length) on foam microstructure for (a) unreinforced polyurethane, (b) 25% wt. fraction of glass fibers, and (c) 75% wt. fraction of glass fibers.

The flexible foam reinforced with chopped glass-fiber strands and other fillers mentioned below typically have partly open and closed cells. Due to the presence of the fillers a large number of nucleation sites for gas-bubble formation are presented by the surfaces of the fillers. Thus a much larger number of bubbles are formed in filled foam as compared to unreinforced foam. When these bubbles grow and eventually form a cell structure in the reinforced polymer they achieve an equilibrium state with a smaller cell size but a larger number of cells per unit volume compared to monolithic foam. This is possibly due to the greater interaction between the bubbles as they grow and also the resistance to growth due to the presence of the fillers. Thus the addition of fillers generally results in a reduced foam density compared to unfilled foam, (see Table I).

Table I: Density of various reinforced polyurethane foams.

Foam Type	Density (kg/m³)	Density (lbs/ft³)
Polyurethane	709.8	44.3
3% spheres	448.7	28.0
5% spheres	481.9	30.1
7% spheres	372.9	23.3
15% milled glass fibers	418.3	26.1
25% milled glass fibers	406.9	25.4
30% milled glass fibers	450.7	28.1
50% milled glass fibers	414.9	25.9
10% glass strands	464.0	29.0
25% glass strands	478.1	29.8
75% glass strands	599.6	37.4
3% milled Fibers – 3% Spheres	361.2	22.5
15% milled Fibers – 3% Spheres	370.1	23.1
5% milled Fibers– 7% Spheres	294.0	18.4

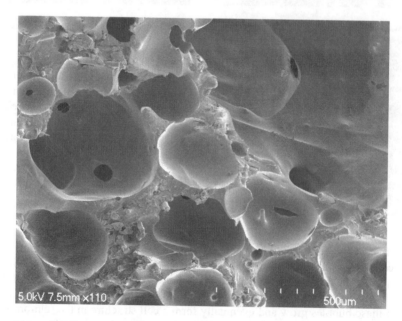

Figure 2: Microstructure of milled E-glass fiber reinforced polyurethane.

(ii) Milled short E-glass fibers: In this type of reinforced foam, the fibers are also typically located in the struts of the cells. Fiber bridging across the cells does not occur. As the fiber weight fraction increased, the cell size decreased similar to that observed with chopped glass-fiber strands. The glass fibers are found to be more uniformly dispersed in the struts than the chopped glass fiber strands, as shown in Figure 2. The density of the foam is lower than the unfilled foam but no particular trend is observed as a function of fiber weight fraction, as shown in Table I.

(iii) Glass micro-spheres: Polyurethane foam reinforced with hollow glass micro-spheres of average diameter 50-µm consists of the reinforcing spheres located in the struts of the cells (see Figure 3). As the microsphere weight fraction increased, the cell size decreased similar to that observed with glass fiber reinforcements, as shown in Figure 3. The microspheres are found to be uniformly dispersed in the struts. The density of foam decreases with increasing microsphere weight fraction, as shown in Table I.

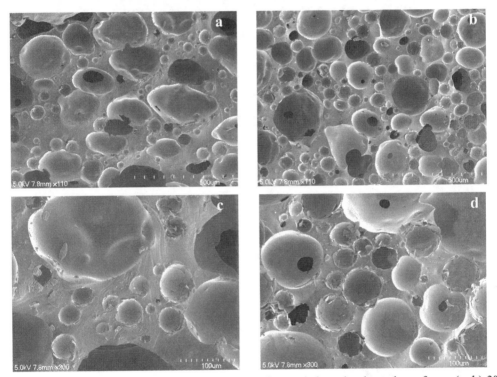

Figure 3: Microstructure of hollow glass microsphere reinforced polyurethane foam. (a, b) 3% wt. fraction, (c, d) 7% wt. fraction.

(iv) Hybrid glass micro-spheres and milled short glass fibers: Figure 4 shows the microstructure of a hybrid foam consisting of 7% wt. fraction micro-spheres and 15% wt. fraction of milled short glass fibers. It may be noticed that the microstructure has become very nonuniform and the glass fibers are also found to bridge across the cells. Thus the hybrid reinforcement tends to make the microstructure more random and the fiber orientation also becomes more random. Variation of the density for some combinations of the hybrid reinforcement is shown in Table I.

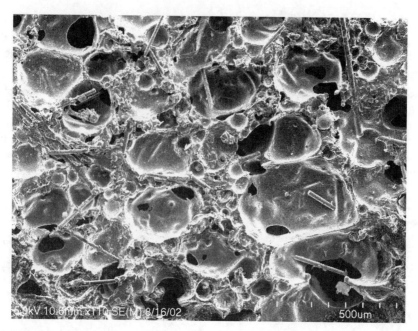

Figure 4: Microstructure of a hybrid glass microspheres and milled short glass-fiber-reinforced polyurethane foam.

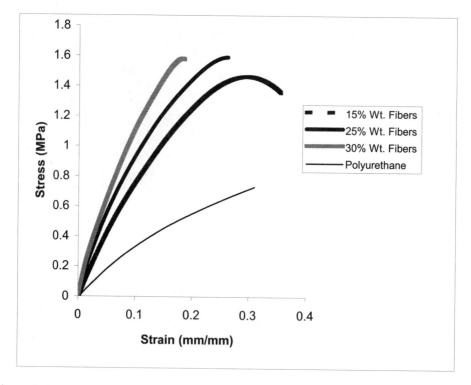

Figure 5: Tensile stress–strain response of milled E-glass fiber-reinforced Polyurethane foam.

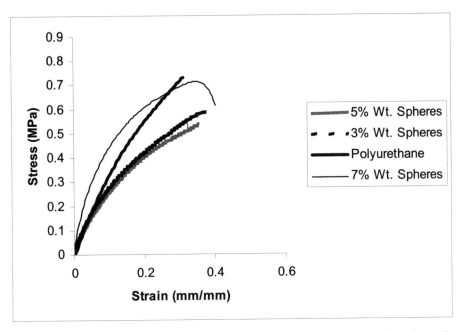

Figure 6: Tensile stress–strain response of glass-microsphere-reinforced polyurethane foam.

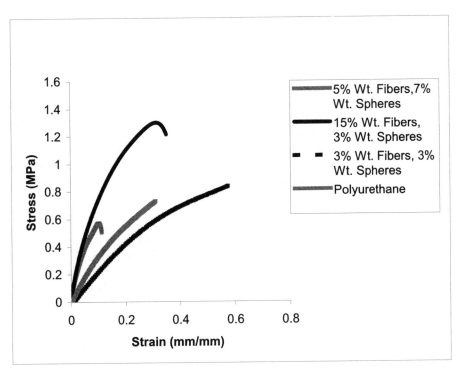

Figure 7: Tensile stress–strain response of hybrid milled E-glass fiber and glass-microsphere-reinforced polyurethane foam.

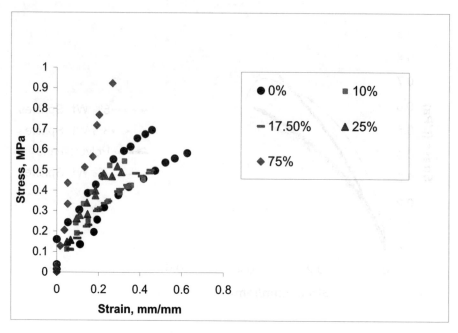

Figure 8: Tensile stress–strain response of chopped glass-fiber-strand-reinforced polyurethane foam.

3.2 Mechanical Properties

Tensile properties: Tensile elastic modulus of the reinforced foam improved with increasing weight fraction of the reinforcing fillers, as shown in Table II. Very low weight fraction of the reinforcement weakened the foam under tensile loading compared to the unreinforced foam. The maximum stress increased with increasing weight fraction of the reinforcement, while the maximum strain decreased with increasing weight fraction of the reinforcement. It has been noticed that glass fibers are more effective in improving the tensile properties of the foam, compared to glass microspheres and the hybrid reinforced foam in the range of filler weight fractions considered in this study. The deformation response of the various reinforced foams when subjected to a tensile load is shown in Figures 5–8.

Compression properties: It was noticed that the compression properties of the reinforced foam are inferior to that of the unreinforced foam for all types of reinforced foams tested, as shown in Figures 9–12. At present compression tests have not be conducted on very high filler weight fraction (order of 50–75%) foams. It is speculated that at higher fiber fractions, the compression properties will become better than the unreinforced foam. The microstructure of the samples with the weight fraction of fillers used show that the cell distribution becomes more random and nonuniform compared to that in unreinforced polyurethane foam. The loss of uniform microstructure possibly results in scattered areas that are weak in compression. Once these areas begin to fail in compression the whole cross-section progressively buckles under the compressive load. It may be postulated that if the filler weight fractions are very high, of the order of 50–75%, it may result in a more ordered microstructure compared to lower filler weight fraction foams.

Table II: Mechanical properties of various reinforced polyurethane foams.

Milled Glass Fiber Wt. %	Elastic Modulus (MPa)	Maximum Stress (MPa)	Maximum Strain (mm/mm)
15	10.77	1.21	0.29
25	13.73	1.44	0.20
30	19.00	1.73	0.18

Glass Fiber Strand Wt. %	Elastic Modulus (MPa)	Maximum Stress (MPa)	Maximum Strain (mm/mm)
10	2.10	0.6	0.41
25	2.40	0.6	0.32
75	6.30	1.0	0.27

Glass Microsphere Wt. %	Elastic Modulus (MPa)	Maximum Stress (MPa)	Maximum Strain (mm/mm)
3	3.74	0.755	0.57
5	2.90	0.540	0.54
7	5.80	0.700	0.34

Milled Fiber & Microsphere Wt. %	Elastic Modulus (MPa)	Maximum Stress (MPa)	Maximum Strain (mm/mm)
3% Fiber 3% Sphere	3.47	0.65	0.66
5% Fiber 7% Sphere	7.80	0.62	0.15
15% Fiber 3% Sphere	11.39	1.05	0.21

Unreinforced Polyurethane Foam	Elastic Modulus (MPa)	Maximum Stress (MPa)	Maximum Strain (mm/mm)
	3.80	0.77	0.55

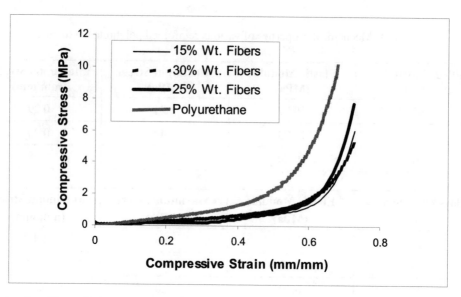

Figure 9: Compressive stress–strain response of milled short glass-fiber-reinforced polyurethane foam.

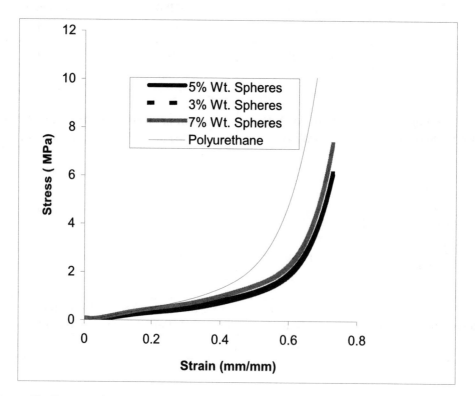

Figure 10: Compressive stress–strain response of glass-microsphere-reinforced polyurethane foam.

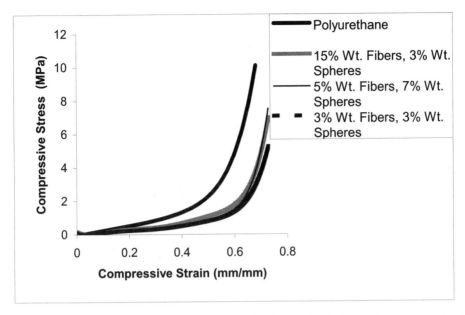

Figure 11: Compressive stress–strain response of hybrid milled short glass-fiber and glass-microsphere-reinforced polyurethane foam.

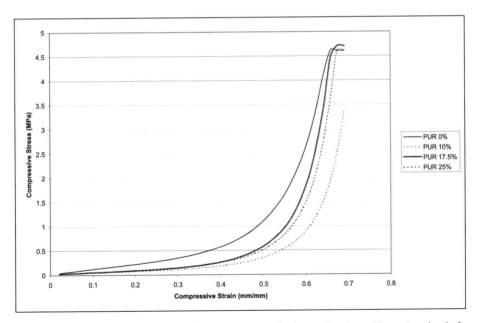

Figure 12: Compressive stress–strain response of chopped glass-fiber-strand-reinforced polyurethane foam.

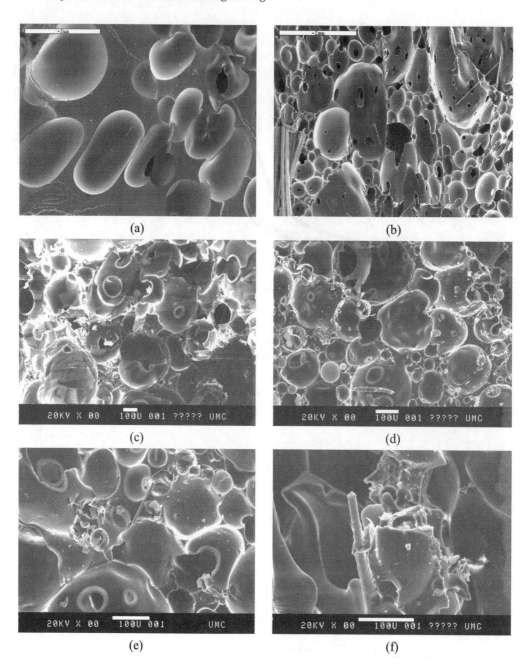

Figure 13: Effect of tensile fracture in foams with (a) unreinforced polyurethane, (b) 25% wt. fraction of glass-fiber strands, (c) 15% wt. fraction of milled E-glass short fibers, (d) 7% wt. fraction glass micro-spheres, (e) hybrid 3% wt. fraction micro-spheres and 3% wt. fraction milled glass fibers, and (f) hybrid 3% wt. fraction micro-spheres and 15% wt. fraction milled glass fibers.

3.3 Tensile fracture of foam

Samples were subjected to tensile loading up to fracture. The fracture surfaces were then examined in a scanning electron microscope and are shown in Figure 13. It is observed that in unreinforced polyurethane and chopped glass-fiber-strand-reinforced foam the cells elongate under tensile stress and acquire a permanent deformation, resulting in a more oval-shaped cell structure (see Figure 13 a, b). In the other type of reinforced foams elongation of the cells is not noticeable.

3.4 3-point bend test

A three-point bend test was conducted with thin aluminum tubes filled with reinforced foam. 6061 aluminum tubes of 1mm wall thickness and 50-mm diameter were filled with foam reinforced with milled E-glass short fibers. This test was done to determine the improvement in the load bearing characteristics of the filled aluminum tube as compared to the hollow aluminum tube. The layout of the test setup is shown in Figure 14. The load-displacement plots are shown in Figure 15. The use of reinforced foam filler helps to improve the flexural rigidity and the load-bearing capacity of a hollow aluminum tube.

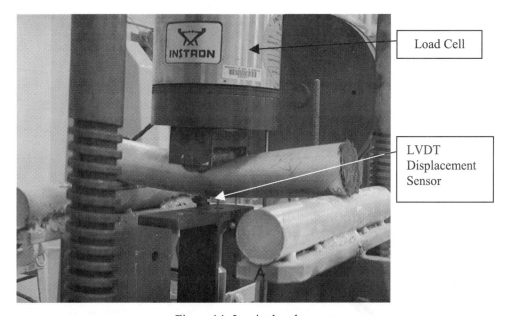

Figure 14: 3-point bend test setup.

3.5 Impact behavior of foam filled thin aluminum tubes

To determine the suitability of glass-fiber-reinforced polyurethane foam for improving energy absorption in thin walled sheet metal structures, 6061 aluminum tubes filled with chopped glass-fiber-strand-reinforced foam were used. Impact tests with other types of filled foams have not been conducted as yet. The following inferences were made from the impact tests: (i) the maximum impact load increases with increasing fiber content; (ii) the maximum load is fairly constant for the impact energy range studied; (iii) the maximum acceleration increases with increasing fiber weight fraction, though the maximum acceleration is nearly constant for each fiber weight fraction for all impact energies; (iv) the duration of impact decreases for increasing fiber content; and (v) duration of impact increases with impact energy and then decreases for higher impact energy.

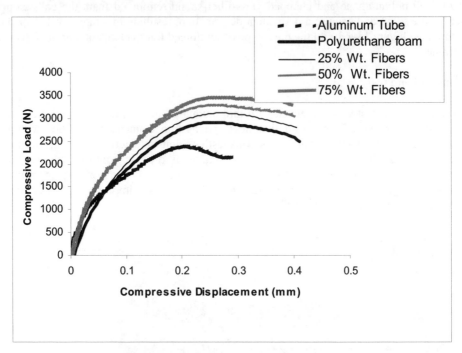

Figure 15: Flexural deformation response of milled glass-fiber-reinforced foam-filled aluminum tube in a 3-point bend loading condition.

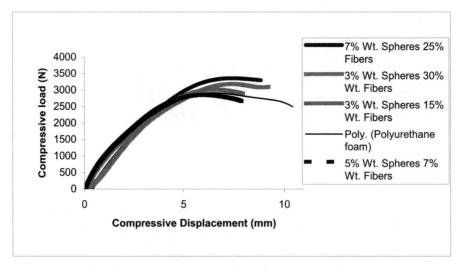

Figure 16: Flexural deformation response of hybrid reinforced foam-filled aluminum tube in a 3-point bend loading condition.

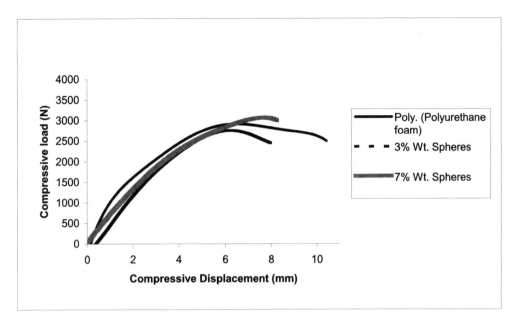

Figure 17: Flexural deformation response of sphere-reinforced foam-filled aluminum tube in a 3-point bend loading condition.

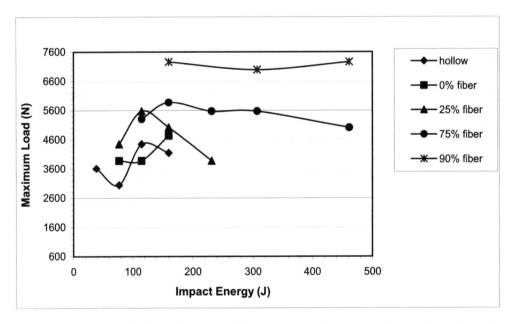

Figure 18: Maximum load as a function of impact energy in a three-point bend configuration on various chopped glass-fiber-strand-reinforced foam-filled aluminum tubes.

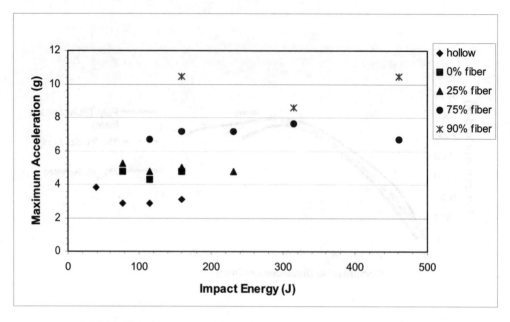

Figure 19: Maximum acceleration as a function of impact energy in a three-point bend configuration on various chopped glass-fiber-strand-reinforced foam-filled aluminum tubes.

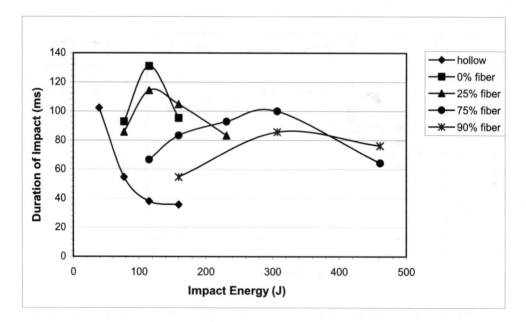

Figure 20: Impact duration as a function of impact energy in a three-point bend configuration on various chopped glass-fiber-strand-reinforced foam filled aluminum tubes.

Figure 21 shows the impact deformation of various foam filled and non-filled aluminum tubes at a constant impact energy level. Figure 22 shows the impact deformation of a 75% wt. fraction fiber-filled foam tube subjected to varying impact energies. It may be noticed that the impact deformation mode changes with varying impact energies and the weight fraction of the filler material.

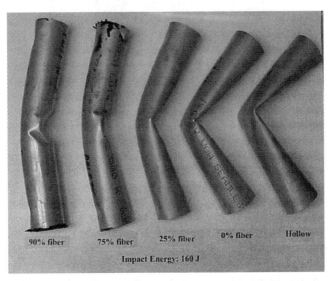

Figure 21: Effect of chopped glass-fiber-strand weight fraction on impact deformation mode of polyurethane-foam-filled aluminum tubes at a constant impact energy.

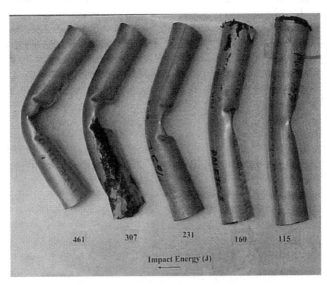

Figure 22: Effect of varying impact energy on the deformation mode of 75% wt. fraction chopped glass-fiber-strand-reinforced polyurethane-foam-filled aluminum tubes.

Under impact a significant degree of cell crushing was noticed, even though the foam is a flexible foam, as shown in Figure 23. This crushing behavior is desirable as it leads to higher energy absorption.

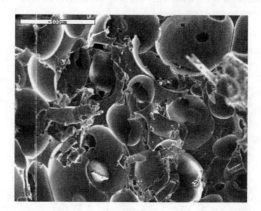

Figure 23: Crushing of cells during impact loading of chopped glass-fiber-strand-reinforced polyurethane foam.

4 Conclusions

Different types of reinforced flexible polyurethane foams have been investigated. The reinforcements used were milled E-glass fibers, hollow glass micro-spheres, and chopped glass- fiber strands. It has been observed that milled E-glass fibers are more effective in improving the tensile and flexural deformation response of the foam compared to other reinforcing fillers. All the reinforced foams show degradation in compressive strength compared to the unfilled polyurethane foam. Currently, the impact response of filled foams shows promise in improving energy absorption during impact; however, more research is required in this regard.

Acknowledgement

The partial financial support of Ford Motor Co., USA, and University of Missouri Research Board is gratefully acknowledged. The assistance of Mary Fivecoat in this investigation is gratefully acknowledged. The glass micro-spheres were donated by 3M Co., USA and the milled E-glass fibers were donated by Fibertec Corp., USA.

References

[1] Reddy, E.S. & Schmitz, G.J., Ceramic Foams. *American Ceramic Society Bulletin*, **81(12)**, pp. 35–37, December 2002.
[2] Yuan, Y. & Shutov, F., Foam in Foam Polyurethane Composites. *J. of Cellular Plastics*, **38(6)**, pp. 497–506, November 2002.
[3] Ebaretonbofa, E. & Evans, J.R.G., *J. of Porous Materials*, **9(4)**, pp. 257–263, December 2002.

[4]   Gibson, L. & Ashby, M., *Cellular Solids: Structure and Properties*. 2nd edn, Cambridge University Press: New York, USA, Ch. 3, pp. 8–10, 1997.

[5]   Foam core-panels, http://doityourself.com/insulate/foamcorepanels.htm, 1995–2001.

[6]   Szycher, M., *Schyzer's Handbook of Polyurethanes*. CRC Press: New York, Ch. 7, 1999.

[7]   Krayem Metal Constructions. *Metal Constructions – Polyurethane Sandwich Panels*. Krayem Metal Constructions, http://www.krayemgroup.com/constructions/panels.htm 2000.

[8]   SWD Urethane Co., *Flexible/Self-Skinning Foams*, http://swdurethane.com/NewFiles/flexfoam.html.

[9]   Russell Products, Medical Coatings, http://www.russprodco.com/page17.html.

[10]   Griffith Polymers, Inc., Polyurethane Products, http://www.polyurethane-1.com/products.htm, 1999

[11]   3M™, http://www.3m.com/US./mfg_industrial/prodprot/poly_home.jhtml;$pageID$-ppp

[12]   Titow, W. & Lanhoam, B., *Reinforced Thermoplastic*. John Wiley and Sons: New York, pp. 266, 1975.

[13]   Saha, P. & Cahine, J., *The Testing Of Vibration Damping Materials*. Sound and Vibration, pp. 38–42, 1995.

[14]   Ratcliffe, C. & Crane, R., Optimizing Reinforced Polyurethane As A Combined Structural And Damping Component. *Advanced Materials for Vibro-Acoustic Applications*, NCA- v 23. ASME, 1996.

[15]   Wagner, D., Gur, Y., War, S. & Samus, M., Modeling Foam Damping Materials in Automotive Structures. *Journal of Engineering Materials and Technology*, **119**, pp. 279–283, July 1997.

[16]   Elastochem Specialty Chemicals, Inc., Polyurethane – Features and Benefits, http://www.elastochem-ca.com/poly.html, 1999–2000.

[17]   PLI, Foam Packaging - Custom Fabrications, http://www.pak-lite.com/foam.htm .

[18]   Zhang, J., Lin, Z., Wong, A., Kikuchi, N., Li, V., Yee, A. & Nusholtz., G., Constitutive Modeling and Material Characterization of Polymeric Foams. *Transactions of the ASME Journal of Engineering Materials and Technology*, **119**, pp. 284–291, July 1997

[19]   Goods, S., Neuschwanger, C. & Whinnery, L., Mechanical Properties of a Structural Polyurethane Foam and the Effect of Particulate Loading. *Material Resource, Symposium Proceedings*, Materials Research Society, **521**, pp. 15–20, 1998

[20]   Shim, V., Tu, Z. & Lim, C., Two-Dimensional Response Of Crushable Polyurethane Foam To Low Velocity Impact. *International Journal of Impact Engineering*, **24**, pp. 703–731, 2000.

[21]   Hilyard, N.C. (ed.), *Mechanics of Cellular Plastics*. Macmillan Publishing Co.: New York, 1982.

[22]   Chang, F.S., Song, Y, Lu, D.X. & DeSilva, C.N. (eds), Constitutive Equations of Foam Materials. *ASME J. of Engineering Materials and Technology*, **120**, pp. 212–217, July 1998.

[23]   Klempner, D. & Frisch, K.C. (eds), *Handbook of Polyurethane Foams and Foam Technology*. University Press: New York, 1991.

[24]   Kumar, V. & Weller, J.E., The Effect of Cell Size on the Tensile Behavior of Microcellular Polycarbonate. *ASME MD*, v76, Cellular and Microcellular Materials, pp. 17–25, 1996.

[25]   Methven, J.M. & Shortall, J.B., Glass Fiber Reinforced Reaction Injection Molded Semi Rigid Polyurethanes. *European J. of Cellular Plastics*, **2**, pp. 83–92, 1979.

[26] Cotgreave, T.C. & Shortall, J.B., A Model For Critical Fiber Length in Rigid Polyurethane Foam. *European J. of Cellular Plastics*, **1**, pp. 137–140, 1978.

[27] Cotgreave, T.C. & Shortall, J.B., The Mechanism of Reinforcement of Polyurethane Foams by High Modulus Chopped Fibers. *J. of Materials Science*, **12**, pp. 708–717, 1977.

[28] Puterman, M. & Narkis, M., Syntactic Foams I. Preparation, Structure and Properties. *J. of Cellular Plastics*, pp. 223–229, July/August 1980.

[29] Narkis, M. & Puterman, M., Syntactic Foams II. Preparation and Characterization of Three Phase Systems. *J. of Cellular Plastics*, pp. 326–330, Nov./Dec. 1980.

[30] Okuno, K. & Woodhams, R.T., Mechanical Properties and Characterization of Phenolic Resin Syntactic Foams. *J. of Cellular Plastics*, pp. 237–244, Sept./Oct. 1974.

[31] Thomas, C.R., Syntactic Carbon Foams. *Materials Science and Engineering*, **12**, pp. 219–233, 1973.

[32] Rizzi, E., Papa, E. & Corigliano, A., Mechanical Behavior of a Syntactic Foam: Experiments and Modeling. *International J. of Solids and Structures*, **37**, pp. 5773–5794, 2000.

[33] Hostis, G.L. & Devries, F., Characterization of the Thermoelastic Behavior of Syntactic Foams. *Composites Part B*, **29B**, pp. 351–361, 1998.

[34] Goods, S.H., Neuschwagner, C.L., Whinnery, L.L. & Nix, W.D., Mechanical Properties of Particle-Strengthened Polyurethane Foam. *J. of Applied Polymer Science*, **74**, pp. 2724–2736, 1999

[35] Titow, W.V. & Lanham, B.J., *Reinforced Thermoplastics*. John Wiley & Sons, 1975

[36] Hornberger, l., Malloy, l. & Kadkol, P., An Evaluation Of The Mechanical Properties Of Glass Fiber Reinforced Polycarbonate Structural Foam. ANTEC 1991

[37] Bledzki, A.K. & Zhang, W., Dynamic Mechanical Properties Of Natural Fiber-Reinforced Epoxy Foams. *J. of Reinforced Plastics and Composites*, **20(14)**, pp. 1263–1274, 2001.

[38] Siegmann, M., Narkis, A., Kenig, S., Alperstein, D. & Nicolais, L., Mechanical Behavior Of Reinforced Polyurethane Foams. *Society of plastic engineers*, **4(2)**, pp. 113–119, April 1983.

[39] Zhang, J., Lin, Z., Wong, A., Kikuchi, N., Li, V.C., Yee, A.F. & Nusholtz, G.S., Constitutive Modelling And Material Characterization Of Polymeric Foams. *Transactions of ASME*, **119**, July 1997.

[40] Elliot, J.A. & Windle, A.H., In Situ Deformation Of An Open-Cell Flexible Polyurethane Foam Characterized By 3D Computer Microtomography. **37(8)**, pp. 1547–1555, April 15 2002.

[41] Narkis, M., Siegmann, A., Kenig, S., Alperstein, D. & Nicolais, L., Effect Of Particulate Reinforcement On Creep Behavior Of Polyurethane Foams. *Society of Plastic Engineers*, **5(2)**, pp. 155–158, April 1984.

[42] Javni, I., Zhang, W., Karjkov, V., Petrovic, Z.S. & Divjakovic, V., Effect Of Nano And Micro-Sillica Fillers On Polyurethane Foam. *J. of Cellular Plastics.*, **38**, pp. 229–239, May 2002.

[43] Petrovic, Z.S. & Zhang, W., Glassy And Elastomeric Polyurethanes Filled With Nano Silica Particles. *Materials Science Forum*, **352**, pp. 171–76, 1984.

[44] Palumbo, M. & Tempesti, E., Fiber-Reinforced Syntactic Foams As A New Lightweight Structural Three-Phase Composite. *Applied Composite Materials*, **8(5)**, pp. 343–359, September 2001.

[45] Jouri, W.S. & Shortall, J.B., Impact Testing of Long Fiber Reinforced Thermoplastics Composites. *J. of Thermoplastic Composite Materials*, **4(3)**, pp. 206–226, Jul 1991,

[46] Kageoko, M., Tairaka, Y. & Kodama, K., Effects Of Melamine Particle Size On Flexible Polyurethane Foam Properties. *J. of Cellular Plastics*, **33(3)**, pp. 219–237, May/June 1997.

[47] Mazzola, M., Masi, P., Nicolais, L. & Narkis, M., Fiberglass Reinforced Polyester Foams. *Journal of Cellular Plastics*, **18(5)**, pp. 321–324, Sep.–Oct. 1982.

[48] Brenner, M., Gibson, L. & Shortall, A.G., Fiber Reinforcement Of Reaction Injection Moulded (RIM) Polyurethane Elastomers. *Cellular Polymers*, **3(1)**, pp. 19–39, 1984.

[49] Hepburn, C. & Alam, N., Influence Of Fillers On Rubber Foam Properties. *Cellular Polymers*, **10(2)**, pp. 99–116, 1991.

[50] Salamone, J., *Concise Polymeric Materials Encyclopedia*. CRC Press: New York, USA, pp. 1425–1426, 1999.

CHAPTER 4

Electroactive polymers as artificial muscles

Y. Bar-Cohen
*Jet Propulsion Laboratory/California Institute of Technology,
Pasadena, California, USA*

Abstract

The potential for developing actuators with performance characteristics that rival that of muscle is increasingly becoming feasible with the emergence of effective electroactive polymers (EAP). Such polymers have many attractive characteristics including low weight, fracture tolerance, and pliability. EAP materials have functional similarities to biological muscles, including resilience, damage tolerance, and large actuation strains (stretching, contracting or bending). EAP-based actuators may be used to eliminate the need for gears, bearings, and other components that complicate the construction of robots and are responsible for high costs, high weight and premature failures. Furthermore, they can be configured into almost any conceivable shape, their properties can be engineered, and they can potentially be integrated with micro-electro-mechanical-system (MEMS) sensors to produce smart actuators. Visco-elastic EAP materials can potentially provide more life-like aesthetics, vibration and shock dampening, and more flexible actuator configurations. Exploiting the properties of artificial muscles may enable even the movement of the covering skin to define the character of the robots and provide expressiveness.

1   Introduction

Throughout history, humans have always sought to mimic the appearance, mobility, functionality, intelligent operation, as well as the decision-making and thinking process of biological creatures. This desire to imitate nature includes even mimicking the characteristics of humans, too. The field of biologically inspired technologies has the moniker biomimetics and it is increasingly introducing systems that are exhibiting realistic appearance and behavior. Robots, which verbally and facially express emotions and respond emotionally to such expressions, are being developed with greater capability and sophistication [Bar-Cohen and Breazeal, 2003]. Imagine a person walking towards you when suddenly you notice something weird about him he is not real but rather he is a robot. Your reaction would probably be "I can't believe it but this robot looks very much real," just as you would react to an artificial flower that is a good imitation. You may even proceed and touch the robot to check if your assessment is correct, but to your astonishment, as opposed to the case of artificial flowers, the robot may be programmed to respond verbally and/or physically to your touch. This science fiction scenario may become a reality as the current trend continues towards developing biologically inspired technologies and robots that appear and behave as human or animals. Beyond the mimicking of appearance and performance efforts are made to maximize the benefits of the biomimetic technologies by incorporating intelligence into the control of these robots.

Biology offers a great model for emulation in areas ranging from electromechanical tools, computer algorithms, materials science, mechanisms and information technology. Some of the implementations of this progress can be seen at many toy stores "near you", where toys appear and behave like biological creatures including dogs, cats, birds, frogs and others. Other benefits of this technology include prosthetic implants or human-aiding mechanisms that may be interfaced with the human brain to assist in hearing or seeing. Technology evolution led to such fields as artificial intelligence and artificial muscles, which are enabling us to consider making more realistic biomimetic intelligent robots.

Science fiction has contributed significantly to the expectations of this field. Human with bionic muscles is synonymous with a superhuman actor in movies or TV series. Driven by bionic muscles, the character is portrayed as capable of strength and speeds that are far superior to human. Recently, effective electroactive polymers (EAP) were developed that induce large strains (stretching, contracting or bending) [Bar-Cohen, 2001]. These materials have earned the moniker artificial muscles and may one day be used to make bionic muscles a reality or even make powerful robots that are actuated by these materials. As this technology evolves, novel biologically inspired mechanisms are expected to emerge with more realistic characteristics, including commercial products, medical devices and robots. EAP-based actuators may be used to eliminate the need for gears, bearings, and other components that complicate the construction of robots reducing their costs, weight and premature failures.

Generally, polymers with actuation capabilities that exhibit large displacement in response to other than electrical signal (e.g., chemical, thermal and light) were known for many years [Chapter 1, Bar-Cohen, 2001]. Initially, EAP received relatively little attention due to their limited actuation capability. However, in the last ten years, the view of the EAP materials has changed due to the introduction of effective new materials that surpassed the capability of the widely used piezoelectric polymer, PVDF2. Currently, efforts are underway to address the many challenges that are hampering the practical application of these materials. Various novel mechanisms and devices were already demonstrated including catheter steering element, robotic arm, gripper, loudspeaker, active diaphragm, and dust-wiper [Kornbluh and Pelrine, 2001; Kennedy et al., 2001; Hanson and Pioggia, 2001; Mavroidis et al., 2001; Jenkins 2001; and Chapter 21 in Bar-Cohen, 2001]. Other applications that are currently being considered include active Braille display for blind people and electroactive clothing, e.g., smart-bra with battery driven shape control. Combining photonic, transducing, sensing and other characteristics of polymers with EAP materials offers enormous potential for the development of multifunctional structures and biomimetic intelligent robots. Other aspects that can be inspired by biology and implemented using EAP can be the use of distributed sensors, multi-functionality and self-repair.

2   Nature as a biologically inspiring model

Evolution over millions of years made nature introduce solutions that are highly power-efficient, and imitating them offers potential improvements of our life and the tools we use. Human desire and capability to imitate nature, particularly biology, has continuously evolved, and with the improvement in the capability more difficult challenges are being considered. Initially, it was limited to making static copies of human and animals, in the form of statues and sculptures, as well as the development of tools to improve humans' life.

One of the early implementation of biologically inspired devices was the bicker of birds, which was adapted as a tool in the form of tweezers. More sophisticated inspirations include the development of aerodynamic structures and systems that use the shape of seeds. Trees disperse their seeds using various techniques where the use of aerodynamics allows them to self-propel with the aid of winds to carry the seeds to great distances. The shape of such seeds has inspired humans to produce objects that can be propelled in air and those have evolved to the boomerang, gliders, helicopter blades and various aerodynamic parts of aircrafts. In Figure 1, an example is shown of a winged seed of the Tipuana tipu (6.5-cm long), which is a street landscaping tree in such places as Southern California. Another plant that offered an inspiring design is the tumbleweed, suggesting a method of mobility that uses wind rather than a power-consuming mechanism. Since wind is blown throughout Mars, producing a spacecraft that imitates the tumbleweed offers an attractive option of designing a vehicle that can traverse great distances on Mars with a minimal use of power. It is not sufficient to mimic the appearance and performance of biology to maximize the benefits of the capability and a critical element of the developed robots is the need to incorporate intelligence into the system control.

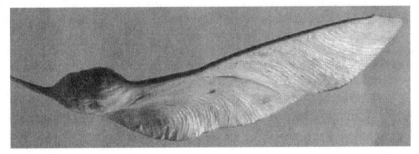

Figure 1: A seed with aerodynamic shape for dispersion with the wind.

It is well known that the introduction of the wheel has been one of the most important invention that humans made allowing us to travel great distances and perform tasks that would have been otherwise impossible within the life time of a single human being. While wheel locomotion mechanisms allow great distances and speeds that are significantly beyond the capability of biological systems to be reached, they are subjected to great limitations with regards to traversing complex terrain with obstacles. Obviously, legged creatures can perform numerous functions that are far beyond the capability of an automobile. Producing legged robots is increasingly becoming an objective for robotic developers and considerations of using such robots for space applications are currently underway. Making miniature devices that can fly like a dragonfly, adhere to walls like gecko, adapt the texture, patterns, and shape of the surrounding as the octopus (that can reconfigure its body to pass thru very narrow tubing), process complex 3D images in real time, recycle mobility power for highly efficient operation and locomotion, self-replicate, self-grow using surrounding resources, chemically generate and store energy, and many other capabilities are some of the areas that biology offers a model for science and engineering inspiration. While many aspects of biology are still beyond our understanding, significant progress has been made.

2.1 Biological muscles as a model for EAP

Muscles are considered highly optimized systems since they are fundamentally the same for all animals and changes between species are small. Natural muscles are driven by a complex mechanism and are capable of lifting large loads with short response time (milliseconds). The operation of muscles depends on chemically driven reversible hydrogen bonding between two polymers, actin and myosin. Muscle cells are roughly cylindrical in shape, with diameters between 10 and 100 μm having a length of up to several centimeters. It is difficult to determine the performance of muscles and most measurements were made on large shell-closing muscles of scallops [Marsh et al., 1992]. A peak stress of 150 to 300 KPa is developed at a strain of about 25%, while the maximum power output is 150 to 225 W/kg. The average power is about 50 W/kg with an energy density of 20 to 70 J/kg that decreases when the speed is increased. Although muscles produce linear forces, all motions at joints are rotary. Therefore, the strength of an animal is not just muscle force, but muscle force modified by the mechanical advantage of the joint [Alexander, 1988], which usually varies with joint rotation. The mechanical energy is provided by a chemical free energy of a reaction involving adenosine triphosphate (ATP) hydrolysis. The release of Ca^{2+} ions is responsible for turning on and off the conformational changes associated with muscle striction.

2.2 Artificial muscles

In spite of the success in making robots that mimic biology, there is still a large gap between the performance of robots and nature creatures. The required technology is multidisciplinary and has many aspects, including the need for actuators that emulate muscles. The potential for such actuators is increasingly becoming feasible with the emergence of effective electroactive polymers (EAP) [Bar-Cohen, 2001]. These materials have functional similarities to biological muscles, including resilience, damage tolerance, and large actuation strains (stretching, contracting or bending). EAP-based actuators may be used to eliminate the need for gears, bearings, and other components that complicate the construction of robots and are responsible for high costs, weight and premature failures. Visco-elastic EAP materials can potentially provide more life-like aesthetics, vibration and shock dampening, and more flexible actuator configurations. Exploiting the properties of artificial muscles may enable even the movement of the covering skin to define the character of the robots and provide expressivity.

Polymers have many attractive characteristics including low weight, fracture tolerance, and pliability. Furthermore, they can be configured into almost any conceivable shape and their properties can be tailored to suit a broad range of requirements. In the last decade, new polymers have emerged that respond to electrical stimulation with a significant shape, or size change and this progress has added an important capability to these materials. Generally, EAP materials can induce strains that are as high as two orders of magnitude greater than the striction-limited, rigid and fragile electroactive ceramics (EAC). Furthermore, EAP materials are superior to shape-memory alloys (SMA) in higher response speed, lower density, and greater resilience. This capability of the electroactive polymers (EAP) attracted the attention of engineers and scientists from many different disciplines. Practitioners in biomimetics are particularly excited about these materials since the artificial-muscle aspect of EAPs can be applied to mimic the movements of animals and insects. In the foreseeable future, robotic mechanisms actuated by EAPs will enable engineers to create devices previously imaginable only in science fiction.

3 Historical review and currently available active polymers

The beginning of the field of EAP can be traced back to an 1880 experiment that was conducted by Roentgen using a rubber-band with fixed end and a mass attached to the free-end and then being charged and discharged [Roentgen, 1880]. Sacerdote [1899] followed this experiment with a formulation of the strain response to electric field activation. Further milestone progress was recorded only in 1925 with the discovery of a piezoelectric polymer, called electret, when carnauba wax, rosin and beeswax were solidified by cooling while subjected to a DC bias field [Eguchi, 1925]. Generally, there are many polymers that exhibit volume or shape change in response to perturbation of the balance between repulsive intermolecular forces, which act to expand the polymer network, and attractive forces that act to shrink it. Repulsive forces are usually electrostatic or hydrophobic in nature, whereas attraction is mediated by hydrogen bonding or van der Waals interactions. The competition between these counteracting forces, and hence the volume or shape change, can be controlled by subtle changes in parameters such as solvent, gel composition, temperature, pH, light, etc. The type of polymers that can be activated by non-electrical means include: chemically activated, shape-memory polymers, inflatable structures, including McKibben Muscle, light-activated polymers, magnetically activated polymers, and thermally activated gels [Bar-Cohen, 2001].

Polymers that are chemically stimulated were discovered over half-a-century ago when collagen filaments were demonstrated to reversibly contract or expand when dipped in acid or alkali aqueous solutions, respectively [Katchalsky, 1949]. Even though relatively little has since been done to exploit such 'chemo-mechanical' actuators, this early work pioneered the development of synthetic polymers that mimic biological muscles. The convenience and practicality of electrical stimulation and technology progress led to a growing interest in EAP materials. Following the 1969 observation of a substantial piezoelectric activity in PVDF2 [Chapter 1, Bar-Cohen, 2001], investigators started to examine other polymer systems, and a series of effective materials have emerged. The largest progress in EAP materials development has occurred in the last ten years where effective materials that can induce over 300% strains have emerged [Kornbluh and Pelrine, 2001].

4 The two major categories of EAP materials

EAP can be divided into two major categories based on their activation mechanism: electronic and ionic (Table 1). The electronic EAP, such as electrostrictive, electrostatic, piezoelectric, and ferroelectric, are driven by Coulomb forces. This type of EAP material can be made to hold the induced displacement while activated under a DC voltage, allowing them to be considered for robotic applications. These materials have a greater mechanical energy density and they can be operated in air with no major constraints. However, in spite of recent developments in making composite EAP, most of the electronic EAP materials are requiring high activation fields (>100 V/μm) that may be close to the breakdown level.

In contrast to the electronic EAP, ionic EAP are materials that involve mobility or diffusion of ions and they consist of two electrodes and electrolyte. The activation of the ionic EAP can be made by as low as 1 to 2 V and mostly a bending displacement is induced. Examples of ionic EAP include gels, polymer–metal composites, conductive polymers, and carbon nanotubes. Their disadvantages are the need to maintain wetness and they pose difficulties to sustain constant displacement under activation of a DC voltage (except for conductive polymers).

The induced displacement of both the electronic and ionic EAP can be designed geometrically to bend, stretch or contract. Any of the existing EAP materials can be made to bend with a significant bending response, offering an actuator with an easy to see reaction (see example in Figure 2). However, bending actuators have relatively limited applications due to the low force or torque that can be induced. EAP materials are still custom made mostly by researchers and they are not readily available commercially. To help in making them widely available, the author established a website that provides fabrication procedures for the leading types of EAP materials [http://ndeaa.jpl.nasa.gov/nasa-nde/lommas/eap/EAP-recipe.htm].

Table 1: List of the leading EAP materials.

Electronic EAP	Ionic EAP
Dielectric EAP	• Carbon nanotubes (CNT)
Electrostrictive graft elastomers	• Conductive polymers (CP) (see Figure 2)
Electrostrictive paper	• Electrorheological fluids (ERF)
Electro-viscoelastic elastomers	• Ionic polymer gels (IPG)
Ferroelectric polymers	• Ionic polymer metallic composite (IPMC)
Liquid crystal elastomers (LCE)	

5   Need for enhanced EAP technology infrastructure

Electroactive polymers can be easily formed in various shapes, their properties can be engineered and they can potentially be integrated with micro-electro-mechanical-system (MEMS) sensors to produce smart actuators. As mentioned earlier, their most attractive feature is their ability to emulate the operation of biological muscles with high fracture tolerance, large actuation strain and inherent vibration damping. Unfortunately, the EAP materials that have been developed so far are still exhibiting low conversion efficiency, are not robust, and there are no standard commercial materials available for consideration in practical applications. In order to be able to take these materials from the development phase to application as effective actuators, there is a need for an established EAP infrastructure (Chapter 1, Bar-Cohen 2001). Effectively addressing the requirements of the EAP infrastructure involves developing adequate understanding of EAP materials' behavior, as well as the availability of standard processing and characterization techniques.

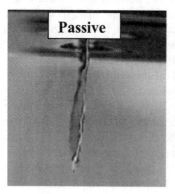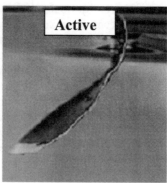

Figure 2: Conductive EAP actuator is shown bending under stimulation of 2 V, 50 mA.

Enhancement of the actuation force studies is sought through improvement of the understanding of the basic principles using computational chemistry models, comprehensive material science, electro-mechanics analytical tools and material-processing techniques. Efforts are underway to gain a better understanding of the parameters that control the EAP electro-activation force and deformation.   The processes of synthesizing, fabricating, electroding, shaping and handling are being refined to maximize the EAP materials actuation capability and robustness. Methods of reliably characterizing the response of these materials are being developed, and efforts are being made to establish a database with documented material properties in order to support design engineers that are considering the use of these materials and towards making EAP actuators of choice.   Various configurations of EAP actuators and sensors are being studied and modeled to produce an arsenal of effective smart EAP-driven systems. In the last four years, significant international effort has been made to address the various aspects of the EAP infrastructure and to tackle the multidisciplinary issues [Bar-Cohen, 2001].   Currently, many researchers and engineers are addressing each of the elements of the infrastructure.   The progress has been documented in the conference proceedings of the SPIE and MRS conferences that are dedicated to the topic of electroactive polymer actuators and devices [Bar-Cohen, 1999 and subsequent years; and Zhang et al. 1999]. The author believes that an emergence of a niche application that addresses a critical need will significantly accelerate the transition of EAP from novelty to actuators of choice. In such case, the uniqueness of these materials will be exploited and commercial products will emerge in spite of the current limitations of EAP materials.

6 Present technology, future possibilities and potentials

Mimicking nature would immensely expand the collection and functionality of the robots allowing performance of tasks that are impossible with existing capabilities. As technology evolves, a great number of biologically inspired robots actuated by EAP materials emulating biological creatures is expected to emerge. The challenges to making such a robot are presented in Figure 3, where a robot dog is shown to hop and express emotion. Both tasks are easy for human to do but are extremely complex to incorporate into a robot.

To promote the development of effective EAP actuators, which could impact future robotics, toys and animatronics, two platforms were developed and were made available to the author for the support of the worldwide development of EAP. These platforms include an android head that can make facial expressions and a robotic hand with activatable joints (Figure 4). The head can be made to move the eyes and the lips, whereas the hand allows moving the index finger. At present, conventional electric motors are producing the required deformations to make relevant facial expressions.   Once effective EAP materials are chosen, they will be modeled into the control system in terms of surface-shape modifications and control instructions for the creation of the desired facial expressions. The robotic hand (Figure 4) is equipped with wire-based tandems and sensors for the operation of the various joints mimicking a human hand. The index finger of this

Figure 3:
Biomimetic robot
(the dog image is
courtesy of
D. Hanson,
University of Texas
at Dallas).

hand is currently being driven also by conventional motors in order to establish a baseline and they would be substituted by EAP when such materials are developed as effective actuators.

The easy capability to produce EAP in various shapes and configurations can be exploited using such methods as stereolithography and ink-jet printing techniques. A polymer can be dissolved in a volatile solvent and ejected drop-by-drop onto various substrates. Such processing methods offer the potential of making robots in full 3D details including EAP actuators, allowing rapid prototyping and quick mass production [Chapter 14 in Bar-Cohen, 2001]. A possible vision for such technology can be the fabrication of insect-like robots that can be made to fly and pack themselves into a box to be ready for shipping once they are made. Another example can be the use of a movie script to produce the needed robots and they can be modified rapidly as needed for the evolving script. Making insect-like robots could help inspection of hard-to-reach areas of aircraft structures where the creatures can be launched to conduct the inspection procedures and download the data upon exiting the structure.

Figure 4: EAP platform for demonstration of EAP actuators.

Left - An android head that makes facial expressions (Photographed at JPL. This head was sculptured by D. Hanson, University of Texas at Dallas and instrumented by G. Pioggia, University of Pisa, Italy).

Right – Biologically inspired robotic hand (Photographed at JPL. This hand was made by G. Whiteley, Sheffield Hallam U., UK. The actuators were installed at JPL by G. Pioggia – University of Pisa, Italy).

6.1 Human–machine interfaces

Interfacing between human and machine to complement or substitute our senses can enable important capabilities for possible medical applications or general use. In the last six years a number of such interfaces, which employ EAP, were investigated or considered. Of notable significance is the ability to interface machines and the human brain. Such a capability addresses a critical element in the operation of prosthetics that may be developed using EAP actuators. A recent development by scientists at Duke University [Wessberg et al., 2000 and Mussa-Ivaldi, 2000] enabled this possibility where electrodes have been connected to the brain of a monkey, and using brain waves the monkey was able to operate a robotic arm, both locally and remotely via the internet. Using such a capability to control prosthetics would require feedback to allow the human operator to "feel" the environment around the artificial limbs. Such feedback can be provided with the aid of tactile sensors, haptic devices, and other interfaces.

7   Lesson learned using IPMC and dielectric EAP

To understand the challenges that are involved with employing EAP materials as actuators, the experience at the Jet Propulsion Laboratory (JPL) that was acquired in seeking applications for IPMC is reviewed herein. The author and his team made extensive efforts to develop effective planetary applications for iuonic polymer/metal composite (IPMC), and a number of issues were identified that hampered its immediate application. While the micro- and macro-electromechanical behavior is still not fully understood, methodic modeling and experimental studies have significantly contributed to the knowledge base [Nemat-Nasser and Thomas, 2001].

Space applications are among the most demanding in terms of the harshness of the operating conditions, requiring a high level of robustness and durability. For an emerging technology, the requirements and challenges associated with making hardware for space flight are very difficult to overcome. However, since such applications usually involve producing only small batches they can provide an important avenue for introducing and experimenting with new actuators and devices. This is in contrast with commercial applications, for which issues of mass production and cost per unit can be critical to the transition of the technology to practical use.

Between 1995 and 1999, under the author's lead, a NASA study took place with the objective of improving the understanding and practicality of EAP materials and identifying planetary applications. The materials that were investigated include IPMC and dielectric EAP, which was named ESSP (electro-statically stricted polymer), and they were used as bending and longitudinal actuators, respectively. The devices that were developed include a dust-wiper, gripper, robotic arm, and miniature rake. The dust-wiper (Figure 5) received the most attention and it was selected as the baseline in the MUSES-CN mission as a component of the Nanorover's optical/IR window.

The use of IPMC was investigated jointly with NASA LaRC, Virginia Tech, Osaka National Research Institute and Kobe University from Japan. The team used a perfluorocarboxylate-gold composite with two types of cations, tetra-n-butylammonium and lithium. An IPMC was used as an actuator to wipe the window with the aid of a unique 104 mg blade having a gold-plated fiberglass brush (Figure 6), which was developed by ESLI (San Diego, CA). When subjecting this blade to a high voltage bias (1 to 2 KV) it repels dust and thus augments the brushing mechanism provided by the blade. A photographic view of the repelled dust and the wiper is shown in Figure 6. Tests showed that the heat losses associated with the activation of the IPMC in vacuum allow the actuator to respond at temperatures as low as $-100°C$.

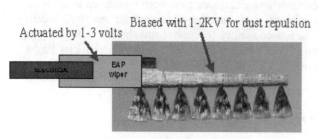

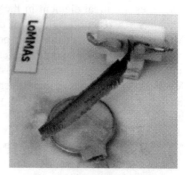

Figure 5: Combined schematic and photographic view of the EAP dust wiper.

Figure 6: A view of the dust wiper activated with high voltage to repel dust

The sensitivity of IPMC to dehydration and the need to maintain its ionic content were addressed using a protective coating (Dow Corning 92-009). This coating was applied after the IPMC was etched to make it amenable to bonding. The application of such a protective coating emulates the role of biological skin that protects and encapsulates the blood and other life-essential body fluids. Experiments have shown that this coating allows the operation of IPMC in air, but the longest period that a protected sample maintained response was about four months. Analysis indicates that the selected coating material is water permeable, limiting the potential of long-term operation in dry conditions. Alternatives, such as the use of multi-layered coatings, possibly consisting of metallic self-assembled monolayering, were considered but the preliminary results were not encouraging. Complication arises when subjecting IPMC actuators to voltages above 1.23V, as a result of the electrolysis that takes place. This process raises concern since hydrogen blisters are formed under the protective coating and are expected to rupture the coating, particularly since there is an extreme vacuum on the asteroid.

Under DC activation, IPMC bends relatively quickly (0.1 to 1 seconds, depending on the size of the cations) followed by a slow recoiling with a permanent deformation [Nemat-Nasser, and Thomas, 2001]. This recoiling can be a serious issue, particularly with Na^+ cations for which there is a bending drift in the opposite direction when the activating voltage is maintained constant. The application of IPMC is further complicated by the fact that permanent deformation is also encountered after intermittent actuation and in its current state it cannot be relaxed by electrical activation. This issue is viewed as a challenge that is not resolved yet and may be addressed by an optimal selection of the ionic content of the IPMC material (Table 2).

Table 2: Challenges and identified solutions associated with the application of IPMC.

Challenge	Potential Solution
Fluorinate base which is difficult to bond	Etching the surface makes it amenable to bonding
Extremely sensitive to dehydration	Apply protective coating over the surface of the IPMC
Off-axis bending actuation	Constrain the free end and use a high ratio of length/width
Operate at low and high temperatures	The issue of extreme temperatures is a major concern. Operating a coated IPMC in vacuum allowed response at $-100°C$.
Removal of submicron dust	Use effective wiper-blade design and high bias voltage
Reverse bending drift under DC voltage	Limit the operation to cyclic activation to minimize this effect, and use cations such as Li^+ rather than Na^+.
Residual deformation particularly after intermittent activation	It occurs mostly after DC or pulse activation and it remains a challenge.
Protective coating is permeable	Develop alternative coating, possibly using multiple layers
Electrolysis occurs at $>1.23V$	Use efficient IPMC that requires low actuation voltage
Difficulties to assure material reproducibility	Still a challenge. May be possible to overcome using mass production and protective coating.
Degradation with time due to loss of ions to the host liquid	Use effective coating or immersion in electrolyte with enriched cation content of the same species as in the IPMC.

8 Summary and outlook

Technologies that allow developing biologically inspired systems are increasingly emerging allowing us to consider the design and construction of biomimetic intelligent robots. EAP materials have emerged with great potential, enabling the development of unique biologically inspired devices. Legged, finned or winged robots may be developed using electroactive polymers that will enable combinations of locomotion techniques including walking, hopping, swimming, diving, crawling, flying, etc., with selectable behavior and performance characteristics. Such robots that are driven by artificial muscles and controlled by artificial intelligence would allow making engineering reality out of what is considered science fiction today.

Using effective EAP actuators to mimic nature would immensely expand the collection and functionality of robots that are currently available. Important additions to this capability could be the application of tele-presence combined with virtual reality using haptic interfaces. Such capabilities are expected to significantly change future robots; however, there is a need for significant research and development to enhance the robustness of EAP and their efficiency. These efforts will require advancement in related computational chemistry models, comprehensive material science, electro-mechanics analytical tools, and improved material-processing techniques. In addition to developing better actuators, a discipline of visco-elastic engineering and control strategies will need to be developed to supplant the traditional engineering of rigid structures.

Figure 7: Grand challenge for the development of EAP-actuated robotics.

There are still many challenges, but the recent trend of international cooperation, the greater visibility of the field and the surge in funding of related research projects are offering great hope. To assist in the development of effective biologically inspired robots, an android head and robotic hand were made available to the author to offer them as platforms for the demonstration of internationally developed actuators. The author's arm-wrestling challenge – a match between EAP-actuated robots and a human opponent (Figure 7) – highlights the potential of this technology. Progress towards winning this arm wrestling match will lead to exciting new generations of robots and is expected to change our daily life. Such changes may include the possibility of robots becoming a household assistant and intelligent companion possibly substituting the dog as our "best friend".

Acknowledgement

Research described in this chapter was partially conducted at the Jet Propulsion Laboratory (JPL), California Institute of Technology, under a contract with National Aeronautics and Space Administration (NASA).

References

[1]   Alexander R. M., Elastic Mechanisms in Animal Movement, The Cambridge University Press: Cambridge, 1988.
[2]   Bar-Cohen Y. (Ed.), *Proceedings of the SPIE's Electroactive Polymer Actuators and Devices Conf., 6th Smart Structures and Materials Symposium*, **3669**, ISBN 0-8194-3143-5, pp. 1–414, (1999).
[3]   Bar-Cohen Y. (Ed.), "Electroactive Polymer (EAP) Actuators as Artificial Muscles - Reality, Potential and Challenges," ISBN 0-8194-4054-X, *SPIE Press*, **PM98**, pp. 1–671, (March 2001) and 2nd Edition (March 2004).
[4]   Bar-Cohen Y., "History, Current Status and Infrastructure," Chapter 1.0, in [Bar-Cohen, 2001], pp. 3–44.

[5] Bar-Cohen Y., "EAP Applications, Potentials and Challenges," Chapter 21, in [Bar-Cohen, 2001], pp. 615–659.

[6] Bar-Cohen Y., V. Olazabal, JPL, J. Sansiñena, & J. Hinkley, "Processing and Support Techniques," Chapter 14.0, in [Bar-Cohen, 2001], pp. 369–401.

[7] Bar-Cohen Y. and C. Breazeal (Eds), "Biologically Inspired Intelligent Robots," SPIE Press, **PM122**, ISBN 0-8194-4872-9 (March 2003).

[8] Eguchi M., *Phil. Mag.*, **49** (1925).

[9] Hanson D., and G. Pioggia, "Applications of EAP to Entertainment Industry," Chapter 18, in [Bar-Cohen, 2001], pp. 535–565.

[10] Jenkins C.H.M., "Shape Control of Precision Gossamer Apertures," Chapter 20, in [Bar-Cohen, 2001], pp. 595–611.

[11] Katchalsky A., "Rapid Swelling and Deswelling of Reversible Gels of Polymeric Acids by Ionization", *Experientia*, V, pp 319–320, (1949)

[12] Kennedy B., C. Melhuish, and A. Adamatzky, "Biologically inspired Robots," Chapter 17, in [Bar-Cohen, 2001], pp. 497–533.

[13] Kornbluh R. and R. Pelrine, "Application of Dielectric EAP Actuators," Chapter 16 in [Bar-Cohen, 2001], pp. 457–495.

[14] Marsh R. L., J. M. Olson, and S. K. Guzik, "Mechanical Performance of Scallop Adductor Muscle During Swimming," *Nature*, **357: (6377)** , pp. 411–413, Jun 4 1992

[15] Mavroidis D., Y. Bar-Cohen, and M. Bouzit, "Haptic Interfacing via ERF," Chapter 19, in [Bar-Cohen, 2001], pp. 567–594.

[16] Mussa-Ivaldi S., "Real Brains for Real Robots," *Nature*, **408**, pp. 305–306., (16 November 2000).

[17] Nemat-Nasser S. and C. Thomas," Ionic Polymer-Metal Composite (IPMC)" Chapter 6.0, in [Bar-Cohen, 2001], pp. 139–191.

[18] Roentgen, W. C., About the changes in shape and volume of dielectrics caused by electricity, *Ann. Phys. Chem.* **11**, pp. 771–786, 1880.

[19] Sacerdote M. P., J. Phys., *3 Series, t*, **VIII**, 31 (1899).

[20] Wessberg J., C. R. Stambaugh, J. D. Kralik, P. D. Beck, M. Lauback, J.C. Chapin, J. Kim, S. J. Biggs, M. A. Srinivasan and M. A. Nicolelis, "Real-time Prediction of Hard Trajectory by Ensembles of Cortical Neurons in Primates," *Nature*, **408**, pp. 361–365, (16 Nov. 2000).

[21] Zhang Q. M., T. Furukawa, Y. Bar-Cohen, and J. Scheinbeim (Eds.), *Proceedings of the Fall MRS Symposium on "Electroactive Polymers (EAP)*," ISBN 1-55899-508-0, **600**, Warrendale, PA, pp. 1–336. (1999).

Section III

Compliant Mechanics

CHAPTER 5

Mechanics of compliant structures

C. H. M. Jenkins[1], W. W. Schur[2] & G. Greshchik[3]
*[1]Compliant Structures Laboratory, Mechanical Engineering Department
South Dakota School of Mines and Technology, Rapid City, USA.
[2]Balloon Projects Branch Code 842, NASA Wallops Flight Facility,
Wallops Island, USA.
[3]Center for Aerospace Structures, University of Colorado, Boulder, USA.*

Abstract

Biological organisms must be structurally efficient. Hence it is not surprising that nature has embraced the compliant membrane structure as a central element in higher biological forms. This chapter discusses the unique challenges of modeling the mechanical behavior of compliant membrane structures. In particular, we focus on several special characteristics, such as large deformation, lack of bending rigidity, material nonlinearity, and computational schemes.

1 Introduction

1.1 Motivation

Biological organisms must be structurally efficient. They have benefited from millions of years of evolution to achieve, for example, high load carrying capacity per unit weight. It is not surprising then to find that compliant membrane structures play a significant role in nature, for membranes are among the most efficient of structural elements. Long ago, engineers adopted membrane structures for solutions where structural efficiency was critical. As an example, consider the working balloon. For a given balloon volume, the total lift available is fixed, implying a zero-sum trade between structure and payload. Modern high-altitude scientific balloons (Fig. 1), made of thin polymer film fractions of a millimeter thick with areal densities of a few grams per square meter, support payloads of a few tons!

Figure 1: Preparing to launch a high-altitude scientific balloon in Antarctica (courtesy NASA).

The subject of the mechanics of membranes is quite broad and challenging, being a special application of nonlinear continuum mechanics, and entire books are written on the topic. This chapter seeks to provide a very concise summary of the important features of membrane mechanics. We hope to give the reader some background and exposure to the subject, a "flavor" if you will, with references provided for those who desire to pursue deeper study. The first part of the chapter is a general foundation used in many applications besides membrane mechanics, while the latter part is more specific to membrane applications

1.2 Brief historical review

The first membrane structures were biological organisms, which may well represent the widest usage of this structural type even today. Examples range from cell walls (Fig. 2) and bat wings, to the bullfrog's inflatable throat. Historical use of membranes in engineering structures may be traced to the sail (Figure 3) and the tent. Kites, parachutes, balloons, and other flying structures followed. Musical instruments, notably drums, were comprised of membranes formed from stretched animal skin or parchment. In modern times, membranes have seen increasing use in civil structures such as temporary storage facilities and large-span roofs. Recently, there has been considerable interest in large membrane/inflatable structures for space applications.

The earliest formal analysis of membranes was begun by acousticians during the Renaissance period. This dynamic analysis was limited of course to simple geometries and linear problems. The first nonlinear analysis occurred during the early part of the 1900s, as a membrane solution to the so-called von Karman plate equations. Only since the advent of modern computers has the solution to problems with strongly nonlinear membranes of arbitrary geometry been accomplished. [For a complete review, see references 1–3.]

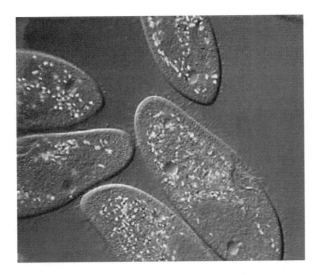

Figure 2: The paramecium wall is typical of cell walls formed from compliant membranes.

Figure 3: The sail may be one of the first human engineered compliant structures.

1.3 Definition and unique behavior of compliant membrane structures

To the structural engineer, membrane may mean an idealized model of a plate or shell structure, wherein the in-plane response dominates away from domain and load boundaries; hence, the stress couples may be neglected in this interior region. To the applied mechanician, membrane may mean a surface (thin film) with zero bending rigidity, resulting in nonexistent compressive solutions. In the present work, the term "membrane model" will be used in the sense of the structural engineer and the term "membrane" will be reserved for zero bending rigidity structures;

the term elastic "sheets" will be adopted for those structures with small but non-negligible bending rigidity.

In the case of membranes or sheets, their lack of bending rigidity, due to extreme thinness and/or low elastic modulus, leads to an essentially under-constrained structure that has equilibrium configurations only for certain loading fields. Under other loading conditions, large rigid-body deformations can take place. In addition, these same characteristics lead to an inability to sustain compressive stress. Time-dependent and nonlinear behaviors are also common features of typical membrane materials. The formalism for describing such behaviors is that of nonlinear continuum mechanics, in which the mathematical language of tensors is central.

2 Tensor analysis

The mathematical analysis of nonlinear continuum mechanics is usually presented using tensors. This is primarily due to the *invariance* of such a formulation, in that it is then general for any coordinate system. A secondary benefit is the conciseness of the resulting mathematics. For a more complete discussion of tensor analysis than can be provided here, see for example references [4, 5].

A *tensor* is a mathematical *operator*, specifically a *linear transformation*. Physical quantities that require a number of descriptors for their specification may be represented by tensors of the required *order*. For example, a quantity like temperature requires only one descriptor (magnitude) and is representable as a *zero-order* tensor (or *scalar*). Force requires more descriptors (magnitude and direction) and is representable by a *first-order* tensor (or *vector*). Stress and strain (9 descriptors) can be represented by *second-order* tensors. In "operator language," we might say that the second-order "rotation" tensor Q operates on the position vector r to form a new (first order) tensor r^*, i.e., $r^* = Qr$.

Two types of notations are used to denote tensors: (i) direct notation – similar to matrix or vector notation, e.g., x or $\{x\}$; and (ii) indicial notation – subscripts or superscripts attached to main letters called "kernel letters," e.g., x_i or x^i, $i = 1, 2, 3$. The number and range of the indices depends on the number of descriptors of the quantity. There is a physical meaning associated with the subscript or superscript notation. Subscripts and superscripts denote "covariant" and "contravariant" components, respectively; the physical meaning is given below.

Two other concepts are important for the understanding of tensor analysis. The first is the *summation convention*. We replace the summation operator Σ with a simple rule: in any given term, whenever an index is repeated once it is a *dummy* variable indicating summation over the range of the index. For example:

$$\sum_{i=1}^{3} a_i x^i = a_i x^i = a_1 x^1 + a_2 x^2 + a_3 x^3 \tag{1}$$

Formally, summation always occurs "along the diagonal" among sub and super indices.

The second concept is that of *expansion in terms of a basis*. Recall that a vector r in the rectangular Cartesian x-y-z coordinate system can be represented as a *linear combination of basis vectors*, say the unit vectors e_i associated with each coordinate direction. Then we may write

$$r = r_1 e_1 + r_2 e_2 + r_3 e_3 = r_i e_i \tag{2}$$

We can expand higher-order tensors in the same fashion, once a suitable basis is identified. The set of so-called *unit dyads* $\{e_i e_j\}$, derived from the outer product of e_i with itself (see below), forms a basis for expansion of second-order tensors, e.g., $\boldsymbol{S} = S^{ij}\boldsymbol{e}_i\boldsymbol{e}_j$. Thus quantities like r_i or S^{ij} are seen to be *components* of the tensor <u>relative to a specific basis</u> (or coordinate system).

A sample of important tensor operations is given below:

- Kronecker delta: $\delta_{ij} = 1$, $i \neq j$; 0, $i = j$

- Inner product of two vectors: $\boldsymbol{u} \cdot \boldsymbol{v} = u_i\boldsymbol{e}_i \cdot v_j\boldsymbol{e}_j = u_k v_k$

- Outer product of two vectors: $\boldsymbol{u} \otimes \boldsymbol{v} = \boldsymbol{uv} = u_i v_j \boldsymbol{e}_i\boldsymbol{e}_j$

- $\boldsymbol{uv}(\boldsymbol{w}) = \boldsymbol{u}(\boldsymbol{v} \cdot \boldsymbol{w})$

- Outer product of two 2nd-order tensors: $\boldsymbol{ST} = S_{ij}T_{kl}\boldsymbol{e}_i\boldsymbol{e}_j\boldsymbol{e}_k\boldsymbol{e}_l$

- Single inner product of two 2nd-order tensors: $\boldsymbol{S} \cdot \boldsymbol{T} = S_{ij}T_{jk}\boldsymbol{e}_i\boldsymbol{e}_k$

- Double inner products of two 2nd-order tensors: $\boldsymbol{S} : \boldsymbol{T} = S_{ij}T_{ij}$, $\boldsymbol{S} \cdot\cdot \boldsymbol{T} = S_{ij}T_{ji}$

The following conventions are used: Latin indices take the values 1,2,3; Greek indices take the values 1,2; capital and lower case Latin letters refer to the undeformed and deformed state, respectively; and bold type indicates vector or tensor quantities.

3 Coordinate systems and configurations

Geometric nonlinearity requires formulating the equilibrium equations in the *deformed* configuration of the body, which may be substantially different from the *undeformed* configuration (and which is not known in advance). We also, however, consider an elastic body to have a *natural, unstressed, reference state*, and we expect the elasticity to be derivable from a thermodynamic potential written in this reference state. Hence, we have a need for coordinate systems in the reference configuration and in the current configuration. Also, for analysis of membranes (as in shells), it will prove convenient to have coordinate systems aligned with the membrane *mid-surface*.

Consider the rectangular Cartesian (RC) coordinates *X-Y-Z* of a point *X* on the reference membrane midsurface that becomes point x on the current midsurface with RC coordinates *x-y-z* (Fig. 4). (Note that *rectangular* refers to *orthogonal* coordinates, while *Cartesian* refers to *straight* coordinate lines.) We also define *curvilinear midsurface* coordinates X^I and x^i in the reference and current configurations, respectively. These coordinate lines will be in general neither straight nor orthogonal, but they remain tangential and normal to the midsurface at every point. It is obvious, then, that a single coordinate system will not suffice for midsurface coordinates. Also, the reference and current configurations are typically taken as the undeformed and deformed states, respectively.

Vectors (*basis vectors*) are chosen that characterize the coordinates (see Fig. 4). In the RC coordinates, the vectors $\boldsymbol{E}_I$ and $\boldsymbol{e}_i$ are orthogonal and of unit magnitude (*orthonormal*). In the curvilinear coordinate system, *covariant* basis vectors $\boldsymbol{G}_I$ and $\boldsymbol{g}_i$ lie <u>tangent</u> to the respective coordinate curves X^I and x^i. In general, they are neither orthogonal nor of unit magnitude. (*Reciprocal bases*, consisting of the *contravariant* vectors $\boldsymbol{G}^I$ and $\boldsymbol{g}^i$ can also be defined, such that $\boldsymbol{G}_I \cdot \boldsymbol{G}^J = \delta_I^J$ and $\boldsymbol{g}_i \cdot \boldsymbol{g}^j = \delta_i^j$, but these bases will not be discussed further here.)

A *metric tensor* $\boldsymbol{g}$ in the deformed state is defined by *metric coefficients* $g_{kl} = \boldsymbol{g}_k \bullet \boldsymbol{g}_l$, where $\boldsymbol{g}_i = \partial\boldsymbol{r}/\partial x^i$ is the basis vector in x^i and $\boldsymbol{r}$ is the position vector from o to x; similarly, in the undeformed state, $G_{KL} = \boldsymbol{G}_K \bullet \boldsymbol{G}_L$, where $\boldsymbol{G}_I = \partial\boldsymbol{R}/\partial X^I$ is the basis vector in X^I and $\boldsymbol{R}$ is the position vector from 0 to X. The significance of the *metric tensor* is that it contains all the information about how <u>length</u>

(specifically squares of length) is measured in different coordinate systems (hence the name *metric*). As a simple example, consider that the (square of the) length of the infinitesimal element dl in rectangular Cartesian coordinates (x, y, z) is

$$(dl)^2 = (dx)^2 + (dy)^2 + (dz)^2 \tag{3.1}$$

But in cylindrical polar coordinates (r, θ, z), the same value is given by

$$(dl)^2 = (dr)^2 + (rd\theta)^2 + (dz)^2 \tag{3.2}$$

since the angular coordinate θ is not of and by itself a measure of length. So to measure length in the θ-direction, in this case one uses the metric coefficient $(r)^2$.

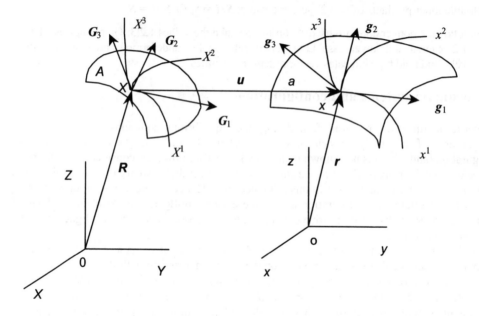

Figure 4: General configuration sketch for nonlinear continuum mechanics.

In the general curvilinear coordinates above, we would have similiarly:

$$(dr)^2 = dr \cdot dr, \ (dR)^2 = dR \cdot dR \tag{4}$$

In order to evaluate these expressions, we realize that

$$dr = \frac{\partial r}{\partial x^i} dx^i, \ \ dR = \frac{\partial R}{\partial X^I} dX^I \tag{5}$$

Substituting in from above we have

$$dr = g_i dx^i, \quad dR = G_I dX^I \tag{6}$$

Then, using the fact that $g_{ij} = g_i \cdot g_j$ and $G_{IJ} = G_I \cdot G_J$, we combine (4) and (6) to get

$$(dr)^2 = g_{ij} dx^i dx^j, \quad (dR)^2 = G_{IJ} dX^I dX^J \tag{7}$$

The use of general curvilinear coordinates (i.e., non-rectangular, non-Cartesian) provides for an elegant and fundamental formalism when developing the general theory of nonlinear membrane response. Noting, however, that the general curvilinear basis is always referred to a rectangular Cartesian basis, some simplifications can be made in the formulation, particularly for computations and in reporting of engineering quantities. To this end, we can establish a *local* rectangular Cartesian coordinate system at each point on the deformed midsurface. We will see how this is accomplished later.

4 Kinematics of Deformation

4.1 Motion and deformation

We take a material particle originally at location X in the reference configuration, and track its *motion* (viz., time-dependent response to loading) to its new location at position x in the current configuration, or

$$x = x(X, t) \tag{8}$$

We assume that matter cannot be created nor destroyed (the *axiom of continuity*), hence the motion is invertible or

$$X = X(x, t) \tag{9}$$

Figure 4: General configuration sketch for nonlinear continuum mechanics. This invertability can equally be expressed through the so-called *Jacobian J* of the deformation as

$$J \equiv \left| \frac{\partial x^k}{\partial X^K} \right| \neq 0 \tag{10}$$

where $|\ |$ denotes the determinant operation.

We can define the *deformation* for each instant of time t of the motion, or as a *quasi-static process*:

$$x = x(X) \tag{11}$$

4.2 Deformation gradient, stretch, and polar decomposition

Consider two neighboring material particles, located at X and $X + dX$, which deform to x and $x + dx$, respectively. Then we can determine dx from

$$dx = \frac{\partial x}{\partial X} dX = F \cdot dX \tag{12}$$

where F is called the *deformation gradient tensor*. Using (12), the initial *gage length dL* ($dL = (dX^T \cdot dX)^{1/2}$ is a natural and convenient choice for measuring deformation) is stretched to a length dl by

$$dx^T \cdot dx = dX^T \cdot dF^T \cdot dF \cdot dX \tag{13}$$

The *stretch ratio* of the gage lengths is

$$\Lambda = \frac{dl}{dL} = \sqrt{\frac{dx^T \cdot dx}{dX^T \cdot dX}} \tag{14}$$

An important postulate in continuum mechanics is that a deformation can be decomposed into a rigid rotation Q followed by a stretch along principal directions (the maximum or minimum stretches possible), or stretch first then rotation, such that

$$F = U \cdot Q = Q \cdot V \tag{15}$$

where U and V are the left and right stretch tensors, respectively. Consequently, V and U describe the stretch relative to the reference and current configurations, respectively.

The rotation tensor Q can be used to define a local RC basis for every point on the membrane surface, as discussed below. Following our convention that the X^I and x^i are RC, the current basis vectors g_i are related to the reference basis G_I by

$$g_i = Q \cdot G_I \tag{16}$$

4.3 Strain definitions

Although stretch provides an adequate measure of deformation, it is convenient to formulate measures that have <u>zero</u> value when <u>undeformed</u> (stretch equals unity in the undeformed state). These measures are called *strain* and are non-unique. It is intuitive, then, to refer strain from the undeformed or reference configuration, i.e., a Lagrangian strain definition.

A very fundamental approach to developing a strain definition is to simply measure the difference in gage lengths before and after deformation (stretching and/or rotation). This accounts for the fact that rigid body rotation should not contribute to strain, i.e., $(dr)^2 = (dR)^2$. Then using (6) and taking the difference:

$$(dr)^2 - (dR)^2 = g_{ij} dx^i\, dx^j - G_{IJ} dX^I dX^J \tag{17a}$$

$$\equiv 2E_{IJ}(X,t)\, dX^I dX^J \tag{17b}$$

Now recalling (12), $dx^i = F^i_J dX^J$, where $F^i_J = \partial x^i / \partial X^J$, and equating (17a) and (17b) above, it must be that

$$E_{IJ}(X,t) = \tfrac{1}{2} (g_{ij} F^i_I F^j_J - G_{IJ}) \tag{18}$$

which are the components of the *Green–Lagrange strain tensor*, and $g_{ij} F^i_I F^j_J$ are components of the so-called *Green's deformation tensor*. It is readily seen that this strain measure is referred to the reference configuration. If, as we have assumed, the midsurface coordinates are RC coordinates, g and G become the identity tensor 1, and the Green–Lagrange strain tensor may be written as:

$$E = \tfrac{1}{2} (F^T \cdot F - 1) \tag{19}$$

(A similar development leads to an *Eulerian* strain tensor, but this will not be discussed further here. Moreover, many materials, including some that may be useful for compliant membranes, have a response that is dependent on the *rate* of straining; this topic will also not be discussed further here.)

5 Stress and balance laws

5.1 Concept of stress

The idea of stress in a body is a way of characterizing the internal force reaction to loads. Physically, the loads create deformations that lead to changes in interatomic distances relative to the unloaded equilibrium state. Resistance to the deformation (e.g., due to van der Waals forces), averaged over a large group of atoms (the continuum *point*), is what we call *stress*. The goal then is to relate the loads to the (internal) stress.

A remarkable hypothesis attributed to Cauchy allows us to do this. It is an extension to deformable media of Newton's law of action/reaction. The first step is to define a *stress vector* or *traction t* that is the limit of an increment of force Δp per unit increment of current area Δa:

$$t = \lim_{\Delta a \to 0} \frac{\Delta p}{\Delta a} \tag{20}$$

Without additional development, we then simply state *Cauchy's Stress Hypothesis*:

> The surface traction *t* (the body load *b* vanishes in the limit) acting on a body, or portion of a body, is related to the *stress* in the neighborhood of the traction by:

$$t = \sigma \cdot v \tag{21}$$

> where v is the outward unit normal to the surface, and σ is the Cauchy (or true) stress tensor.

Newton's law of action/reaction follows since $t(-v) = -t(v)$. The components of *t* and likewise σ depend on the coordinate system chosen as a basis.

5.2 Stress definitions

The Cauchy stress is the most accurate measure of stress at a point. However, for constitutive relation development, other forms of the stress tensor are desirable (see the discussion below on *stress conjugacy*.) Several options are available:

- *Kirchhoff* stress: $\tau = J\sigma$ (simply a "weighted" Cauchy stress)
- *1st Piola–Kirchhoff* stress: $P = JF^{-1} \cdot \sigma$ (which is not a symmetric tensor)
- *2nd Piola–Kirchhoff* stress: $S = JF^{-1} \cdot \sigma \cdot F^{-T}$ (for small strain, the 2nd P – K stress can be shown to be merely the Cauchy stress rotated as if acting on the originally oriented surface)

5.3 Energy, mass, and momentum balance

The principle of energy balance (energy conservation) states that the time rate of change of the kinetic plus internal energy is equal to the sum of the rate of work of external forces plus all other power (energy/time) sources or sinks (e.g., from heat energy, electrical energy, chemical energy, etc.). Mass balance (conservation of mass) provides the mathematical description for the physical observation that matter can neither be created nor destroyed. Moreover, mass must be invariant under motion.

For linear elastostatics, the equilibrium equations are special cases of the balance of momentum equations. In this case, the inertia term is neglected, either due to vanishing mass and/or acceleration of the body. The equilibrium equations can be grouped into force (translational) and moment (rotational) equilibrium.

For *global* translational equilibrium, we sum all of the surface tractions t and body forces b over any arbitrary portion of the body of volume v and enclosing surface area a in the current configuration:

$$\oint_a t\,da + \int_v b\,dv = 0 \tag{22}$$

The internal stress within the volume can be related to the surface tractions through the Cauchy stress hypothesis (21):

$$\oint_a \sigma \cdot n\,da + \int_v b\,dv = 0 \tag{23}$$

The surface integral on the left can be converted to a volume integral through use of Gauss's theorem [6], giving, after some manipulation:

$$\int_v (\nabla \cdot \sigma + b)\,dv = 0 \tag{24}$$

Since the original volume v was arbitrary, it must follow that

$$\nabla \cdot \sigma + b = 0 \tag{25}$$

This single *local* vector equation contains the familiar three scalar equations of translational equilibrium.

Rotational or moment equilibrium follows in a similar fashion, namely

$$\oint_a (t \times x)\, da + \int_v (b \times x)\, dv = 0 \tag{26}$$

Again, use is made of Gauss's theorem to convert the closed surface integral to a volume integral. The conclusion drawn from the result is that the stress tensor σ must be symmetric. Conversely, the symmetry of the stress tensor automatically satisfies rotational equilibrium. (This result assumes, however, that there are no local "stress couples").

For nonlinear elastostatics, the moment equilibrium may be satisfied in an interesting way. Since the body can deform largely, global moment equilibrium is automatically satisfied, as shown in Figure 5.

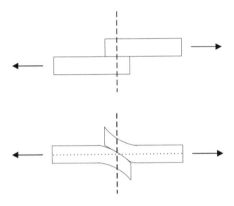

Figure 5. A single lap joint rotates to satisfy moment equilibrium

5.4 Weak form of translational equilibrium

For computational purposes, it is convenient to replace (25) with an equivalent single scalar *weak* or integral form. The *pointwise* equation (25) is multiplied by a test function and integrated over the *entire* body. If the test function is the virtual velocity field δv (which is an arbitrary function that must satisfy kinematic constraints), the weak form is called the *principle of virtual power*:

$$\int_v (\nabla \cdot \sigma + b) \cdot \delta v \, dv = 0 \tag{27}$$

After some manipulation [6], we get

$$\int_v \sigma : \delta d\, dv = \int_a t \cdot \delta v\, da + \int_v b \cdot \delta v\, dv \tag{28}$$

where d is the deformation rate tensor. Stated plainly, the rate of work done by the external forces for any virtual velocity field is equal to the rate of work done by the internal stresses for the same velocity field.

5.5 Conjugate stress and strain

As stated earlier, we expect the elastic response of a material to be derivable from a thermodynamic potential function that is referred to the original, undeformed state (i.e., has zero potential when undeformed, which implies that the stress and strain are zero as well). Hence, we form the rate of work per unit volume in the reference state as

$$d\dot{W} = [\text{stress}]: d[\text{strain}]$$

where [stress] and [strain] are *work conjugate* stress and strain tensors, respectively.

We now generalize the concept of conjugacy by considering the virtual power (work rate) equation previously derived:

$$\int_v \boldsymbol{\sigma} : \delta d \, dv = \int_a \boldsymbol{t} \cdot \delta v \, da + \int_v \boldsymbol{b} \cdot \delta v \, dv \tag{29}$$

where the integration was taken over the current volume v. Knowing that $dv = J \, dV$, we can take the integration over the reference volume (recall that work conjugacy is referred to the reference state). Then the internal virtual power (left hand side) can be taken as:

$$\int_v \boldsymbol{\sigma} : \delta d \, dv = \int_V J\boldsymbol{\sigma} : \delta d \, dV \tag{30}$$

We conclude that $\tau = J\boldsymbol{\sigma}$ is work conjugate to the strain whose (deformation) rate is $\boldsymbol{d}$; τ is the *Kirchhoff* stress tensor.

Other conjugate stress–strain pairs are possible, including that the 2nd Piola–Kirchhoff stress S is work conjugate to the Green–Lagrange strain E, and that the Cauchy stress $\boldsymbol{\sigma}$ is work conjugate to the *Hencky* or logarithmic strain

$$\ln(\boldsymbol{U}) = \tfrac{1}{2} \ln (\boldsymbol{F} \cdot \boldsymbol{F}^T) \tag{31}$$

where $\boldsymbol{F} \cdot \boldsymbol{F}^T$ is the *Finger* tensor. (Remark: although it is conceivable to write the constitutive relations in the current configuration, there are fundamental reasons [7] and practical reasons [6, 8] that call this approach into question.)

6 Constitutive equations

6.1 Introduction

Many structural materials exhibit at sufficiently small strains, i.e. under sufficiently small stresses, a linear-response regime. In that regime the accumulation of damage due to cyclic loading is typically relatively small. At higher stress levels the strain response typically deviates from linearity. Generally, the rate of accumulation of damage due to cyclic loading or due to sustained loading increases with the stress level. The onset of non-linear response often signals some irreversible changes and the acceleration of damage accumulation. Therefore, in technological applications, the operational design-strength threshold, at least in a nominal sense, is often limited to well below the onset of significant deviation from linear response.

Some materials deviate from this response behavior. Materials that exhibit linear strain response up to failure are brittle. Their technological application is quite limited; it requires special precautions. Successful technological applications of brittle materials typically avoid features that locally raise stress levels as predicted by the theory of elasticity solutions, such as holes and voids within the load path, or re-entrant corners. These features cause local stress peaks that exceed the stress level of the remote uniform cross section in the load path by a large factor (in strength of material terminology, this is the stress concentration factor). To reduce that effect it is generally necessary to round out re-entrant corners using as large a radius as possible. Unless the stress peaks in a brittle component are accurately predicted, it is generally necessary to severely limit the exploitation of the tested material strength. Applications may require the limitation to be one quarter to less than one tenth of the tested strength.

Technological applications of the materials discussed so far justify the use of linearly elastic constitutive laws in the analysis of structural systems. In general, theories developed for linearly elastic materials are limited to small strains.

There are materials that exhibit elastic, hence reversible response well into their non-linear range. Some of those materials remain elastic for very large strains. These are elastomers. In continuum mechanics, they are termed hyper-elastic. Theories developed for hyper-elastic materials typically extend into large strains.

The analytical methods and tools available since the last quarter of the 20th century, such as the non-linear finite element method, allow in principal the analysis of structural systems that use a far broader collection of classes of material. In principal, in an incremental analysis such as performed via the non-linear finite element method, any response mechanism can be programmed and hence executed during the numerical process. For the outcome of the solution process to make sense, however, it is necessary that the implemented constitutive laws mimic the material responses and satisfy the conservation laws of mechanics and the first and second fundamental laws of thermodynamics. In developing new constitutive relations that do not fit within established formulations from empirical observations on test specimens, it is necessary to assure that these laws are not violated. For a loading process that is adiabatic and isothermal, this requirement can be simply stated: Under monotonic up-loading from the unstrained state the external load system must perform non-negative (non-negative rather than positive is used here to include the friction of an incompressible material) work on the solid element upon uploading, that is:

$$d\sigma_{ij}\, d\varepsilon_{ij} \ge 0. \qquad (32)$$

This requirement demands that the incremental (or tangent) moduli of the material for direct stress, shear stress, and hydrostatic stress must be positive. An application of this requirement yields the range of possible Poisson's ratios for isotropic solids.

6.2 Thermomechanics

Events in solid mechanics are governed by three types of equations that must be solved simultaneously. These are 1) the equilibrium equations, which may be either static or dynamic, 2) the kinematic relations, and 3) the constitutive laws. The equilibrium equations and the kinematic relations are general. The equilibrium equations are directly derived from physics. The kinematic relations connect displacements to the deformation quantities, i.e., they are just geometric relations. The constitutive laws by contrast are material specific; and, they can be quite complex. Indeed it may be difficult if not impossible to specify such a law for a specific material that suits all its applications. Often the analyst must be satisfied with a constitutive law that in some narrow way captures the material response that is pertinent for his particular application. In an earlier time, when analytical solutions were principally of the closed-form type, i.e. the strong solution of differential equations, constitutive laws were sought that made the solution of solid mechanics problems by these methods tractable. This limitation on the choice of constitutive equations was quite severe. Modern analysis methods such as the various discretization methods and semi-discretization methods accept a much broader class of constitutive laws. Using these methods, which are usually available to the analyst as a commercially supplied numerical tool, even material failure modes can be included in the analysis. This section describes a number of mechanical material response phenomena connecting stress, strain and temperature and it provides an overview of their mathematical description in sufficient detail to be useful to the analyst. A given material may exhibit one or more of these phenomena. Where appropriate and expedient, the description is limited to the two-dimensional sheet.

Not until the second half of the 20th century did the field theory of thermomechanics come into being. By contrast the field theory of mechanics dates back to 1775 for fluids, due to Euler, and 1822 for solids, due to Cauchy. Thermodynamics, which treats the state of matter and transformation of energy within matter is due to Carnot (1824) and Clausius (1850). Until recently, it has been limited to the treatment of homogeneous states. Still, its importance in the development of constitutive relations in mechanics has long been recognized. The limitations placed on constitutive laws by the first and second fundamental laws of thermodynamics have been properly regarded. An example of this will be discussed in the section that deals with linear elasticity.

The first fundamental law of thermodynamics, when written for an element of matter, states that there exists a state function $u(a_k, \theta)$, the internal energy per unit mass, such that:

$$du = dw + dq \tag{33}$$

The second fundamental law of thermodynamics identifies a second state function $s(a_k, \theta)$, the entropy per unit mass, that satisfies

$$\theta \, ds \geq 0 \tag{34}$$

Here θ is the absolute temperature, dw is the external work supply per unit mass, dq is the heat supply per unit mass, and the a_k are the collection of external and internal parameters that combine with external and internal force quantities in products that have the dimensions of work per unit volume. The entropy increment has two parts, a reversible part

$$d^{(rev)}s = dq/\theta \tag{35}$$

which is due to heat flow, and an irreversible part, the entropy production inside the element

$$d^{(ir)}s \geq 0 \tag{36}$$

Unlike ds, $d^{(rev)}s$ and $d^{(ir)}s$ are not total differentials. In the dynamic case, i.e., when matter accelerates, the first fundamental law as stated above must be amended by the addition of kinetic energy supply.

6.3 The linearly elastic isotropic solid

The constitutive relation that governs the response of a linear-elastic solid in an isothermal and isentropic process is Hooke's law. Written for the general stress state of an anisotropic solid it is given by

$$\sigma_{ij} = D_{ijkl}\, \varepsilon_{kl} \,. \tag{37}$$

Both the stress tensor and the strain tensor are symmetric in their subscripts, and in addition the tensor $D_{(ij)(kl)}$ is symmetric with respect to the 1st and 2nd group of index pairs
The symmetries of the 4th-rank material tensor reduce the number of independent constants to 21. The additional symmetries of an isotropic solid reduce the independent elastic constants to two. These are the Lamé constants λ and μ. Hooke's law for this solid is given by

$$\sigma_{ij} = \lambda\, \varepsilon_{kk}\, \delta_{ij} + 2\, \mu \varepsilon_{ij} \tag{38}$$

The response to uniaxial stress is

$$\varepsilon_{11} = (\lambda + \mu)/[\mu\,(3\lambda + 2\mu)]\, \sigma_{11} = \sigma_{11}/E \,, \tag{39}$$

where E is the elastic modulus (or Young's modulus).
The shear response is

$$\varepsilon_{ij} = \sigma_{ij}/(2\,\mu) = \sigma_{ij}/(2\,G) \,, \tag{40}$$

where $G = \mu$ is the shear modulus.
The response to hydrostatic stress is

$$\varepsilon_{kk} = \sigma_{kk}/(3\lambda + 2\mu) = \sigma_{kk}/(3\,K) \,, \tag{41}$$

where K is the bulk modulus.
The two independent elastic constants used in the engineering literature are Young's modulus and Poisson's ratio

$$\nu = (\lambda/2)/(\lambda + \mu) \tag{42}$$

The shear modulus in terms of these constants is

$$G = E/[2(1 + \nu)] \tag{43}$$

Young's modulus characterizes the strain response in the direction of a uniaxial applied stress. Poisson's ratio is the ratio of contraction in a direction that is perpendicular to an elongation caused by a tensile stress that is in line with the elongation.
Thermodynamic considerations require that E, G, and K are non-negative. These requirements limit Poisson's ratio for an isotropic material to the range between -1.0 and $+0.5$. There is no real isotropic material known that has a negative Poisson's ratio. Therefore, one may postulate for the

range of Poisson's ratio $0.0 \le \nu \le 0.5$. Typically, cork and other porous materials have Poisson's ratios near the lower end and elastomers such as rubbers have Poisson's ratios near the upper end of that range.

For later convenience, the stress tensor and the strain tensor may be decomposed into their isotropic part σ_{kk} and deviatoric part

$$\sigma'_{ij} = \sigma_{ij} - \delta_{ij}\,\sigma_{kk}/3 \tag{44}$$

for stress, and isotropic part ε_{kk} and deviatoric part

$$\varepsilon'_{ij} = \varepsilon_{ij} - \delta_{ij}\,\varepsilon_{kk}/3 \tag{45}$$

for strain. The shear response can then be written as

$$\varepsilon'_{ij} = \sigma'_{ij}/(2\,G). \tag{46}$$

6.4 The linearly elastic isotropic membrane

The stress state of interest in compliant membrane mechanics is plane stress. For this state the constitutive equation for the isotropic membrane can be reduced to

$$
\begin{Bmatrix} \gamma_1 \\ \gamma_2 \\ \gamma_6 \end{Bmatrix} =
\begin{bmatrix}
1/E & -\nu/E & 0 \\
-\nu/E & 1/E & 0 \\
0 & 0 & 2(1+\nu)/E
\end{bmatrix}
\begin{Bmatrix} \sigma_1 \\ \sigma_2 \\ \sigma_6 \end{Bmatrix}
\tag{47}
$$

The inverse relation is an obvious simplification of the corresponding equation for the orthotropic membrane discussed below. The notation used here is common in the engineering community that deals with thin sheets and laminates:

$$\gamma_1 = \varepsilon_{11},\ \gamma_2 = \varepsilon_{22},\ \text{and}\ \gamma_6 = \varepsilon_{12};\ \sigma_1 = \sigma_{11},\ \sigma_2 = \sigma_{22},\ \text{and}\ \sigma_6 = \sigma_{12} \tag{48}$$

6.5 The linearly elastic orthotropic membrane

The relations connecting stresses and strains in orthotropic films, when written in the material principal directions, are

$$
\begin{Bmatrix} \gamma_1 \\ \gamma_2 \\ \gamma_6 \end{Bmatrix} =
\begin{bmatrix}
1/E_1 & -\nu_{21}/E_2 & 0 \\
-\nu_{12}/E_1 & 1/E_2 & 0 \\
0 & 0 & 1/G
\end{bmatrix}
\begin{Bmatrix} \sigma_1 \\ \sigma_2 \\ \sigma_6 \end{Bmatrix}
\tag{49}
$$

and

$$
\begin{Bmatrix} \sigma_1 \\ \sigma_2 \\ \sigma_6 \end{Bmatrix} =
\begin{bmatrix}
E_1/(1-\nu_{12}\nu_{21}) & -\nu_{12}E_1/(1-\nu_{12}\nu_{21}) & 0 \\
-\nu_{21}E_2/(1-\nu_{12}\nu_{21}) & E_2/(1-\nu_{12}\nu_{21}) & 0 \\
0 & 0 & 1/G
\end{bmatrix}
\begin{Bmatrix} \gamma_1 \\ \gamma_2 \\ \gamma_6 \end{Bmatrix}
\tag{50}
$$

In any other reference coordinate system, the forms of the constitutive relations for the orthotropic membrane are indistinguishable from those for a general anisotropic membrane, i.e. the matrix $[D_{ij}]$ and its inverse $[C_{ij}]$ are fully populated.

In determining the thermodynamic restrictions for the Poisson's ratios v_{12} and v_{21}, it is necessary to take the through-thickness direction into account. These Poisson's ratios may indeed be larger than 0.5. There is no general relation for G in terms of the E_i and the v_{ij}.

An orthotropic membrane may be isotropic in the plane. In that case (47) holds but without the restriction on Poisson's ratio in the plane to not more than 0.5. Also, balanced orthotropy in the plane, i.e. $E_1 = E_2$, does not imply isotropy in the plane. While $E_1 = E_2$ implies $v_{12} = v_{21}$, it does not imply $G = E /[2(1 + v)]$.

6.6 Generalized elasticity: the Cauchy, hyperelastic, and hypoelastic solids

Linear elastic materials obey (37), where the coefficients C_{ijkl} are independent of stress and strain; they may, however, be dependent on temperature. These coefficients are restricted on grounds of the symmetries of the stress and strain tensors and the fundamental laws of thermodynamics. In particular, specific linear combinations of them, the elastic moduli, the shear moduli, and the bulk modulus, must be positive. The concept of elasticity can be expanded to more generality. Truesdell [9–11] categorized three classes of elasticity, which are:

1) A material is said to be elastic (Cauchy material) if it possesses a homogeneous stress-free state, the natural state, and if in some neighborhood of this state there exists a one-to-one correspondence between a work-conjugate pair of stress and strain tensors

$$\sigma_{ij} = F(\varepsilon_{kl}) \tag{51}$$

2) A material is said to be hyperelastic if it possesses a homogeneous stress-free state, and if there exists a strain-energy density function $\rho_0 W$, which is an analytic function of the strain tensor, the work done by the stresses equalling the gain in strain energy

$$\partial(\rho_0 W)/\partial\varepsilon_{ij} = \sigma_{ij} \tag{52}$$

3) A material is said to be hypoelastic, if the stress rate is a homogeneous linear function of the rate of deformation

$$d\sigma_{ij}/dt - \Omega_{kj}\,\sigma_{ik} - \Omega_{ki}\,\sigma_{kj} = C_{ijkl}\,d_{kl}. \tag{53}$$

Here

$$\Omega_{ij} = \tfrac{1}{2}\left(\partial v_j/\partial x_i - \partial v_i/\partial x_j\right) \tag{54}$$

is the spin tensor.

In this definition the coefficients C_{ijkl} are functions of stress or strain. The definition of the hypoelastic material can be restated by substituting the time derivatives of any work-conjugate pair of stresses and strains so that

$$d\sigma_{ij}/dt = C_{ijkl}\,d\,\varepsilon_{kl}/dt. \tag{55}$$

Furthermore, without violating the concept, one can replace the time derivatives with derivatives of a generalized evolution parameter. With this identification it is clear that the only difference in the definitions of the Cauchy material and the hypoelastic material is the requirement of the homogeneous stress-free state in the Cauchy material. Clearly, the Cauchy material includes the hyperelastic material. Thus, the hypoelastic material is the most general definition of an elastic material.

Note: Some writers have questioned the admissibility of hypoelastic materials on thermodynamic grounds. While we caution anyone who develops a mechanical constitutive model for a material to make sure that under a complete loading cycle net energy cannot be extracted from a material, it is quite conceivable that the micro-structure of a continuum may contain elastic instabilities that exhibit snap-through like response at the sub-continuum mechanics scale. Such a material can be modeled as hypoelastic.

Interest in hyperelastic models has focused primarily on large deformation for which the dilatory component is deemed insignificant, so that only distortion is of concern; in that case the body is considered incompressible. It is clear from the context that the strain under discussion here is the logarithmic strain and the stress is the Cauchy stress in a reference frame that is rotated with the principal stretch axes. Also, since there is no volume change, the hydrostatic pressure does no net work.

A particular form of the elastic potential, which is due to Mooney, is

$$W(I_1, I_2) = C_1 (I_1 - 3) - C_2 (I_2 - 3) , \qquad (55)$$

where I_1, I_2 are "stretch invariants", and C_1 and C_2 are constants, seems to provide a suitable energy function for certain rubber-like materials. With $C_2 = 0$ this function becomes the strain energy function for the so-called neo-Hookean solid of Rivlin.

The coefficients in the constitutive equation of a hyperelastic material satisfy the fundamental laws of thermodynamics automatically. In developing constitutive equations for a Cauchy solid or for a hypoelastic solid, it is necessary to assure that the coefficients of the tangent stiffness are such that during monotonic uploading the external load system performs positive work on the element for each load increment.

6.7 Visco-elasticity

Visco-elastic solids are dissipative; i.e., they can undergo thermodynamically irreversible processes during deformation. They may or may not be restorable to their initial state by simply unloading and letting sufficient time pass. A convenient way to characterize the response behavior of these materials, at least in a qualitative sense, is to envision them to be performing like viscous elements (dash-pots) and elastic elements (springs) in some combination of series and parallel arrangement. Some examples of such visualizations in linear visco-elasticity are the Maxwell model – a non-restorable system, the Voigt model – a restorable system, and the standard linear model – also a restorable system.

A model that exhibits, at least qualitatively, most observed phenomena in the early response phases of many technological materials used in structural systems combines the Maxwell model and the Voigt model in series. This model, when loaded by a step load, which is maintained constant over time (this is the creep test), exhibits an instantaneous elastic response, a primary creep phase, which is transient, and a secondary creep phase with a constant flow rate.

Real materials that may, at least qualitatively, be characterized by the Maxwell and Voigt model in series, exhibit a tertiary creep phase of accelerated creep towards failure as a result of cross section reduction due to Poisson's effect.

Particularly in polymers, but in other materials as well, visco-elastic response is very sensitive to temperature. For some materials it has been observed that there is a time–temperature correspondence that allows establishing a master curve together with a time-shift rule (these materials are sometimes referred to as thermorheologically simple). This reduces the analysis of visco-elastic response for a variable-load/variable-temperature history to a formulation with the dummy time variable of integration replaced by a scaled time.

If non-linear response can be similarly reduced to the master curve by some other time-shift rule, then the analysis of visco-elastic response to a variable-load/variable-temperature history can again be reduced to a formulation with the dummy time variable of integration substituted by the scaled time.

The creep function $J(t)$ and the stress-relaxation function $G(t)$ for complex visco-elastic response behavior can typically be characterized by a series made up of exponential terms, a so-called *Prony series*. Such a series is not an orthogonal series. Fitting a Prony series to test data can be done in two ways. The more traditional way is to choose exponential terms with the time decay coefficient separated by about a decade, and then using some weighted-integral method to determine the appropriate coefficients. Another way that generally requires a smaller number of terms is to determine both the coefficients associated with each term and the time decay coefficients in each term, using an optimization method. Both processes require the availability of appropriate software.

While with today's computers and software the determination of the coefficients in a Prony series is rapid, the acquisition of suitable creep data or stress relaxation data is time consuming and expensive. Structural analysis tools, such as non-linear finite element codes, may require both the creep formulation and the stress-relaxation formulation during the incremental analysis. To avoid resource-intensive test repetition, one can invert the Prony series for creep to obtain a Prony series for stress relaxation and vice versa [12].

6.8 Fabrics

While fabrics were one of the first structural materials used by humans in applications to membrane structures, to the structural analyst they are the least understood. Contrary to claims otherwise, a fabric does not behave like a two-dimensional continuum. Fabrics have internal mobility. This characteristic can be further classified into two distinct types of mobilities; these are the angular mobility and the transport mobility. Both types of mobilities contribute in different ways to the early success of fabric-made structural membranes, and to the difficulties that they pose to the analyst.

Angular mobility refers to the lack of resistance to shear distortion in the material reference frame. If this mobility is the only one active, then during deformation adjacent material points remain adjacent to each other, and in the topological sense in the same relative position. In particular, the crossing points of warp yarns and fill yarns do not shift. The recently developed solid mechanics subfield, theory of nets [13], is capable of addressing this aspect. As of now, it is still primarily an academic enterprise.

The standard apparatus of the theory of continuum mechanics is an inadequate tool for the analysis of structures that possess this characteristic. This is easily demonstrated by the following experiment. Fabrics have significant stiffness in both the warp and the fill (weft) direction. These can be characterized to some approximation by the elastic moduli E_W and E_F, respectively. Fabrics exhibit Poisson's effect, which can be characterized to some approximation by the Poisson's ratios v_{WF} and v_{FW}. The resistance to shear (angular distortion) in the material reference frame of the fabric (x_{W}, x_{F}) is typically several decades smaller than the resistance to extension in the material directions. Hence G, the shear modulus, is very small. It is observed when subjecting a simple weave fabric to uniaxial tension diagonally (in a reference direction rotated $\pi/4$ relative to the warp direction) to the material reference coordinates, then, at least for small deformations, little resistance to the deformation is experienced.

Transport mobility refers to yarns sliding relative to each other. This aspect is even more difficult to formulate in a theoretical model. It is also responsible for the incredible toughness of fabrics, particularly loosely woven ones. This mobility prevents the stress concentrations that are found in linearly elastic solid continua to occur.

Still, fabrics make excellent structural membranes. Successful designs that use fabrics as structural membranes usually are constructed such that, under design critical loadings, the material directions are nearly coincident with the principal stress directions. To small deviations from this condition the fabric will respond by undergoing some significant but most often harmless angular distortion. Fabric structures, designed to this condition, can be analytically assessed by the methods of continuum mechanics as the shear stiffness, or lack thereof, plays a negligible role.

7 Approximations

Similar to other technical fields, membrane theory is characterized by principles that can be stated in a relatively straightforward form, and problems that may involve prohibitive difficulties in using those principles. These difficulties necessitate the careful choice of a line of attack that often involves approximations. However, approximations may affect the predicted responses of membranes more profoundly than of other, more traditional structures. To appreciate and quantify these effects in the context of a given technical application, the engineer must be aware of how the final results may be influenced.

The quality degradation of response predictions due to solution approximations depends on the problem and is generally not straightforward to assess. We here address some selected aspects of the issue only. First, the relevance of the problem of approximations is placed in the context of up-to-date computational tools. The general sensitivity of membrane solutions to approximations is illuminated next. The discussion of some selected approximations follows, and a simple illustration is given. Finally, the notion of solution accuracy is addressed.

7.1 Approximations in the era of computational mechanics

Familiar with some of the gross simplifications needed for the solution of some mechanical problems prior to the computer age, one may be tempted to ignore the issue of approximations in the context of current technology. Indeed, solution approaches such as the finite element method (FEM) are almost universally applicable and are capable of close to arbitrary solution accuracy for certain problems. However, the need for the awareness of approximations is not eliminated by the availability of such tools. One should not ignore the issue of approximations because:

- Numerical solutions also involve approximations.

- Before their predictions can be deemed acceptable, numerical models must be benchmarked *both* within their own context (convergence and parameter sensitivity studies) *and* against alternative solutions. The alternative solutions often need to be derived symbolically because physical test results for membranes with a quality comparable to numerical/theoretical predictions are virtually non-existent and are often prohibitively difficult to obtain.

- Parametric studies with a need for only limited accuracy may be based on closed-form formulas, as opposed to numerical models.

- The knowledge of underlying approximations may prevent the abuse of numerical analysis in some cases.

By the way of the last point we stress that the unintentional abuse of a numerical tool may be due to attempts to obtain results despite the unusual difficulties of a membrane problem. Such difficulties are typically related to overcoming a common limitation of many analysis programs, namely, the inability of most regular numerical solution procedures to handle singular structural states such as a flat membrane state with no lateral stiffness, before pressurization or prestressing. In order to obtain results at all, one may have to "trick" a program through such a singular configuration. In so doing, one should take care not to modify the problem in a mechanically or mathematically illegitimate manner, such as via adding bending stiffness to the film.

Regardless of whether an analysis tool has to be outsmarted to produce results, typical membrane problems generally necessitate *full* geometric nonlinear capabilities in the program. One of the problem features necessitating nonlinear analysis is the extreme sensitivity of membranes to physical details, and membrane models to modeling details. As geometric nonlinearity is a standard feature of modern computational tools, one may safely require its use in *all* membrane analyses. This requirement becomes imperative for precision applications such as inflatable RF reflectors.

So far in this section we peculiarly omitted concerns of material nonlinearity. This omission reflects the state of the art in membrane engineering in the aerospace industry where, despite the availability of more "exotic" material models, the engineer is still practically limited to linear elasticity in the overwhelming majority of cases. This limitation need not cause concern when the subject membrane is smooth and is operated with sufficiently low stresses. However, stresses potentially higher than the material proportionality limit *or* a creased membrane state (which increases global film compliance in a highly nonlinear fashion) clearly call for nonlinear material models. Unfortunately, properly quantified (measured) parameters of constitutive behavior beyond the proportional limit of films commonly used in space are rarely available and the rigorous test study of wrinkled membranes is still in its infancy [14, 15]

7.2 The nonlinear nature of membrane problems

Film bending and compressive compliance entails a malleable global geometry: membranes re-configure their shape, at the cost of wrinkling if necessary, to enable the bearing of certain loads. "While their thinness makes them incapable of sustaining bending moments, it also renders them incapable of ... preserving their shape under certain kinds of loading" [16].

That, except for some simplistic examples, the re-configuration of geometry is an integral aspect of their response renders membrane behavior similar to post-buckling response in that geometrically linear analysis is simply incapable of capturing their mechanics. Thus geometric simplifications — approximations — can have a significant impact on a membrane solution. A pronounced example of this influence is illustrated in Figure 5.16 on page 263 of reference [17]. Shown among the insets of this figure are the shapes of a membrane cylinder subject to a perimeter load as predicted with shell theory with bending effects, with small-strain nonlinear membrane theory, and with large-strain nonlinear membrane theory. The three shapes differ significantly.

7.3 Approximations in the context of the governing equations

A subject of mechanics, the behavior of membranes is governed by the three sets of equations stating equilibrium, stress–strain relations, and geometric compatibility. To prepare the illustration of solution approximations, we first present these equations in a complete and general form uncorrupted by any simplification. (Equivalent forms of these equations other than those presented below also exist: our choice is for convenience only.) We then discuss some classic types of approximations.

7.3.1 An exact form of the governing equations

Describe membrane mechanics locally at an internal, smooth point. Use a rectangular coordinate system with its x and y axes tangent to the membrane mid-surface and aligned in the directions of the surface principal curvatures in the load-carrying state. (These mutually perpendicular directions exist at any point on any smooth surface.) Thus the third, z, axis will be the surface normal. Define all (stress, strain, etc.) quantities in this coordinate system, and interpret all derivatives with respect to these coordinates.

Also, ignore membrane thickness: use through-thickness resultant quantities (such as membrane forces obtained by stress integration through the membrane thickness). Accordingly assume that, where necessary, even relations often stated in a general continuum-based form (such as the constitutive law) are now modified to involve through-thickness resultant quantities.

State equilibrium as

$$\partial n_x/\partial x + \partial n_{xy}/\partial y + q_x = \rho a_x \tag{56}$$

$$\partial n_y/\partial y + \partial n_{yx}/\partial y + q_y = \rho a_y \tag{57}$$

$$n_{xy} = n_{yx} \tag{58}$$

$$p - n_x/R_1 - n_y/R_2\, p = \rho a_z \tag{59}$$

where n_x, n_y, and n_{xy} are the direct and shear membrane stress resultants in units of force per deformed length, q_x and q_{qy} are the in-plane surface loads in the x and y directions, p is the surface load normal to the surface (such as pressure), ρ is the membrane surface density, a_x, a_y, and a_z are the components of the acceleration vector, and R_1 and R_2 are the principal radii of curvature along the properly aligned x and y coordinate axes.

The constitutive law F can be generally stated as

$$N = F(history(E)) \tag{60}$$

where N is the tensor of membrane stress resultants and the term "*history(E)*" refers to the full history of the strain tensor E to accommodate time- or path-dependent nonlinear material responses. As an example we recall that for linear elasticity F is

$$N = F(history(E)) = F(E) = C{:}E \tag{61}$$

where C is a fourth-order tensor and ":" denotes double contraction. As no time dependence is involved, history is limited to the current instant. (By rearranging the membrane force and strain tensor components into a vector and those of C into a simple matrix, Eq. (61) is often presented as a matrix equation.)

Finally, geometric compatibility implies a proper displacement-based definition of the strains

$$E = L(u) \tag{62}$$

where L is a differential operator and u is the displacement vector field.

The constitutive and geometric relations, Eqs. (60) and (62), have been presented in a rather general form in comparison to the equilibrium equations to permit variations. Strains can be defined in a number of ways, with the constitutive law varied accordingly and also according to the assumed material behavior. The equilibrium conditions, however, can only vary in form, not in essence.

The difficulties in directly using relations, Eqs. (56) through (62), for the solution of a particular problem can be enormous. Consider, for example, the xyz coordinate system used. This reference frame, which permits writing the *exact* equilibrium equations in the relatively simple form Eqs. (56) through (59), is defined according to the instantaneous geometric conditions on the load-bearing membrane. These conditions generally vary over the surface as well as through the loading process, as the membrane shape evolves. Moreover, it is typically this very evolution — or its final state — that is sought by the solution. To manage the field equations in a frame of reference defined point-wise over a spatial surface among ephemeral conditions varying in an initially unknown manner would be difficult, to say the least.

To illustrate another practical difficulty, consider the membrane stress resultants n_x, n_y, and n_{xy}. For the equilibrium conditions Eqs. (56) through (59) these are defined as force per *distorted length* — a membrane-thickness resultant version of what is called the Cauchy stress in continuum mechanics. However, the constitutive laws often relate strain to the material response referred to the *stress-free* state. (For example, according to the common approach to linear elasticity, the Young's modulus E is obtained by dividing the load endured by a test coupon with the *initial* coupon cross section, as opposed to the one laterally contracted under the load due to Poisson's effect.) To avoid all approximations, the governing equations should involve the translation of the latter membrane force definition to the former.

Similar difficulties could be identified for most of the other variables as well. As a result, the above equations are rarely used as is. Instead, they are cast in equivalent forms in coordinate systems defined conveniently for particular problems. To manage the complexities of these alternative forms, approximations must be used. Resulting equations, derived for particular (classes of) problems, are established, analyzed, and solved in a number of reference works for shells and membranes — see, for example, [17] or [18]. (Shell-governing equations stated in terms of stiffness reduce to membrane equations as the bending and lateral shear stiffnesses diminish.)

7.3.2 Some geometric approximations

We here review three classes of geometric approximations. For this illustration, we borrow the nomenclature of [17], and denote by α the angle of slope with respect to a reference plane (at a generic point) of the unloaded membrane surface. Furthermore, the angular change of this slope during the loading process is denoted β.

Moderate rotation theory

Moderate rotation theory assumes that the angles of rotation β experienced by membrane surface points are small: $o(\beta) \ll 1$ Consequently, $o(\beta^2) \lll 1$ is also implied and the following substitutions can be made:

$$cos\ (\alpha + \beta)\ = cos\ (\alpha) - \beta\ sin\ (\alpha)$$
$$sin\ (\alpha + \beta) = sin\ (\alpha) - \beta\ cos\ (\alpha)$$
$$cos\ (\alpha) - cos\ (\alpha + \beta) = \beta\ sin(\alpha) + 1/2\ \beta^2\ cos\ (\alpha)$$
$$sin\ (\alpha + \beta) - sin\ (\alpha) = \beta\ cos(\alpha) - 1/2\ \beta^2\ sin\ (\alpha)$$

where α is the initial slope of the surface with respect to a reference plane, measured in the direction where β is taken.

Shallow shell theory

If, in addition to moderate rotations, the initial slope α of the surface is also low ($o(\alpha) \ll 1$, $o(\alpha^2) \lll 1$), the following approximations can be used:

$$cos\ (\alpha + \beta) = 1$$
$$sin\ (\alpha + \beta) = \alpha + \beta$$
$$cos\ (\alpha) - cos\ (\alpha + \beta) = \alpha\beta + 1/2\ \beta^2$$
$$sin\ (\alpha + \beta) - sin\ (\alpha) = \beta$$

The same approximations can be stated in other forms as well, depending on the frame of reference adopted. For example, an alternative but equivalent condition is $\sqrt{(z_{,x}^2 + z_{,y}^2)} \ll 1$, where x and y are coordinates within the particular reference plane, and z is the surface position normal to this plane [17, p.442].

Föppl–Kármán equations

The Föppl–Kármán equations, a classic formulation of the axishell (axisymmetric shells under axisymmetric loads) equations, involve small-strain approximations in the context of a particular version of shallow shell theory [17].

7.4 On accuracy and modeling

The need for faithful response prediction pervades by nature the entire gamut and history of engineering. The following discussion of this need is particularly relevant for precision inflatable space structures where application tolerances, manufacturing reliability, and modeling capabilities often appear at conflict.

Accuracy — in the sense of how well intent or assessment turns out to coincide with reality — is directly relevant to almost all steps of the engineering process. A few of these steps are presented in Table 1 with the errors qualitatively referred to and the statistical issues ignored.

One can state as a general condition for successful engineering endeavor that

$$e_a > e_f \tag{63}$$

In plain English: fabrication must adhere to tighter tolerances than necessary for the operation of the product.

Table 1: Modeling errors.

Error	Associated accuracy	Example
e_a ("application")	The accuracy required of a particular application: how close to ideal the hardware should be in terms of shape, material, etc.	The maximum *rms* surface error acceptable for a reflector.
e_f ("fabrication")	Workshop accuracy: how close to the specifications can the product be fabricated	Fabrication tolerances, quality scatter.
e_m ("modelling")	The accuracy of modeling assumptions: how well the principles underlying a model correspond to reality.	Is the material really linear elastic? Can dynamic effects really be ignored?
e_s ("solution")	Accuracy of solving the model: how well the mathematical and physical principles in the focus of the model are actually reflected by the solution.	Prediction errors due to the math. approximations that rendered the governing equations solvable. Numerical errors.
e_{pr} ("prediction")	Response prediction accuracy: how well physical reality can be predicted. e_{pr} is a compound of e_m and e_s.	Calculated vs. measured response, if all significant aspects of the test are accounted for in the calculation.

For the responses that drive a design (those onto which much of the engineering effort focuses), prediction must be better than the allowable tolerances for the operability of the final product for the governing responses:

$$e_a > e_{pr} = e_m + e_s \tag{64}$$

Furthermore, one can also observe that, in terms of the governing responses, an analysis tool must also reliably predict the impact of likely (fabrication and other) errors on the operational conditions for the governing responses:

$$e_a > e_f > e_{pr} = e_m + e_s \tag{65}$$

The state of the art of space inflatable structural engineering in general, and of precision inflatables in particular, does not yet consistently reflect the relative order of error magnitudes just outlined.

Historically, classical shell and membrane theory has been primarily concerned with e_s, with improving model solution accuracy by alleviating as many of the solution approximations as possible for membranes of various characteristics and geometries. In some way, the development of solution methods for additional classes of problems (such as wrinkled membranes) also falls in this category because it aims at enabling the solution at all of certain models.

The concern with the solution error e_s is secondary today because properly designed and used numerical tools can reduce e_s to limits of computer arithmetic and discretization.

However, these methods do not reduce any of the other errors reviewed above. Actually, it is the uncertainties and the magnitudes of the fabrication error e_f and of the modeling error e_m that primarily hamper precision membrane engineering. While generally no established estimates, prediction methods, or rules of thumb exist for the assessment of these errors, they clearly violate the rules spelled out above in some of cases. For example, the modeling with a linear elastic material model of a reflector canopy subject to low to moderate pressurization after deployment from a creased stowed state is clearly inadequate for a precision application because the creases entail a highly nonlinear material behavior. Such a wrong modeling approach entails

$$e_m > e_a \tag{66}$$

which is in obvious violation of Eq. (64) and thus renders the results useless. Another faulty approach that entails the same contradiction is to benchmark precision membrane shape predictions to approximate symbolic or empirical membrane shape formulas (such of those collected in [19]).

Modeling errors similar to those just highlighted continue to haunt recent membrane engineering efforts. (Some of these common mistakes are examined quantitatively in [20].) The trend to overlook such mistakes in the context of newly pursued precision membrane applications (which include RF and even optical reflectors) is unfortunate. The operational error limit e_a of such devices can be orders of magnitude lower than common structural engineering tolerances. An engineer not keenly aware of this fact may consider his results acceptable because e_f, e_m, and e_s are within the limits he is used to. However, a low value of e_a can still render the predictions unacceptable by violating conditions (64) through (66).

8 Analysis of wrinkled membranes

8.1 Introduction

Due to their lack of bending stiffness, membranes cannot sustain compressive stresses. The membrane responds to an in-plane contraction, due to external agencies other than that of Poisson's effect from tensile stresses that act perpendicular to the contraction, by out-of-plane displacements that oscillate about the mean plane; i.e., the membrane wrinkles (Fig. 6). Wrinkles are seen in biological organisms, such as the wrinkles in the skin of humans (Fig. 7).

The strength of material model for the membrane cannot model this response behavior. A suitable model for this response behavior is the tension field (TF). Different from other strength of material models, the TF model is non-linear. This is the case even when the membrane material is linearly elastic.

The TF responds to a planar strain field where one of the principal strains is extensional the other contractive by a stress field with a single non-zero stress component of tension in the direction of the extensional principal strain. All other components of the stress tensor are zero.

The first mention of a tension field model was due to Wagner (1929) [21]. Wagner was concerned with the load-carrying capability of web-stiffened steel plate girders that were capable of carrying loads with a buckled web far in excess of their load carrying capability in the unbuckled state. The mode of performance of these plate girders is akin to the mode of performance of parallel cord trusses, where the bending moment is carried by the cords in tension and compression, respectively, and the shear stress resultant is carried by vertical cross members in compression and by diagonal cross members in tension. In the case of the plate girder, the stiffeners take the role of the vertical members of the truss, and the wrinkled web takes the role of the diagonal tension members. Wagner's theory is an equilibrium theory only. The full set of solid mechanics equations as specialized to the structural elements is only used to predict the onset of buckling, not the tension field response. By contrast, the TF model for membrane mechanics uses the full set of solid mechanics equation as specialized to the two-dimensional sheet.

Figure 6. Wrinkles in a thin metallized polymeric foil are easily observed.

Figure 7. Wrinkles in the skin are seen under the eye.

TF theory ignores the minutia of out-of-plane wrinkling, neither the amplitude, nor the frequency of wrinkles are of concern. The direction of the wrinkles is determined and the total amount of in-plane contraction of the mean mid-plane of the field in excess of that due to Poisson's effect are determined by displacements at the boundary of the tension field.

Since Wagner's early work, numerous researchers have contributed to the development of TF theories. No attempt is made here to give a full account if these efforts. Reissner (1938) [22], Kondo et al. (1955) [23], and Mansfield (1970) [24] developed solutions for geometrically linear problems. Wu (1981) [25] developed a model for finite plane stress theory. Pipkin (1986) [26], and Steigmann and Pipkin (1988) [27] used the concept of relaxed strain energy density. Roddeman et al. (1987) [28] modified the deformation tensor. Jenkins and Leonard (1993) [29] used modified strain energy and a modified dissipation function in the analysis of the dynamic wrinkling of visco-elastic membranes.

A particular simple approach for solving membrane mechanics problems that include wrinkling response is due to Schur (1994) [30, 31]. This approach is particularly suitable for use with a non-linear finite element (FE) code (be it a special purpose type or a commercially supplied general purpose code) [32, 33]. It treats the wrinkled region as a degenerate membrane for which it modifies the constitutive equation via a penalty parameter. This process diminishes the stiffness of the membrane in the wrinkling direction without rendering the stiffness matrix non-singular. By nature, this method is approximate. This method is outlined below.

8.2 Tension-Field modeling via a penalty parameter modified constitutive law

The modification of the analysis process so to enable TF response remains entirely within the material module (i.e. the application of the constitutive law) of the FE code. In a non-linear finite element analysis an interim solution step starts with the strained state $^{(i-1)}\varepsilon$ of the previous instance and advances under a load increment to the new strained state $^{(i)}\varepsilon = {}^{(i-1)}\varepsilon + \Delta\varepsilon$. The inverse of the tangent stiffness matrix D_{TAN} is used to advance the stress to its new state $^{(i)}\sigma$. If the principal stresses of this state are both (plane stress) positive, then the membrane is non-degenerate, i.e., the membrane model is appropriate and the constitutive model for the membrane sheet can be applied unmodified for the determination of the element tangent stiffness matrix. However, if one of the principal stresses is negative, then the membrane is degenerate.

There are two degrees of degeneracy. When both principal stresses are negative then the membrane is locally fully degenerate. The TF state exists when one of the principal stresses is positive and the other is negative.

For analysis to proceed in the fully degenerated state, it is necessary to return a zero stress state and a tangent stiffness that is severely diminished but not identically zero. If a zero tangent stiffness matrix were to be returned, then the analysis would terminate due to a singular stiffness matrix. The magnitude of that diminution must be supplied by the analyst, and methods are available to assist in choosing the optimum value [32]. It should be such that the solution can proceed yet the results of the analysis remain meaningful.

In the TF case the stiffness matrix is transformed to the principal stress axes. The off-diagonal coefficients in the transformed matrix are set to zero. The stiffness coefficient on the diagonal of the transformed matrix that is associated with the compressive principal stress is diminished by a penalty parameter of the analysts choosing and the compressive stress is set to zero.

Inversion of the diagonal tangent stiffness matrix is trivial. The tangent stiffness (or compliance) and the stresses are returned after transformation back to the material reference coordinate system. The transformation matrices that are required for this process are presented in the section on multi-layered membrane sheets.

This process is well suited for single-integration-point finite elements. In the case of elements with more than one integration point there exists the possibility that the iterative analysis process toggles indefinitely; thus preventing the progress of the solution process.

Although the classical TF model ignores details of the wrinkles themselves, progress has been made on predicting the wrinkle parameters of number of waves, wavelength, and wave height [32, 34].

9 Experimental analysis

9.1 Unique challenges for experimental analysis of membrane structures

Their extreme thinness is central to the unique challenges when making experimental measurements on membrane structures. Thinness contributes in large part to the lightweight and high compliance of these structures. In addition, membrane materials are often comprised of polymer films, with lower modulus, higher elongations at failure, and time, temperature, and frequency dependence. Also, membrane space structures may be considerably larger than more conventional space structures.

All of this points to the fact that, in most measurement situations involving membrane structures, noncontact methods are usually called for. The following table summarizes some of these issues.

Table 2. Contact problems in membrane measurements, and noncontact solutions.

Measurement	Contact Issues	Noncontact Methods	Limitations
Static Deformation	Artificial stiffening Mass loading	Eddy-current probes	Measurement range Single-point measure
		Capacitance probes	Measurement range Single-point measure
		Moiré	Optically quiet environ. Set up, grid placement
		Electronic speckle	Expensive
Dynamic Deformation	Artificial stiffening Mass loading	Eddy-current probes	Measurement range Single-point measure
		Capacitance probes	Measurement range Single-point measure
		Laser vibrometer	Expensive Not true full-field
		Holography	Sensitivity to noise, vibration
		Moiré	Optically quiet environ. Set up, grid placement
		Electronic Speckle	Expensive
Thermal Deformation	Artificial stiffening Mass loading	Infrared thermography	Surface measure only Calibration

Details about each of these issues and solutions will be briefly discussed below.

9.2 Static deformation measurement

Measurement of displacement and strain are often required and essential in membrane mechanics. However, conventional contact instruments like dial gages and strain gages cannot be used; the former may artificially add displacement, while the latter artificially stiffens material immediately surrounding the gage. Clip-on extensometers can be used for testing of some material coupons.

The simplest noncontact techniques are electric field techniques, such as eddy current and capacitance probes. These inexpensive techniques are usually fairly precise over a small measurement range, which is limited typically to a few millimeters. They also are restricted to single-point measurements. Jenkins and co-workers reported on using capacitance techniques for measuring membrane wrinkling [35].

Optical techniques offer high precision, full-field measurement, but only a few of the techniques are applicable to large deformations. The moiré family of interferometric techniques has considerable history in structural measurements. Since a typical object grating applied to the membrane would provide significant artificial stiffness, shadow moiré techniques are often used [36]. Speckle methods also hold much promise for displacement and strain measurements. A serious drawback is their expense and the need for complex data-analysis routines. Optical extensometers are available.

9.3 Dynamic displacement measurement

Conventional vibration measurement using accelerometers will not work on membrane structures, due to mass loading and artificial stiffening. Electric field techniques mentioned above are also applicable for dynamic displacement measurements. However, high frequency response may be a problem, and they are still single-point techniques.

Moiré interferometry described above may also be used for dynamic measurements, but data analysis becomes more challenging as the frequency increases, and lack of time-series may also be a problem. Holography has been used for the vibration analysis of plates for many years, but it requires a very quiet optical environment, which makes the technique less robust for many applications.

The laser vibrometer is a powerful tool for noncontact membrane vibration analysis. Vibrometers measure velocity changes due to the doppler (frequency) shift of laser light reflected from the moving surface. Lock-in amplifiers give good noise rejection. Scanning systems allow for fast raster scanning of the object, but this is only quasi full-field (in steady-state vibration). Full systems are expensive. Jenkins and co-workers have reported on laser vibrometer measurements of membrane structures [3, 37].

9.4 Thermal measurements

Conventional structural temperature measurements are performed using the ubiquitous thermocouple. Thermocouples are inexpensive and relatively precise. As in the other cases described above, attaching thermocouples to membranes artificially stiffens and loads them.

Infrared (IR) techniques provide good noncontact alternatives to thermocouples [38, 39]. High-precision IR sensors are available, some of them supercooled by liquid nitrogen for good noise rejection. The primary disadvantage of IR techniques is that they are surface temperature measurements only (thermocouples can be embedded). For thin membranes at thermal equilibrium this is not too much of a problem. The other disadvantage is that the IR/temperature conversion is dependent on the emissivity of the membrane surface, which may be a function of temperature. Hence careful and frequent calibration may be required.

10 Conclusion

The analysis of compliant structures in general and membrane structures in particular, is complicated by the nonlinear nature of the deformations and/or the materials involved. The natural language to describe such behavior is nonlinear continuum mechanics. This chapter has attempted to provide some insight into the mathematical formalism, physical quantities, material constitution, and analysis issues associated with the nonlinear continuum mechanics.

References

[1] Jenkins, C.H. & Leonard, J.W., Nonlinear Dynamic Response of Membranes: State of the Art. *Appl. Mech. Rev.*, **44**, pp. 319–328, 1991.

[2] Jenkins, C.H., Nonlinear Dynamic Response of Membranes: State of the Art – Update. *Appl. Mech. Rev.*, **49(10)**, pp. S41–S48, 1996.

[3] Jenkins, C.H., Membrane Vibrations: a Review and New Experimental Results. *1999 ASME Joint Applied Mechanics and Materials Summer Conference*, Blacksburg, VA, 1999.

[4] Eringen, A.C., *Nonlinear Theory of Continuous Media*, McGraw-Hill, 1962.

[5] Fung, Y.C., *Foundations of Solid Mechanics*, Prentice-Hall, 1965.

[6] Bonet, J. & Wood, R.D., *Nonlinear Continuum Mechanics for Finite Element Analysis*, Cambridge University Press, 1997.

[7] Ogden, R.W., *Nonlinear Elastic Deformations*, Dover, 1997.

[8] Leonov, A.I., On the Conditions of Potentiality in Finite Elasticity and Hypo-Elasticity. *Int. J. Solids Structures*, **37**, pp. 2565–2576, 2000.

[9] Truesdell, C., Hypo-elasticity. *J. Rational Mech. Anal.*, **4**, pp. 83–133, 1019–1020, 1955.

[10] Truesdell, C., Foundation of Elasticity Theory. *Int. Sci. Rev. Ser.*, Gordon & Breach: New York, 1965.

[11] Truesdell, C. & Toupin, R., Handbuch der Physik. **3(1)**, *The Classical Field Theories*, 1960.

[12] Taylor, R.L., Inversion of Prony Series Characterization for Visco-elastic Stress Analysis. *Int. J. Num. Meth. Eng.*, **5**, pp. 499–502, 1973.

[13] Steigmann, D.J. & Pipkin, A.C., Equilibrium of Elastic Nets. *Phil. Trans. R. Soc. Lond. A.*, **335**, pp. 419–454, 1991.

[14] Ruggiero, T.J. & Mikulas, M., A One-Dimensional Constitutive Model for Wrinkled Thin Polymer Films. *Contractor Report CR-1999-209129*, NASA Langley Research Center, Hampton, VA 23681–2199, April 1999.

[15] Murphey, T.W., A Nonlinear Elastic Constitutive Model for Wrinkled Thin Films. *Ph.D. Dissertation*, University of Colorado, Boulder, 2000

[16] Calladine, C.R., *Theory of Shell Structures*, First edn, Cambridge University Press, 1983.

[17] Libai, A. & Simmonds, J.G., *The Nonlinear Theory of Elastic Shells*, Second edn, Cambridge University Press, 1998.

[18] Timoshenko, S. & Woinowsky-Krieger, S., *Theory of Plates and Shells*, Second edn, McGraw Hill, 1959.

[19] Young, W.C., *Roark's Formulas for Stress and Strain*, Sixth edn, McGraw-Hill, 1989.

[20] Greschik, G., Palisoc, A. & Mikulas, M., Approximations and errors in pressurized axisymmetric membrane shape predictions. *Proceedings of the 39th AIAA/ASME/ASCE/AHS/ASC Structures, Structural Dynamics, and Materials Conference and AIAA/ASME Adaptive Structures Forum*, April 20–23, Long Beach, CA, **4**, pp. 2761–2771, AIAA-98-2101-CP, 1998.

[21] Wagner, H., Ebene Blechwandtraeger mit Sehr Duennem Stegblech. *Z. Flugtechnik u. Motorluftschiffahrt*, 1929.

[22] Reissner, E., Tension-field Theory. *Proc. 5th Int. Congr. Appl. Mech.*, pp. 88–92, 1938.

[23] Kondo, K., Iai, T., Moriguti, S. & Murasaki, T., Tension-Field Theory. *Memoirs of the Unifying Study of Basic Problems in Engineering Science by Means of Geometry*, Vol. 1, C.-V., 61–85,; Gakujutsu, Bunken Fukyo-Kai, Tokyo 1955.

[24] Mansfield, E.H., Load Transfer via a Wrinkled Membrane. *Proc. R. Soc. Lond. A.*, 316, 269, 1970.

[25] Wu, C.-H., Wrinkling in Finite Plane Stress Theory. *Q. Appl. Math.*, **39**, pp. 179–199, 1981.

[26] Pipkin, A., The Relaxed Energy Density for Isotropic Elastic Membranes. *J. Appl. Math.*, **36**, pp. 85–99, 1986.

[27] Steigmann, D.J. & Pipkin, A., Wrinkling of Pressurized Membranes. *ASME, Trans. J. Appl. Mech.*, **56**, pp. 624–628, 1989.

[28] Roddeman, D.G., Drukker, J., Oomens, W.J. & Jannsen, J.D., The Wrinkling of Thin Membranes. *J. Appl. Mech.*, pp. 884–892, 1987.

[29] Jenkins, C.H. & Leonard, J.W., Dynamic Wrinkling of Viscoelastic Membranes. *J. Appl. Mech.*, **60**, pp. 575–582, 1993.

[30] Schur, W.W., Tension Field Material Model for Thin Films. *32nd AIAA Aerospace Science Meeting*, Reno, NV, 1994.

[31] Schur, W.W., Tension Field Modeling by Penalty Parameter Modified Constitutive Law. *24th Midwestern Mechanics Conference*, Iowa State University, Ames, Iowa, 1995.

[32] Liu, X., Jenkins, C.H. & Schur, W.W., Fine Scale Analysis of Wrinkled Membranes. *Int. J. Computational Engr. Sci.*, 2000.

[33] Liu, X., Jenkins, C.H. & Schur, W.W., Large Deflection Analysis of Pneumatic Envelopes using a Penalty Parameter Modified Material Model. *Finite Elements in Analysis Design*, **37**, pp. 233–251, 2001.

[34] Liu, X., Jenkins, C.H. & Schur, W.W., Fine Analysis of Degenerate Membrane States using a Penalty Parameter Modified Constitutive Relation. *Fifth U.S. National Congress on Computational Mechanics*, Boulder, CO, 1999.

[35] Jenkins, C.H., Haugen, F. & Spicher, W.H., Experimental Measurement of Wrinkling in Membranes Undergoing Planar Deformation. *Exp. Mech.*, **38**, pp. 147–152, 1998.

[36] Jenkins, C.H. & Khanna, S.K., Determination of Membrane Wrinkling Parameters using Shadow Moire. *1999 Spring Conference, Society for Experimental Mechanics*, Cincinnati, OH, 1999.

[37] Jenkins, C.H. & Tampi, M., Local Membrane Vibrations and Inflatable Space Structures. *Space 2000*, Albuquerque, NM, 2000.

[38] Jenkins, C.H. & Faisal, S.M., Thermal Load Effects on Precision Membranes. *J. Spacecraft Rockets*, 2001.

[39] Jenkins, C.H. & Faisal, S.M., Thermal Load Effects on Precision Membranes. *1999 AIAA Adaptive Structures Forum*, St. Louis, MO, 1999.

Section IV

Compliant Structures
in Engineering

CHAPTER 6

Pressurized membranes in nature, technology and engineering

W.W. Schur
Physical Science Laboratory, New Mexico State University, USA

Abstract

This chapter presents a broadly inclusive definition of pressurized membranes. It then describes a variety of occurrences of this efficient structural element in nature together with similar applications in technology from early to modern technology. These are grouped by performance features. Though the sweep of this chapter attempts to cover significant ground; no claim to completeness can be made. Also, by covering a broad range of different types of application, there is no way of providing exhaustive detail. Rather the aim of this chapter is to whet the appetite of those interested in technology to look at nature for inspiration.

1 Introduction

Efficient systems are characterized by minimum effort required to serve a specific purpose, be that purpose to maintain a specific state or to facilitate or perform a specific task. High efficiency may be just sufficient to be enabling, or it may preserve resources for multiple purposes and follow-on tasks. In the constant struggle for survival in a competitive or hostile environment, while not giving guaranties, efficiency provides for an improved chance of success. At least in a statistical sense, success and ultimately survival side with the efficient. These observations are very general; they apply to technology, biology, both fauna and flora, and to social organization, and warfare.

Load transfer in structural systems is most efficient in pure tension where a structural element can be stressed evenly throughout the cross section. Any other load transfer, particularly over long distances, requires non-uniform stress distribution, or is limited by stability considerations that do not allow the full exploitation of the material strength. One-dimensional structural elements of the pure tension type are typified by ropes and cables, while two-dimensional structural elements of the pure tension type are typified by thin membranes. Many or even most structural systems that include pure tension-type structural elements either anchor to some base or contain structural elements that transfer load via other response modes that include compression, tension and shear. There are some structural systems that are entirely tensile in type and do not include anchoring in any way. An example of an essentially one-dimensional structural system of the pure tension type is a hoop-band that holds the staves of a barrel together. An example of an essentially two-dimensional structural system of the pure tension type is a pneumatic envelope such as a spherical balloon. However, external equilibrium, be it dynamic or static, is always satisfied by some means. So in the presence of a gravitational field – the real-life situation – the balloon must be buoyed by some fluid or must rest on some base, as for example a beach ball lying on the ground. This article deals with thin pressurized membranes, their versatility and their almost endless variety in nature, and in technology, pre-industrial, industrial and modern. Specifically excluded from consideration are some structural systems that have well into the middle of the 20th century been analyzed by structural engineers using classical membrane theory but that have primarily compressive internal forces. Spectacular examples of the latter in architecture are domes that cover large internal spaces and the hyperbolic cylinders of large cooling towers. In these excluded structural systems, the structural elements that were analyzed using classical membrane theory are actually able to resist significant bending moments; as structural elements they are classified as shells; they are not membranes. Our concept of a thin membrane is then an essentially two-dimensional structural element that is only able to sustain internal tensile force systems in its tangent plane. Any transverse force system imposed on the membrane, be the force system external, or be it inertial or gravitational, induces curvature into that membrane. This chapter also includes pre-stretched membranes that admit only small departures from their assembled shape under service-life states, which only in a narrow interpretation violate the notion of compliant structures.

Thin pressure envelopes can be categorized in many different ways. One such way is grouping them into closed envelopes and semi-envelopes, which are open to the surroundings. Another categorization differentiates between the type of matter held by the envelope, whether liquid, gaseous, solid particulate, or any combination thereof. Still another differentiation distinguishes pressure envelopes by general functionality such as providing buoyancy by enclosing a less-dense fluid than the ambient, being a conduit for transport, or serving static containment, the latter two both with and without facilitating or allowing some internal processing, chemical or otherwise. And, of course, one can distinguish them by the type of construct, whether a pressure envelope consists of skin alone or is a heterogeneous structure where a tendon[1] system provides the global pressure confining strength, while the skin provides a barrier and functions in local load transfer to the tendons.

Often in nature the skin may be multi-layered with each layer having different characteristics. Such layers may include sensors and actuators. The inclusion of sensors and actuators into structural elements in technology is only a recent accomplishment of the modern age (here meaning information age). In the industrial age, the period preceding the information age, sensors and actuators were generally external to the structural elements, and articulation depended on discrete articulation joints with the structural element of the actuators either being a cable system or expected to be nearly rigid. Still more categorizations that distinguish between different mechanical characterizations, or other characterizations of the envelope

---

[1] Here the term tendon is used in a generic sense, it could refer to cables, tapes or other essentially one-dimensional tensile structural elements.

materials are possible and appropriate in context. We will address some of these issues on examples found in nature and technology.

2 Causes of pressure loading on the structural membrane

To recognize the versatility of the structural membrane in technology or biology, we must be broad in our acceptance of the causes of the transverse pressure, lest we omit some of the most important instances where structural membranes play important roles.

Membranes perform well in transferring distributed transverse pressure load of any cause. In the region where transverse pressure load is applied to the membrane, the membrane is curved so as to affect equilibrium with the in-plane stress resultants. The transverse pressure loading may be asserted by a fluid as either static or dynamic pressure. Both gases and liquids are fluids, but they are distinct. If a liquid of a certain density is insufficient to fill an available space, it will, under the effect of a gravitational field, fill a sub-region of that space under an equi-potential surface. By contrast a gas will expand into all available space. The transverse pressure load may also be caused by solid particulate matter that in some macro sense behaves somewhat similar to a liquid. If not sufficient to fill a space, solid particulate matter will in the presence of a gravitational field also fill a sub-region, but the free boundary of that sub-region may differ from an equi-potential one by up to the angle of repose of that particulate matter. The angle of repose is dictated by grain shape, size and mix of the particulate matter. There is certainly matter that does not fit neatly into these categorizations and that is hybrid between liquid matter and solid matter, and that is contained by or separated from other matter by a membrane.

3 Other types of loading on the structural membrane

Membranes are well suited for force systems with forces acting in the plane of the membrane. These forces may be surface or line forces. Line forces occur most generally at the boundary of membranes with other structural elements or the support system of the membrane.

Concentrated transverse (point) loads are less well tolerated even if distributed over a finite sub-region rather than actually a point. Such loads generally cause abrupt direction changes in the membrane surface with high stress resultants at the point of application. Both nature and the engineer make provisions to accommodate concentrated transverse loads that are expected at predetermined positions on a membrane by introducing some reinforcing elements and by shaping the membrane to better accommodate that load.

4 Nature's edge on technology

While membranes in technological application are generally very simple in their construction and often single purpose, nature's membranes are often quite complex in their construction, and they perform multiple functions other than those of barrier and load transfer. Moreover nature's membranes grow, i.e., they are being under construction while performing their functions, while man-made membranes are generally fabricated before being deployed into service. The growth of nature's membrane is often, if not generally, affected by the stimulus of the current loading on the membrane.

In what way man has glanced at nature and attempted to emulate it may not be precisely ascertained. But particular applications of membranes by man do suggest a direct connection.

Fortunately, nature's "inventions" are not protected by copyright and patent laws. Clearly though, persons who are responsible for and involved in technological development are well advised to look at nature as a fountain of ideas from which to draw nourishment for their imagination.

Over the millennia man-made membranes have changed little, except that slowly over time more uses for these efficient structural elements have been found. New materials have been put into service. The sizes of man-made membranes have extended in both directions: growth to gargantuan size, and miniaturization to sizes that make them invisible to the unaided eye.

There is one aspect where man has recently encroached on what was before clearly the domain of nature's membrane design. The introduction of piezoelectric elements into solid mechanics structures and into solid mechanics theory has enabled a significant leap in technology. Both sensors and actuators can now be buried in a membrane and in other structural elements. Local observations on the membrane can now be responded to by local and global configuration changes of the membrane and other structural elements. The potential of this technological advance has just been tapped and its promise for the future can only be imagined.

5 The membrane was there in the beginning and it persists

The membrane was there in the beginning, an integral part of the most primitive form of life. It provided protection, and still does, of the working parts of single-cell organisms. The membrane separates the ambient from the interior and assures the integrity of the cell, which may be quite complex and perhaps in many instances as yet not fully understood in the details of its functioning. The outer boundary of most cells in fauna, primitive or advanced, is a membrane. And even at a smaller scale, internal parts of cells such as organelles are surrounded by and contained within thin membranes. While the cell walls and the boundary membranes of the organelles separate their interior from their ambient, beneficial molecular traffic through these walls provides fuel to the cells, and metabolic energy conversion within the organelles transforms the energy content of that fuel into energy forms that enable the cell to perform its assigned role within the organism. Generally, exceptions granted, cell boundaries in flora do have significant bending stiffness to disqualify them as membranes.

Though the cell boundary and sub-cell boundary are the most abundant membranes in fauna, they are generally too small to observe with the naked eye or at least are not easily observed; they can be assumed to have not contributed to man's development of the membrane as a technological element. Still, man has recognized that thin membranes can allow significant molecular through-traffic, and he uses osmotic membranes in chemical processing. Similar to the functioning of a cell wall, these membranes function as separators for fluids on both sides, but allow transport of some chemical species through the wall from one fluid to the other.

Another aspect of cells is that except for very simple forms of life, a large number of cells are assembled to form an organism. Taking some liberty, one could liken this to the stacking of sacks, which is a good example for man's use of membranes in technology from the ancient to the modern times. The potato sack, or grain sack, which holds globular or granular mass goods, respectively, and the pouches used for intravenous feeding or for medication, are all technological applications of the membrane. So are the water sacks that have been used for millennia to provide storage of potable water during desert transit, and so are the double skinned wine flasks of Iberian origin. But nature provides us with macro-scale examples of the sack. The skin or pelt of mammals and most fish are an abundant example, just far less in number than nature's example of micro-size. The careful observer might object to some animal skin, particularly fish skin, to be viewed as structurally separate from the flesh. After all, the removing of the skin from a fish in the filleting operation, as any fisherman knows, requires a sharp knife. But where do we draw the line?

Perhaps to the hunter and gatherer of prehistoric times, some internal organs of his prey provided a lesson and suggested use of these organs in some technological manner outside the animal's body similar to how they are used in-vivo. Maybe it is unreasonable to suggest that food preservation and storage in intestines, the making of sausages, dates back to prehistoric times. But do we really know the age of the sausage? Sausages are found in Asian cuisine at least in China, and throughout Europe, with the current day center of sausage making in the ethnically German regions. The intestine is a membrane tube. The bladder is a sack. When filling the sausage casing, the filling exerts considerable pressure on the outside wall, the membrane. The filling is generally an amalgam of soft particular matter that behaves very similar to a fluid. However, the consumer sees generally a rigidized state of the sausage at which the shape of the content of the skin is stable even without the support provided by the casing.

6 The membrane as device for storage and protection

Examples of sacks in nature and technology have already been discussed in the preceding section. But there are other interesting examples of membranes as storage and protection devices in nature. The skin-fold of marsupial animals, which holds the young offspring of the species, provides storage and protection. Marsupials are found in the Americas with a single representative species, the possum on the North-American subcontinent. They are the dominant group of mammals in Australia. The kangaroo is perhaps the most well-known species. The young, when born, crawls on the pelt and into the pouch where it attaches itself to a nipple from which it obtains its nourishment for further growth and development. The pouch provides a secure container and a connection to the mother.

Technological applications abound. Packaging containers for diverse purposes are made of membranes. Early examples are made of leather or fabric and many modern ones are made of polymer sheets.

7 The membrane as container for liquids

Ticks (Class Arachnida, suborder Metastigmata) are blood-sucking parasites that store their booty in the abdominal section of their body. Their distribution is worldwide. About 850 species have been described. They belong to two families, soft ticks (Family Argasidae) and hard ticks (Family Ixodidae). During their various life stages, they feed off mammalian hosts. When feeding on the host's blood, the abdominal section enlarges to become a large sack. In the last stage the fertilized female tick gorges itself and fills its abdomen with an enormous (in relation to the size of the unfed tick) amount of blood, expanding the volume of the abdomen perhaps more than one hundred-fold.

In technology from ancient to present, there are examples of sacks as containers of liquid. Some have been mentioned earlier in a different section of this chapter such as water sacks used in desert transit, Iberian double-skinned wine flasks, and intravenous feeding bags.

Another more recent example is the replacing of glass bottles for merchandizing some of the cheaper wines. They are now often filled into polymer-lined aluminum sacks and marketed in paper boxes.

8 The membrane as an airfoil

A very different use of pressurized membranes is their use under dynamic pressure. Bats, of which there exist approximately 1000 species worldwide, are unique in the world of mammals; they are the only mammals that achieve true flight. Their wings are made of a support structure that consists of the extremely elongated "finger" bones of their front feet and a wing surface, which is a leathery membrane stretched between them. The webbed feet of certain waterfowl are very similar in that sense and serve in a very similar manner as hydrodynamic surfaces, though they do not contribute to the flying ability of these birds. The fins and the tail of fish generally consist of a comb-like assembly of bony spikes. The space between them is spanned by thin skin membranes. The spikes are articulated by muscles. The fins and tail function as hydrodynamic control surfaces and hydrodynamic propulsion surfaces. Insect wings are of a similar structural composition in that they feature a relative stiff support structure that is spanned by a thin skin surface. However, physiological studies on most species have probably not focused on such details as whether that surface is better classified in its function as a structural element as thin plate or shell, or as membrane.

Technological examples over untold millennia abound. They span well from pre-stone-age technology to modern technology. The sail of seafaring cultures is perhaps the prime example of man's use of the membrane as an aerodynamic surface. It is perhaps astounding that peoples of Oceana[2] have developed a sail, the crab claw sail, that at a considerable range of angles of attack has a significant advantage over the most efficient modern yachting sail, the Bermuda sail. (The angle of attack is the angle formed by the cord of an airfoil and the direction of the free stream flow. If the vertex of the angle is placed at the aft end of the cord, then an upstream parallel to the free-stream direction that goes through that vertex and the cord line enclose the angel of attack.) Still, the usual short triangular racing course of sailing regattas favors the Bermuda sail, which performs favorably at very small angles of attack, and which allows swift tacking maneuvers at the vertices of the course while the crab-claw-sail-equipped boat must undergo a time wasting shunting maneuver. Note though that the modern Bermuda sail was developed by drawing on the insights and analytical methods of modern fluid dynamics, while by contrast the crab-claw design is a product of a primitive technology. To some it may be surprising that the fabrication of a good Polynesian sail with the natural materials available to these ocean-going peoples took significantly more effort by them than the construction of the floating platform. These were dugout canoes arranged as either two hulls separated and structurally connected by a framework, or a single hull and an outrigger float similarly connected. Not only is the design of the sails remarkable, but also the fabrication that implemented the design. Modern sail-makers will appreciate this fact, as their craft is still an art where trade secrets are highly guarded. At this juncture it should be mentioned that the ocean-navigating civilizations of the pacific at the period of first contact (with Europeans) used primarily, or even exclusively, wooden tools and weaponry. (Hence in the view of this writer, technological age does not track with calendar age, and technological solutions from an earlier technological era can on occasion be superior to those developed by newer technology. One

---

[2] As used here, the geographic term refers to the Islands of the North and South Pacific.

wonders how much technology of the past has been lost because of an inability to record, or because records were lost due to man-made or nature-made disasters.)

Both inland-waterway navigators and seafarers of many cultures and over the times have developed and used many different sails and sail assemblies on boats and ships. Sails have been made of hides, rough natural fiber weaves, woven cloth such as canvas and even silk, modern (i.e. polymer) woven cloth, and thin (polymer) films. Here it may be remarked for the benefit of the technology minded that the design and fabrication of sails made of woven fabrics is still an art. This is because analytical predictions for the performance of such sails still poses significant difficulties as woven fabrics cannot be treated in an analysis in the same manner as two-dimensional continua for which proven and reliable theories exist. Reliable analytical models that mimic the general response behavior of fabrics do not exist as yet despite the perennial claims made by some academic authors who offer nothing more than orthotropic models, which may be suitable for thin sheets but fall far short in representing the response behavior of fabrics.

Membranes have also been used to harvest wind energy for other industrial purposes for many centuries. Examples are the windmills of the Mediterranean and those of Northern Europe, particularly the Netherlands.

A more modern use of the membrane as an airfoil is the Wright Brother's airplane that ushered in the age of manned flight. Other early airplanes including WWI military aircraft used fabric skins to cover fuselage structure, wing structure and the structure of control surfaces. All these skins function as membranes. Since then most aircraft are made of more rigid materials.

But there are many other aeronautical applications that use membranes as aerodynamic components: these are parachutes, para-foils, kites, fans, hang gliders and the ultra-light aircrafts. Sea anchors for small watercraft may also use membranes that are supported by cantilever beams. These beams extend radially from an axial member, which is attached upstream to a cable.

Here it is appropriate to take a peek into the not too distant future. Humans plan again to set sail to explore the unknown, sending craft under sail to distances as yet not explored. And again as in the era of global exploration, when we harvested inexhaustible wind-power for propulsion, humans plan to use inexhaustible power harvested from nature to provide propulsion for their forays. Currently several international government-funded agencies have research spacecraft on their drawing boards that will be driven by quantum packets of energy that are emitted from the sun. And as in the time of the great explorers, Christopher Columbus and James Cook, to name just two of many, power is harvested and turned into a propulsive force by large membranes that are supported by cables or tendons and a rigid frame structure.

9 Aerostatic and hydrostatic devices

The internal airbladder of many fish species controls both buoyancy and attitude of the fish body. Similar functions are served by the ballonets in airships. The ballonets are internal bladders whose volumes are actively controlled generally by some mechanical devices.

Balloons are perhaps the most recognized buoyant aircraft. Starting with the Montgolfier brother's hot-air balloon, these are all membrane structures. Modern balloons, both the hot-air sport balloons and the stratospheric balloons, assume their flight configurations only under internal pressure. They are usually folded up in their stowed configuration, thus they take up little space during ground stowage and transportation. Hot-air balloons are usually fully inflated on the ground and are maintained at full inflation throughout their flight. Ground inflation of stratospheric balloons fills only a small fraction (usually less than ½%) of the available volume. These balloons fill out as they approach float altitude. Depending on their mode of operation, stratospheric balloons are divided into two general classes, which are commonly designated as zero-pressure balloons and as super-pressure balloons.

The lifting gas of zero-pressure balloons communicates with the ambient air through openings at the height of the nadir or through openings in vertically suspended ducts some short distant below the nadir. These provisions, which allow the balloon to "breathe", i.e. exchange gas with the environment, are necessary to protect the balloon from pressurization to levels that are not sustainable by the balloon envelope. The balloon is essentially a large radiative heat exchanger. At latitudes (other than in polar regions) where the radiative environment changes over the day, the temperature of the internal gas changes significantly, and if the gas mass is confined to the same volume, then the pressure increases proportionally to its absolute temperatures. So starting with night-time equilibrium, as the gas heats up with day-rise, the zero-pressure balloon expels excess lifting gas, but then with the arrival of night time when the internal gas cools, ballast must be dropped to maintain the desired float altitude. Clearly this type of operation is limited by the amount of ballast that is carried and typically does not exceed two diurnal cycles.

By contrast, super-pressure balloons are closed systems. They are allowed to pressurize during daytime. The high internal pressure attained by the gas limited earlier designs, which were of the spherical type, to very small balloons that could at most carry 150 kg payloads to rather modest altitudes, while zero-pressure balloons achieved payload capacities of over 4000 kg lifted to higher altitudes. Recently, NASA adopted a new design scheme in which the global pressure confining strength is provided by one-dimensional structural elements, which are load tendons; the membrane is relegated to the role of gas barrier and local load transfer of the pressure load to the tendons. These new balloons will achieve load-carrying capacities comparable to current (2003) zero-pressure balloons and are expected to survive in the order of 100 days sustained altitude keeping flight at mid-latitudes. This balloon type is currently still in its test phases.

Another rather spectacular class of primarily aerostatic pneumatic envelopes is the airship. Because the airship is required to move relative to the surrounding fluid, its design must have an aerodynamically efficient shape. In general, the airship has the form of an elongated axi-symmetric body akin to a fat cigar. From the vantage point of structural design, airships can be grouped into two design classes, the "rigid airships" and the "pressure airships". The hull shape of the pressure airship is maintained by the pressure of the lifting gas. Pressure airships that have no rigid structure to accommodate any of the utility components, like the power plant or the gondola, are referred to as "non-rigid"; these are the so-called "blimps". Pressure airships that are outfitted with a structural keel that participates in the accommodation of bending loads and that provides hard attachment points for the gondola, the power plant, and other installations are referred to as "semi-rigid". By contrast, rigid airships carry the global loading through a fabric-covered lightweight frame structure that is held in shape by transverse frames that are strut and wire braced. The transverse frames divide the airship longitudinally into compartments. The lifting gas is contained in multiple gasbags that are distributed over the compartments. This construction is only feasible for large airships. The pressure in these gasbags can be significantly lower than the pressure required to retain the shape of pressure airships. Pressure airships have a distinct advantage over rigid airships in the sense that they can accommodate collision forces by large deformations without sustaining permanent damage, making them much more tolerant to maneuver mishaps during landing and anchoring exercises. All these airbags and pressure hulls are pressurized membranes; the fabric skin of the rigid airship is also a membrane.

Perhaps the Hindenburg disaster in the late 1930s is the primary reason for the airship to fall out of favor. But there is currently (around 2003) an interest in returning the airship to technological use again. There are several industrial niches where the airship has been recognized as offering probable economic advantage over existing or proposed alternatives, for example: 1) the use of airships as heavy-lift devices in difficult to access and generally difficult to maneuver terrain; 2) the use of stationary airships, either tethered or powered, over large urban areas for signal transmission; 3) the use of roving airships as early warning platforms or observation platforms for military, policing and drug interdiction purposes; and 4) the use of airships for medium-long-distance transport of perishable produce.

10 Gas-filled floats at fluid interfaces

The Portuguese-Man-of-War, a "jelly-fish", is somewhat of an unusual biological arrangement. While often thought of as a single animal, it is rather a colony of four interdependent highly specialized kinds of polyps. Visible to the above water surface observer is a single individual, the float (pneumatophore), a warning to man, as the sting of the Portuguese-Man-of-War is not only painful but can be deadly. The float is filled with gas, mostly nitrogen. It supports the rest of the colony, which is fully submerged. The tentacles (dactylozooids) are polyps that detect, capture, incapacitate and then deliver prey to the gastrozooids, polyps that specialize in the digestion and the extraction of nutrients from the food. The gonozooids specialize in reproduction. Whole fleets of hundreds and perhaps thousands of colonies can be observed drifting, propelled by wind, on the water surface of warm seas and oceans. The Portuguese-Man-of-War most commonly occurs in the tropical and subtropical regions of the Pacific and the Indian Ocean, and in the northern Atlantic Gulf Stream.

Rubber rafts or similar pneumatic rafts function in a role akin to that of the pneumatophore. Such rafts when deflated stow away into small spaces hence are ideal for rescue missions launched from larger craft. Since the pneumatic raft is pressurized, no internal structure is required to provide rigidity. The compressed air in its envelope provides a pneumatic skeleton to the craft. And since it is light, the craft can be made to skim over water and reach high speeds. The skin of such rafts is mostly made of fabric that is impregnated with a highly elastic material to provide water and air tightness. When the fabric is made of one of the modern high-stiffness, low-density fibers that are suitable for ballistic applications, then they are highly suitable for military use.

Pneumatic buoys have even a closer affinity to the pneumatophore as they are either tethered to some anchor or support some utilitarian subsurface system such as fishnets.

11 The membrane as a compressed-gas reservoir

The bullfrog (American specie: Rana Catesbeiana; African specie: Pyxiecephalus edulis) makes a rather conspicuous display of its pressurized throat. The throat is a very compliant membrane; it forms one boundary of a pressurized gas reservoir. The release of pressurized gas is used by the frog in various ways to generate sound. A number of musical instruments use pressurized membranes to excite sound producing elements; examples are bagpipes, accordions, and concertinas. The bellows used by the smith from the ancient metalworking age and well into the industrial age employed the membrane as part of the outer boundary of a pressure reservoir.

The airbladder in domestic water tanks separates air that is compressed when water is being pumped into the tank. The compressed air provides the pressure in the water pipe circuit allowing frequent water demand without the need for pump startup at the demand frequency, saving both energy and wear and tear on the pump.

12 The membrane as an energy-storage device with explosive release

Pilobolus, the shotgun fungus, has a remarkable self-propagation mechanism. Pilobolus grows on dung of certain grass-eating mammals, such as bovines and horses, where it obtains its nutrients. The multicellular structure of this fungus grows like spokes on a wheel radially outward from the location where the spore germinated. These spokes are the mycelia. A swelling, the trophocyst, develops at or near the end of the mycelium out of which grows a vertical stalk, the stipe. A swelling on the top of that stipe, the sporangium develops, and in it subsequently spores develop. The sporangium performs the function of a lens that directs light in such a manner to the wall of the stipe that a light-triggered growth mechanism bends the stipe towards the light source, thus aiming the sporangium in the average direction of the light source. Considerable liquid pressure develops in the stipe during its growth toward maturity. When reaching maturity, the sporangium is violently discharged propelled by a liquid squirt-mechanism that hurls the sporangium to a distance of up to approximately 1.8 m.

Equally remarkable are some early air guns. In our context it is appropriate to mention the Austrian military rifle that was designed by B. Girandoni about 1779. It used a detachable ball-shaped membrane, which together with its metal fittings made up a pneumatic envelope that could be pressurized to high internal pressure levels. The empty reservoir could be exchanged in battle for a fully charged reservoir. This 20-shot repeater could discharge its ingenious rapid-fire magazine filled with 11.5-mm heavy metal bullets in about one minute. This weapon was deadly up to about 137 m, a formidable weapon when compared to the muzzle-loaders commonly used by the militaries of the time. The smoke from the powder of those muzzle-loaders was an irritant to the shooter, while the air-rifle marksman was not similarly impaired. This rifle saw battle against Turkey, France, and a confederation of German states.

13 The membrane as a conduit of matter

The earthworm ingests earth at the front end of its segmented body, transports the earth through its gut, an internal tube, and the essentially identical segments of the body extract nutrients from the ingested mass; and finally the leached and loosened mass is expelled through the anus region. The lowly earthworm belongs to a large group in the animal kingdom, Phylum Annelida (segmented worms), with nearly 14000 species identified. The phylum contains three classes, 1) Polychaeta, which includes lugworms, polychaetes, ragworms, and sandworms; 2) Oligochaeta, which includes earthworms and a group of related species, primarily freshwater species; and 3) Hirudinea, which are the leaches. All members of this phylum have a well-developed large true coelom, a body cavity that is lined with a mesoderm.

Annelids have segmented bodies. With the exception of the gut, all of the major body systems such as circulatory, excretory, reproductive, nervous, and the muscular structure are repeated in each segment. The segments are separated by transverse membranes. With the exception of leeches, the coelom in annelids is partially subdivided at the segment boundary by membrane walls, the septa. The coelom is filled with a fluid. Its longitudinal walls contain muscles that contract segment-wise. Hydrostatic pressure is maintained throughout the coelom across segments. Thus it provides a hydrostatic skeleton that maintains body rigidity, which allows segment-wise muscle contraction to bend the body freely thus, aiding locomotion through a complex path with great efficiency in burrowing. We observe then various roles of pressurized membranes in Annelids. The walls of the coelom contain and bound its pressurized fluid contents. One may also view the tubular construct of the worm's body as a complex composite membrane with the muscles as imbedded activators. Mass transport through this tube is then achieved by massaging the contents of the gut by muscular contraction. The colon of a mammal, though also a tubular membrane for mass transport of liquid and particularized solid matter is of less structural complexity than the worm. The urinary tract is similar but dedicated only to the transport if liquid, neglecting here the pathological case of passing a kidney stone.

Technological examples of tubular membranes for mass transfer abound. Though, generally the driving force affecting the transport is hydrostatic pressure applied on the inlet side. Suction applied at the outlet side, as is possible in rigid tubes, will collapse the membrane tube. Typical examples are (some) garden hoses and fire hoses, and similar hoses of heavier construction and much larger diameter for the transport of slurries. The construction industry uses hoses to transport concrete in its fresh state, through complex paths over obstacles, bridging over gaps, to its intended location where, after discharge, it will set, solidify, harden and cure into a strong solid capable of bearing loads.

14 The membrane as a sound transducer–the tympanum

The eardrum is a thin membrane. It is a sound transducer capable of responding effectively to very small pressure variations. It is part of the sound sensors of many species in fauna. It is particularly conspicuous on bullfrogs where it is external and relatively large. In the American specie, Rana Catesbeiana, the male is smaller than the female but it has a larger tympanum than the female. The American frog is a very large frog. Various maximum sizes are reported for this specie in the literature; the apparently largest claimed is 20 cm.

Technological applications of the use of stretched membranes as sound transducers reach from prehistoric epochs to the present. Various musical instruments of the percussion type from primitive to modern civilizations use a tympanum. Also, the sound of low-frequency drums carries over long distances, and in some cultures drums of various types have been used from prehistoric times for communication purposes. Significant sophistication had been reached in sub-Saharan Africa, in the use of drums for long-distance communication well before the age of colonization by European powers. Communicating drummers exploited similarities to the spoken language and in addition found ways to build into their message redundancy not unlike as is done with modern tele-messeging that uses error-correcting codes. Some modern loudspeakers use stretched membranes as sound transducers as well, others use elements that are better categorized as thin plates but they respond primarily in a membrane mode.

15 Tents

Perhaps one of man's earliest applications of the membrane is as cover and as strength element of lightweight shelters, the tents. The earliest cover materials for tents were animal hides that were sewn together. Two examples of hides being used as tent covers in relatively recent history are the teepees of the native inhabitants of North America and the yurts of the nomads of Central Asia. Low structural weight and ease of assembly make tents portable. Roaming hunting parties used tents as temporary shelters. Tents are particularly suited for the nomadic life. The tent cover serves as space separator, separating the protected space from the hostile environment, and it carries loads to other structural elements and anchor points. These loads include structural weight, distributed snow load and wind pressure load. At some time, early in technological advancement, fabrics substituted for the hides. Tents were indispensable military campaign accessories from well before recorded history, and they are still that today.

Until very recently the evolution of tents was very slow and gradual. But recent technological advances enabled architects and structural analysts to collaborate in rather spectacular tent designs. Certainly advances in material science and fabrication played an important role in that development. But the crucial element here is the advance in the ability to analytically predict both the in-service performance of heterogeneous membrane structures and their structural performance during all critical fabrication stages. Advantage is taken of the self-tension capability of anticlastic membranes and of suitably designed cable-truss-membrane systems so that large spans are bridged by pure tension elements only. Spectacular examples are the Hajj Terminal in Jeddah (Saudi Arabia), the Denver International Airport (USA), the roof over the Rothenbaum Stadium in Hamburg (Germany), and the Opera House in Sydney (Australia).

16 Summary

This chapter focused on one of the two most weight-efficient structural elements, the membrane. The membrane is essentially a two-dimensional structural element, its thickness being very much smaller than its extensions in the two other orthogonal directions. It functions both as a spatial barrier and as a load-transfer element for distributed loads that act on its two large surfaces. It carries distributed transverse loads as in-plane tensile stress resultants only. Both in nature and in technology it is adapted to serve a wide variety of very different tasks that are seemingly very dissimilar yet in some sense are very similar indeed. A sample of varied technological application from primitive to modern technology is presented. It speaks of human genius at any technological age. Examples of applications of the pressurized membrane in nature are discussed together with similar applications in technology. Clearly such an exposition cannot be exhaustive; it only scratches the surface. Some order is preserved, although an arbitrary one, by presenting the various applications in broad categories. Even these categories are only a small selection of the types of application of pressurized membranes in technology and nature. Human genius has found many ways to adapt this structurally efficient model to serve many purposes. Yet nature has been there long ago, and it has traveled paths that technological man has still to find. It is hoped that this chapter inspires readers with interest and competence in technological solutions to human needs to look at nature at any scale, from micro to macro, for suggestions of effective solutions to technological problems.

Acknowledgements

The material in this chapter has been collected from various sources in the literature. Great ease is provided by the Internet, and much of the information was collected from websites of academic institutions, museums, and from web postings of individuals of various affiliations. An effort has been made to check data against several sources to increase the chance of being accurate. This effort led to the rejection of some interesting examples in nature simply because contradictions between different physiological descriptions from reputable sources could not be resolved. My thanks go to the many unnamed individuals and institutions for the excellent descriptions they made available to public access. But no matter how the information came to me, I made the selection and chose the form of presentation. Any errors acquired by this process are mine.

I wish to thank two individuals who have made his effort easier. These are Ms. Jane Riddle of the NASA Goddard Space Flight Center who provided instructions on some finer points of automated search of library resources and introduced me to Mr. Chaz Vaubel, then a biologist well in the final stages of a doctoral program. Chaz provided some interesting biological examples, but more importantly, by the choice of these examples opened my eyes and caused a reorganizing of this chapter into what I believe to be a more suitable one for the presentation of the subject.

CHAPTER 7

Rope and rope-like structures

J.J. Evans[1] & I.M.L. Ridge[2]
[1]*Randall Division of Cell & Molecular Biophysics, Kings College London, UK*
[2]*University of Reading, School of Construction Management and Engineering, UK*

Abstract

A rope may be defined as a load-bearing structure that is efficient at supporting tensile loads, yet is very flexible in bending. A rope differs from other structures such as a chain, in that it is a multiple redundant structure made from a number of parallel load-bearing elements, which are usually twisted together in some way to allow the assembly to operate as a cohesive whole.

This chapter discusses some of the wide range of rope and rope-like structures found in engineering and nature. Initially the mechanics and behaviour of helical structures are discussed before moving on to examine the similarities in the design and manufacture of man-made ropes and nature's rope-like structures. Examples taken from nature include: polysaccharides (cellulose and plant cell walls) and polypeptides (collagen, tendon, arterial walls and spiders silk), which we discuss at molecular, cellular and organic levels.

Although it would be difficult to prove any direct 'inspiration from nature' on the part of rope and cable designers, a comparison of the technology of rope and similar structures such as hoses and umbilical cables reveals striking parallels with the rope-like structures in nature.

1 The mechanics of the helical structure

Some of the key mechanical features of groups of helical fibres are discussed in the following sections (for a more detailed discussion see Evans [1]).

1.1 Geometrical nature

A helix can be defined by two parameters: its radius, R, and lay (helix) angle α (α and R are defined in Figure 1). The important geometrical properties are the curvature κ and 'torsion' τ (the geometrical twist in the helix – not to be confused with mechanical torsion). In the case of a circular helix, κ and τ are constant and non-zero throughout the structure. They can be expressed by the following simple expressions:

$$\kappa = \frac{\sin^2 \alpha}{R} \quad \text{and} \quad \tau = -\frac{\cos \alpha \sin \alpha}{R}.$$ (1)

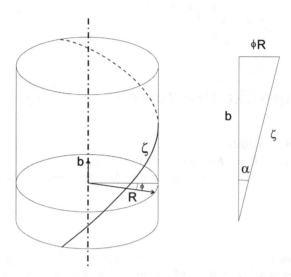

Figure 1: The geometry of a right-hand helix (defined in the same manner as a right-hand screw thread), where b is the helix length and ζ the helix space curve length.

1.2 Flexibility

One highly desirable feature of a structure consisting of helical fibres is that it can have a high axial strength and a low bending stiffness. The bending properties of any component are dependent on the distribution of cross-sectional area resisting the bending with the highest stresses furthest from the neutral plane of bending. The bending resistance of a cross-sectional shape is given by the second moment of area, which for a solid circular cross section with radius r about its centre line is:

$$I_c = \frac{\pi \cdot r^4}{4}.$$ (2)

If a solid circular fibre is subjected to bending about an axis that is offset from its own centre line by a distance d_i then its second moment of area about that axis, I_i, is:

$$I_i = I_c + Ad_i^2.$$ (3)

A bundle of fibres that are held together in such a way that the fibres cannot move relative to one another will have a second moment of area the sum of the individual values of the fibres about the centre line of the bundle. If calculated in this manner, the second moment of area for a circular bundle of fibres, will be roughly that of a circular bar of the same overall radius.

If, however, the fibres can slide freely past each other such as if they are wound in a helical fashion then the Ad^2 term in the above equation disappears, resulting in a huge reduction in the second moment of area. This is because the change in length in a helical fibre when the bundle is bent is zero, hence the only remaining contribution to the overall bending stiffness is the bending stiffness of the fibre about its own centre line, I_c.

The above theory assumes that there is no friction between fibres within the helix. However, in practice there will be friction between wires, which will make the structure stiffer than the above theory implies. The frictional effect will become more significant with each increasing helical layer and one mechanism for introducing more inter-fibre slip is through helical hierarchies as discussed in the next section.

1.3 Structural hierarchy

If it is assumed that the value of the coefficient of friction between fibres does not change depending on the layer within a helical bundle (i.e. the same amount of friction per unit length of fibre), there will be a greater force resisting slipping at greater radii as the fibre length for one turn increases. Consequently the first layer in a spiral strand will be the closest to the full-slip approximation, and the assumption will get progressively worse until at some layer the wires will have so much frictional force restricting it that it will virtually behave like a solid tube. The solution to this is to build up helical units within units. This can be done a number of times creating a repeating helical hierarchy. The advantage is that slippage is introduced at a number of levels and so a much greater flexibility can be achieved.

1.4 Crack propagation

In a parallel fibre structure, the nature of the structure itself offers an extremely useful mechanism for preventing crack propagation [2]. In a solid structure, a single crack may propagate and cause the failure of the entire structure. For a fibrous system to fail, a crack must move from within a fibre, across an interface and then into the next fibre, and so on if it is to propagate. If the interface between fibres is sufficiently weak, the highly concentrated region of tensile stress that exists just ahead of the crack tip will cause a separation of the fibre interface and blunting of the crack (effectively arresting the crack). In the case of most ropes, there is no substrate and the mechanism of load transfer between neighbouring fibres is essentially through frictional forces caused by the contact load between them. This frictional adhesion is only effective in shear across the interface. Hence the tensile stress region ahead of an advancing crack will cause a separation of the wires, and the crack will be arrested and will not continue into the neighbouring wire.

The frictional forces between the fibres, has another structural advantage. A broken fibre within the structure carries no load at the actual location of the break. However, moving away from the break, the fibre gradually takes up the load until at some distance from the break it regains its full share again. The axial length over which this occurs is known as the 'effective length'. Even a structure made of continuous long elements, such as a wire rope, may have every individual wire broken and still be able to operate. This does of course require that the wire breaks are sufficiently distributed along the rope (i.e., separated by more than twice the 'effective length'). Man-made fibre structures such as cotton rely on this effect to spin short fibres into much longer yarns or ropes.

1.5 Energy absorption

The inter-fibre shear mechanism in a parallel element type structure can be designed with significant levels of hysteresis within a load cycle, and – which may be time dependant – visco-elastic behaviour (in the case of a viscous fluid interface) or time-independent Coulomb type damping (for a frictional interface). This property can prove useful for shock absorption or for damping oscillating loads.

1.6 Tensile efficiency

The helical structure of the fibres or wires in a rope means that the structure is very flexible in bending, increasingly so at higher lay angles α. However, the higher the lay angle, the less efficient the component is at transmitting tensile load. Thus the nature of a rope will be a compromise between its ability to perform its primary function of bearing tensile load and the level of flexibility required.

An example of a rope that does not need to bend in service is the stay cable on a bridge. In this application the rope used may be of the spiral-strand construction (see Figure 6a). Spiral strand ropes are very stiff in bending and, more importantly from the bridge designer's point of view, very stiff under axial loading. The stiffness in bending is due to the fact that the wires are spun in (usually many) concentric layers at a very low helix angle. The helix angle is designed to be sufficient to hold the rope together so it may operate as a whole (it must be remembered that there will be some bending in the strand's life – especially for transportation where the strand must be spooled). The efficiency of this single helix type of rope, η, will be given by:

$$\eta = \sum_{i=1 \, to \, n} \cos\alpha_{i \, wire} \tag{4}$$

where n is the number of layers in the spiral strand. As α tends to zero the efficiency tends to 100%.

In a much more flexible stranded rope (for example, Figure 8) with a wire lay angle within the strand of α_{wire} and strand lay angle within the rope of α_{strand}, the efficiency will be lower and will be given by

$$\eta = \sum_{i=1 \, to \, n} \cos\alpha_{i \, wire} \cdot \cos\alpha_{i \, strand} . \tag{5}$$

1.7 Torsional behaviour of axially loaded helical structures

Another consequence of spinning fibres (or wires) in a helical arrangement is that when under tension, as well as the axial force in the rope, there will be an additional radial force. This effect has been noted and analysed for wire ropes (see for example [3–6]), a summary of which is given here.

We consider the simple case of six fibres about a central core. On loading (Figure 2a), because of the angle that the strands make with the axis of the rope, the fibre load (R_f) will be composed of a vertical (R_ℓ) and horizontal component ($R_f \sin\alpha$) – Figure 2b. The magnitude of the forces R_f and $R_f \sin\alpha$ will depend upon the applied load R_ℓ and the lay angle α, that is the angle the fibres make with the centreline of the rope. If we assume that each of the fibres is similarly loaded (at any one layer or level – in this example there is only one layer), then the moment M will be a function of the rope load and lay angle, the number of strands N_{fibres} and the radius R at which the force $R_f \sin\alpha$ acts (Figure 2c). Thus:

$$M_{total} = \sum N_{fibres} \cdot R_f \sin\alpha \cdot R .\qquad(6)$$

The rotational characteristic of helical structures can cause considerable problems in rope applications, especially those where the end is not fixed, which will result in rotation of the rope under load. Consequently, rotation-resistant ropes have been designed to avoid these problems. The rotation resistant rope is a multi-layer rope with one or more layers spun in the opposite direction. Thus the sum M_{total} in eqn. (6) can be designed to be zero or as near zero as possible.

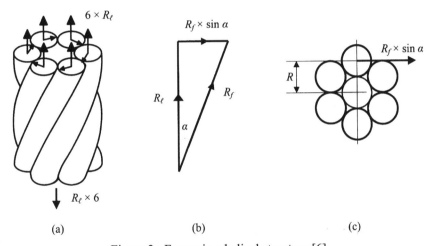

Figure 2: Forces in a helical structure [6].

Another problem related to the effect of the resultant twist in a rope structure is the effect of imposed twist; that is, twist forced into a rope by an external source. This can cause considerable damage to both non-rotation resistant (six strand, etc.) and especially rotation resistant (spiral, multi-strand) types of construction. Twist may be forced into the structure by connection to a component that is either in a twisted state or is of a different torsional stiffness [7], or, may be caused by interaction with the system in which the rope operates [8].

1.8 The effect of helical lay angle on pressure containment

A rope-like structure that has similarities with rope, but differs in its primary function, is a reinforced hose. In this structure, the requirement is not the transmission of tensile load, but control and containment of a pressurised fluid. In order to contain the pressure, yet maintain a flexible structure, a helical armouring of one or more layers of high tensile wire is used. As the armoured hose may well have fixed ends, it is important to maintain a dimensionally stable structure.

Consider a helical hose reinforcement wire wound at a lay angle, α, which is purely in tension, the axial and circumferential forces, F_a and F_c, respectively, must be related to the lay angle by the following relationship:

$$\tan \alpha = \frac{F_c}{F_a}, \tag{7}$$

where the axial force, F_a, can be calculated from the pressure, P, and the cross-sectional area of the end of the hose as follows:

$$F_a = P\pi R^2 \; ; \; F_c = PRS , \tag{8}$$

where the pitch, S, can be calculated from the reinforcement geometry in terms of the winding radius and lay angle. Combining these equations and solving for the lay angle, α, gives the 'neutral angle' as:

$$\alpha = 54.74° . \tag{9}$$

If fibres are wound at this angle, then the wires will be completely in tension and a single-layer design will be optimised. At any other angle, when the hose is pressurised it will tend to get either longer and thinner or shorter and fatter as the wires move toward the neutral angle.

2 Engineered rope-like structures – ropes and hoses

2.1 Brief historical introduction

2.1.1 Ropes

Ropes have been in use to transmit or support loads for as long as man has used tools. The first 'ropes' were vines that might have been used to help climb trees or rock faces to collect, for example, fruits or honey. Later, strips of animal hide were cut and plaited to produce stronger ropes. By the time of the Egyptians, ropes of hemp or manila fibres were spun to combine and lengthen fibres to produce ropes that were capable of transmitting significant loads [9]. Figure 3 found in the tomb of Tehuti-Hetep, which dates from 2000–1800 BC shows the production of continuous fibre through the various stages of manufacture [10]. Figure 4 from the same tomb gives some idea of not only the lengths of rope that the Egyptians were capable of producing, but of the breaking loads obtainable. Ridge [11] estimates the tractive force required to move the colossus at 12.5 tonnes, implying a breaking strength of each rope to be about 3 tonnes.

By using such materials and manufacturing techniques, stronger ropes could be made by simply spinning more fibres together and increasing the load-bearing area. One of the largest recorded natural-fibre ropes was a four-strand core fibre rope 15 inches in diameter, which according to Hipkins [12] was used in the launch of Brunel's *Great Eastern* in 1858. This great size of rope would obviously have been difficult to handle, yet there was a growing demand for ropes capable of transmitting larger and larger loads. This requirement led to development of the wire rope: in 1834 Wilhelm Albert made the first experiments using wire ropes in the 'Caroline' pit at Clausthal in the Harz mountains, Germany.

Figure 3: Manufacture of palm fibre rope, 2000–1800 BC [10].

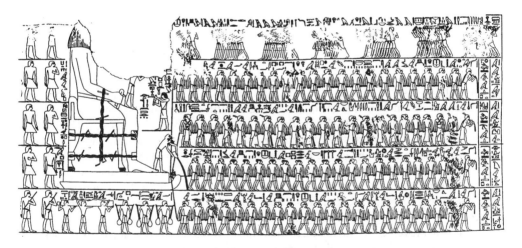

Figure 4: Transport of a colossus using fibre ropes, 2000–1800 BC [10].

The wire rope was rapidly adopted, and manufacturers were quick to experiment with different constructions. Figure 5 shows some of the types of wire rope offered by the English manufacturer Andrew Smith [13].

Figure 5: Examples of early wire rope designs from Smith [13].

2.1.2 Hoses

In parallel to these developments, as early as 400 BC hose was being used to transport water for fire fighting [14]. In this era, the hose was made out of ox gut. Firemen filled bags with water and then forced them into the ox gut by either sitting or stomping on the bag.

In 1673, two Dutchmen, Van der Heiden and his son, developed fire "hoase". These 50-foot lengths of leather tubes were sewn together in a similar fashion to the way shoemakers made boots. In 1807, two members of the Philadelphia Hose Company, James Sellers and Abraham Pennock revolutionised fire hose when they developed a way to rivet leather strips together. The hoses were made of the thickest and best rear-quarter cowhides. In Boston, in 1825, the Mayor reported 100 feet of hose doing the work that formerly required 60 men hauling buckets.

The next improvement came in 1821, when James Boyd received a patent for rubber-lined, cotton-webbed fire hose. Another major advancement came when Charles Goodyear discovered the vulcanisation process for rubber in 1839; the technique effectively cross-links rubber and gives a much more robust material. By this time a number of manufacturers existed and the number of hose designs began to proliferate significantly.

A growth in the number and quality of available materials (such as wire drawing, production of synthetic polymer fibres), coupled with a constantly evolving and increasing number of applications needing specific solutions, has led to a wide range of constructions of ropes, hoses and related structures available in the modern world. A description of some of the common constructions are detailed in the following sections.

2.2 Wire ropes

The building block of the wire rope is the wire, several of which are spun together into the basic unit, termed a strand. At its simplest, a strand is a group of wires spun together, usually a helical layer of wires over a straight central core (or 'King' wire).

As discussed earlier in Section 1, if increased strength is required, maintenance of flexibility can be accomplished by adding more helical layers rather than simply using larger wires, although in all practical rope design the final choice will be a compromise between the two factors. Additionally, depending upon the mechanical properties required in service from the rope, different types of wires and strands will be combined in different ways.

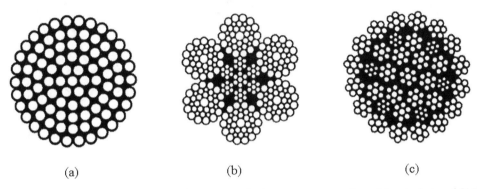

(a)   (b)   (c)

Figure 6:Examples of the three main groups of wire rope construction: (a) spiral strand [15], (b) six strand with IWRC [16]; and, (c) rotation-resistant [16].

We can define three main classes of rope that are discussed in more detail:
1. spiral strand (Figure 6a);
2. six (or eight) strand with independent core (Figure 6b); and,
3. multi-strand (also termed semi-rotation resistant or rotation-resistant) (Figure 6c).

2.2.1 Spiral strands

The spiral strand is the simplest form of rope, consisting of concentric layers of helically spun wires (Figure 6a). The wires tend to be spun at a low lay angle in order to achieve greatest efficiency (see Section 1.6), but still retain some form of cohesive structure. Owing to the dense packing of the wires that may be achieved in a spiral strands, and the low lay angle, the spiral strand is a very stiff rope type, both in bending and axially. These properties make the construction ideal for applications such as bridge stays, which will not operate over pulleys and require high axial stiffness.

An additional feature of the spiral strand is, that by careful design, it can be manufactured so that when subject to an axial load, the resultant moment of the layers is zero (Section 1.7). In order to achieve this balance, it is necessary to spin some layers in the opposite direction (hand) to others. Since the outer layers of wires will dominate the reaction of the rope, owing to the fact that not only are the wires further away from the King wire but there will also be more of them per layer (assuming the wires have the same or similar diameter), there will not be the same number of layers of each hand. Furthermore, the layers of wires are not spun alternately left hand (LH) and right hand (RH), but tend to be grouped, for example starting from the core: LH, LH, LH, RH, RH. This grouping of the hand of the layers of wires has the additional advantage of reducing the number of cross or 'trellis' contacts that will occur through the strand (Figure 7a).

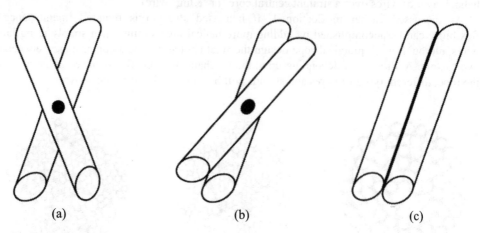

(a)   (b)   (c)

Figure 7: Types of contacts between wires: (a) trellis; (b) cross lay; and, (c) equal lay.

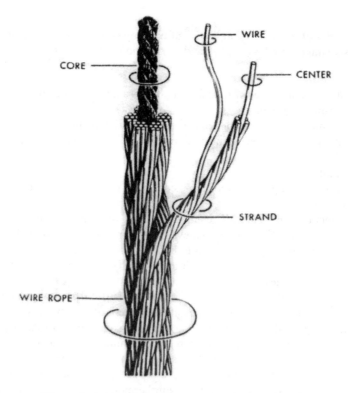

Figure 8: A stranded wire rope from Costello [17].

2.2.2 Stranded wire rope

The stranded wire rope is made up of typically six or eight strands spun helically about a central core (Figure 8 and 9). The three strand rope is an exception to this rule, being formed without a core (Figure 9a). Ropes with four or five outer strands are not generally used as they do not give a very circular cross section. Unlike the spiral strand discussed in the previous section, the fundamental property of the stranded rope is flexibility, and the ability to operate over a pulley (also termed sheave). Thus, the layers of wires in the strands are all spun in the same direction in order to avoid the damaging cross contact between wires.

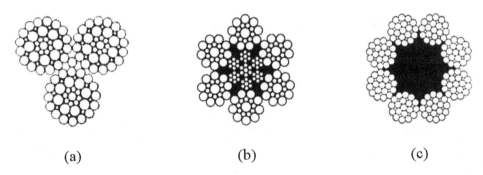

| (a) | (b) | (c) |

Figure 9: Different classes of stranded wire rope: (a) three strand [18]; (b) six strand with IWRC [16]; and, (c) eight strand with fibre core [19].

2.2.2.1 Strand constructions In order to provide a uniform load sharing between the layers, the concentric layers of wires in the strand must have the same lay angle. However, owing to the difference in radius between concentric layers, this will mean that different layers will have different lay lengths. The constant-lay-angle strand was the basis of the first strands used in stranded rope, the most common type being the 12/6/1, built up of wires of the same diameter as shown in Figure 10a. A strand built up of layers with a constant lay angle would have been easier to manufacture as there would be no need to change the gearing of the stranding machine for each layer. As a result of the different lay lengths, even though the layers are spun in the same direction there will be discreet cross-contact points, as shown in Figure 7b. This type of construction is therefore known as 'cross-lay'. Any advantages that the cross-lay construction accrues from equal load sharing between its layers are outweighed by the disadvantage of the stress concentrations caused at the inter-layer point contacts.

It should be noted that this argument also applies to the spiral strand discussed above; however, since the lay angle of the layers is lower than that of a stranded rope, the load sharing between layers is already better. A different lay angle may be used in a layer or layers of wires to aid in the torque balance of the whole structure.

By accepting that for stranded ropes it is more important for the wires in different layers to lie parallel to each other so that they have equal lay lengths rather than equal lay angle a much better contact condition is obtained. The wires in and between the layers now have a line rather than cross contact (see Figure 7). This type of construction is termed equal-lay, and is now by far the most commonly used.

In addition to the contact benefits described above, if wires in one layer can be arranged to sit in the groove wires of the adjacent layer, the packing efficiency will be further improved.

This idea is the basis for constructing strands with different wire diameters. There are three common constructions of two layer equal-lay strands: Seale, Warrington and Filler.

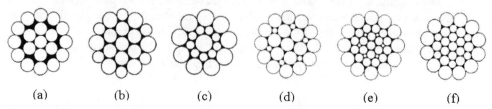

(a)   (b)   (c)   (d)   (e)   (f)

Figure 10: Common strand constructions used in stranded rope applications:(a) simple strand (12/6/1) cross-lay, note the common wire size; (b) Warrington (6+6/6/1) equal-lay; (c) Seale (9/9/1) equal-lay; (d) Filler wire (12/6+6F/1) equal-lay; (e) Filler-Seale (12/12/6+6F/6/1) equal-lay; and, (f) Warrington-Seale (12/6+6/6/1) equal-lay [20].

The Seale construction (patented in 1885 by Thomas Seale [21]) consists of a number of large wires laid around an equal number of smaller wires, in such a way that each outer wire lies in the valley of the two underlying wires, as shown in Figure 10c. This has a very good packing density and, because of the large diameter of the outer wires, excellent wear properties, although with a reduction in rope flexibility. Where flexibility is not a major consideration, this is considered the best equal lay construction [22]. The Filler wire construction (patented in 1894 by W. B. Brown [23]) consists of an even number of wires laid around an inner layer of half that number, where each valley is filled with a small wire (Figure 10d). The number of valleys is thereby doubled so in the next layer, each outer wire beds in the valley formed by one main wire and one of the filler wires. This construction is more flexible than the Seale, but has a poorer packing density. The Warrington construction (patented by Dixon in 1888 [23]) has an outer layer of wires with twice as many as the inner layer. The outer layer of wires consists of alternate wires of two diameters (see Figure 10b). This construction has very good flexibility, but a poorer wear resistance than the Seale [11]. For equal lay-strand construction with three or more layers, generally some combination of Warrington, Seale or Filler wire is used (e.g., the Warrington–Seale and Filler–Seale as shown in Figure 10e and f).

2.2.2.2 Types of strand lay Strands can either be wound in a left-hand or right-hand helix within the rope, the only difference between these being the direction of the resultant torque that will be produced upon loading. In addition to the strand lay, there are two possibilities of wire lay direction within the strand: ordinary lay and Lang's lay. In ordinary lay, the strands are laid in the opposite direction to the wires within the strand (Figure 11a and b). In Lang's lay (patented by John Lang in 1879 [24]), wires are spun in the same sense as the strands (Figure 11c and d). Under tensile loading, both ordinary and Lang's lay ropes will rotate. Lang's lay rope is especially prone to this, and will untwist indefinitely if the ends are allowed to rotate. For this reason, stranded ropes must only be used where the ends are restrained from rotating. The main advantage of Lang's lay rope is its increased resistance to wear owing to the fact that a longer length of individual wire is exposed on the surface of the rope – this is especially useful in running-rope applications.

Figure 11: Types of rope lays: (a) right-hand ordinary lay (RHO); (b) left-hand ordinary (LHO); (c) right-hand Lang's lay (RHL); and, (d) left-hand Lang's lay (LHL) [20].

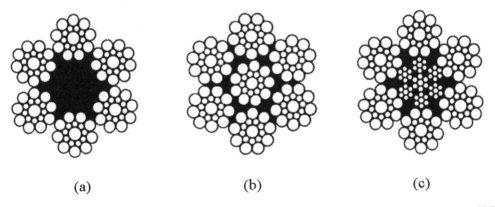

(a)   (b)   (c)

Figure 12: Three different kinds of cores used in stranded rope as follows: (a) Fibre core (FC) so the rope is 6×19(9/9/1) + FC [16]; (b) Wire strand core (WSC) the rope is 6×19(9/9/1) + WSC [15]; and, (c) Independent wire rope core (IWRC), the rope is 6×19(9/9/1) + IWRC [16].

2.2.2.3 Types of core   The main function of the core within a stranded rope is to provide support for the outer strands. The three types of core are shown in Figure 12 and are as follows:

- The fibre core (FC), which consists of a bundle of thermoplastic fibres. This construction has good flexibility and the core may be heavily lubricated to give good lubrication during service. However, this type of core may not be sufficiently rigid to prevent cross-sectional distortions where there is significant lateral loading in service (Figure 12a).

- The wire strand core (WSC) is a simple solution to the problem of lateral loading. The core is another strand similar to the outer strands. This does, however, give an inherently stiffer rope (Figure 12b).

- The use of an independent wire rope core (IWRC) - a core that is a rope in its own right, gives a rope good flexibility while providing a good support for the outer strands against lateral forces. The IWRC also gives a much better contact with the outer strands because of its circular profile (Figure 12c).

2.2.3 Multi-strand ropes

A more complex variation of the stranded rope, which combines the flexibility of a stranded rope with the possibility to resist rotation under load characteristic of the spiral strand, is the multi-strand or rotation resistant rope (Figure 13). One of the simplest classes of rotation-resistant rope is the 17×7 (seventeen strands of seven wires each), as seen in Figure 13a. However, with only two layers of strands, it is not possible to create properly balanced construction, and this type of rope is termed semi-rotation resistant.

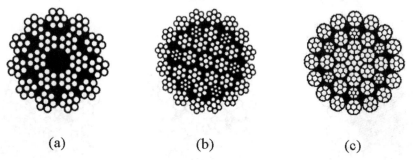

(a)   (b)   (c)

Figure 13: Semi-rotation-resistant and rotation-resistant rope constructions (a) 17×7; (b) 35LS; and, (c) 34LR die-form® [16].

Multi-strand ropes with three or more layers of strands can be designed to give rotation resistance. Figure 13b shows a 35-strand rope where the outer strands are spun about the rope axis in the opposite direction to the inner strands. This type of rope is ideal for use on cranes.

A major drawback of the rotation-resistant classes of rope is that in service they tend to fail from the inside owing to the cross contacts between the first and second layers: very few if any wire failures will be visible on the outer strands, whilst the core may have hundreds of breaks! This makes accurate inspection very difficult, and effectively prohibits the use of this type of rope in some safety-critical applications [25].

One variant that improves the contact conditions of the wires in the rope and of the rope as it operates over pulleys is the die-form construction (Figure 13c). The die-form type of rope is so called because each of the strands are put through a die or alternatively rolled, to compact the strands and create a more circular section.

2.2.4 Rope constructions with shaped wires or strands

A further development in strand construction is to use shaped wires. The most common reason for using shaped wires is to give the outside of a spiral strand a more circular cross section and better wear properties. Two examples of this are the half-lock and full-lock spiral strands as shown in Figure 14a, b. These two constructions are very stiff, but have excellent wear properties. A locked-coil rope would typically be used as a track rope for an aerial cable way, whilst the half-lock might be used as the guide rope for a car in a mine hoist system.

Where flexibility is still required, stranded ropes with a more circular cross section can also have similar advantages to those described above. This is achieved by the use of shaped strands. The strands are usually either oval or triangular shaped (Figure 14c, d). For example, triangular strands consist of a triangular-shaped king wire that is then spun in the usual manner with standard circular wires (usually with a Seale construction).

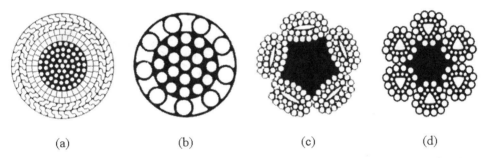

| (a) | (b) | (c) | (d) |

Figure 14: Examples of constructions with shaped (non-round) wires or strands: (a) full-lock coil structural strand (44Z/38S/38T/32T/24/18/12/6/1) [26]; (b) a half-lock strand (9+9H/12/6/1) [16]; (c) flattened-strand 5×28(16/11/1) + FC [18]; and, (d) triangular six strand 6×25(12/12/Δ) + (FC) [27].

2.2.5 Production of wire rope

Figure 15 provides a simplified over-view of the stages involved in the production of a wire rope. Starting from the steel billet the rod is first produced, then subject to heat treatment. The heat-treatment process known as "patenting" is a crucial part of the manufacture of medium- and high-carbon steel wires, giving them sufficient ductility to be drawn, while retaining the high strength advantages.

The patenting process involves an austenization of the wire at high temperature followed by an extremely rapid cooling to temperature below the transformation temperature of 723°C. This results in an almost isothermal transformation of the austenite structure into a pearlite with a very fine laminate structure (an order of magnitude finer than the course pearlite structure found in plain carbon eutectoid steel). The undrawn patented wire has a tensile strength of between 800 and 1300 N/mm^2 depending on the inter-laminar spacing of the pearlite [28] (a finer spacing giving a higher strength). The drawing process is capable of more than doubling this strength caused by work hardening and increased alignment of the grain structure along the wire axis. Typical wire grades in wire ropes are 1770, 1960 and 2160 N/mm^2. Following heat treatment, the wires must be cleaned and fluxed to prepare for the initial wire drawing.

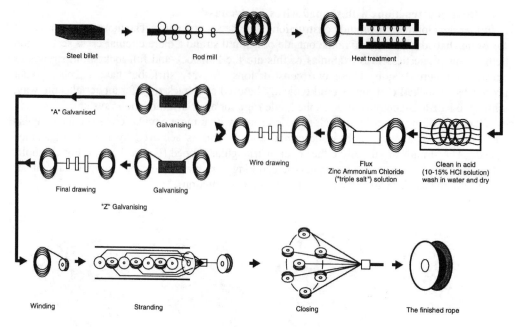

Figure 15: Stages in the production of a wire rope (after Bridon [16]).

Depending upon whether the wires in the rope are to be galvanised or bright (natural) finish, the next stage in the process is to galvanise the wires. Galvanising used to be applied using the electro-deposition technique, but this method is not used now, hot-dip galvanising being preferred. The thickness of the zinc coat applied to the wire will be a function of the speed of travel of the wire through the bath and the temperature of the bath. The elevated temperature will cause some softening of the wire, and where a higher strength is required the wire will undergo a final drawing after galvanising. Since the final drawing process will remove some of the zinc coat it is not used where the heavier 'A class' of galvanising is required. ('A class' galvanising is used typically for ropes in marine applications.)

The wires are now ready for stranding (creating the rope strands) and are spooled onto bobbins. Depending upon the capacity of the machine and the numbers of wires in the strands, the strands may be formed in one or more than one pass of the stranding machine. Following stranding, the rope strands are assembled in a closing machine to form the final rope.

One aspect of stranding and closing that deserves mention here is the removal of the twist in the wire or strand as it is being spun about the central core (which passes along the centre axis of the machine). The route to the development of helical winding was the invention of the Cordelier, by Edmund Cartwright in 1786. Although the Cordelier (Figure 16) was designed for yarns in the weaving industry, it incorporates the basic principle of epicyclic gearing to add or remove any twist in the yarns as they are spun together.

Dickinson describes the principle of the Cordelier thus: 'The spools of yarn are supported in a rotatable frame; on the axis of each spool is a toothed wheel, gearing through an idle wheel, with a corresponding toothed wheel on the axis of the frame. The toothed wheel on the spool is the same diameter as the wheel on the axis and therefore as the frame is rotated, the spool remains stationary relative to the axis. By altering the diameters of the two wheels, the spools may be made to overtake or else lag behind the revolutions of the axis, and thus put in or leave out twist as desired; uniformity in laying is thus ensured.' [29].

An additional manufacturing process that has been found to be beneficial to the final mechanical properties of rope (and hose) is that of pre-forming of the wires and strands into a helix before they are wound into the final component. This has the result of reducing contact stresses within the component and also reduces the level to which a free end will try to unwind. Figure 17 shows a close-up of a pre-forming head such as will be used in a wire rope closing machine (Figure 18).

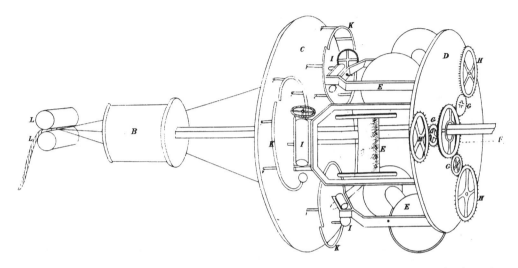

Figure 16: Cartwright's 'Cordelier' showing the principle of the gearing used to take the twist out of the fibres as the strand is spun. From Cartwright's patent [30].

Figure 17: Pre-forming head on a rope-closing machine [20].

Figure 18: Rope-closing machine. Note the bobbins to the right of the picture and the closing head in the centre [20].

An essential element to the wire rope construction that has not been discussed until now is the lubricant. Lubricant has two purposes: firstly, and primarily, it is to reduce the friction between contacting wires, allowing them to slide freely and reducing the effects of fretting fatigue during use. Secondly, the lubricant has the added benefit of acting as coating to help prevent corrosion. Lubricant is heated to the melting point to allow easy application at the closing head during all stages of making a strand. The lubricant is applied to the wires just before they enter the guide (or 'nips'), and again to the strand as it emerges from the nips. More lubricant is applied in the closing stage of the rope manufacture. Once a rope has been assembled it is extremely difficult to lubricate the interior, particularly in the case of the spiral and multi-strand type constructions, consequently the rope must be thoroughly lubricated at all stages of manufacture. Different grades of lubricant are used depending upon the service of the rope, for example a light lubricant for a lift rope, whilst for ropes offshore, a heavy bituminous marine lubricant would be used.

2.3 Hose

Hoses typically consist of a number of fundamental components [31]: the inner core; reinforcement; and, an outer cover (see Figure 19).

2.3.1 Inner core
The inner core is a tube the main function of which is to contain the hydraulic or pneumatic medium, it is usually made of either polymer or elastomer. The inner core prevents leakage of the fluid and it is loaded in almost hydrostatic conditions

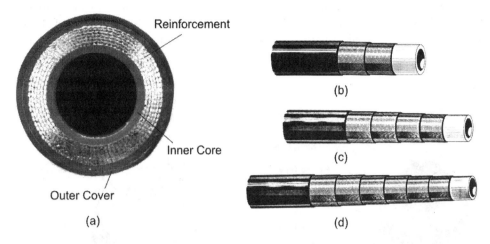

Figure 19: (a) The cross section of a six-layer Polyflex hose, indicating the basic components of the hose. (b) two-layer spiral hose, (c) four-layer spiral hose, (d) six-layer spiral hose (from Polyflex [32]).

2.3.2 Reinforcement

The reinforcement is the main load-bearing component and consists of layers of fibres or wires wound around the inner core. The reinforcement will be either braided or spiral wound.

Braiding involves weaving both left- and right-hand helical fibres on the same layer to produce a jacket or sheath such as shown in Figure 24a. In order to braid the wires effectively they must by thin enough to bend into place. The braiding has the advantage that upon loading or pressurisation, the hose will not twist. However, the strength of the braiding may not be sufficient for all applications.

Where greater strength is required, spiral armouring is used. This created a structure that is similar to the spiral strand rope described in Section 2.2.1, with the core wires replaced by the tube. Depending upon the strength required, the armouring will be built up in layers. As with the spiral strand, some level of torsional stability may be achieved if more than one layer of armouring is used. It must also be remembered that the armouring may be required to maintain axial-dimensional stability as described in Section 1.8.

2.3.3 Outer cover

The outer cover is concerned mainly with protecting the reinforcement from wear and corrosive attack. It contributes little to the strength or stiffness of the hose structure.

2.3.4 Related structures – flexible risers and umbilical cables

When oil is transported from the sea bed to a floating platform it is done by means of a flexible riser, the most common type of which is known as a non-bonded flexible pipe (for example, see Figure 20).

These are a much larger diameter than hoses and an important consideration is to prevent collapse from the external seawater pressure while retaining flexibility. Consequently such structures have layers such as locked coils and corrugated carcasses to prevent internal collapse, as well as wire layers for hoop and longitudinal strength.

Another requirement of floating platforms is to control the well head remotely from the platform. This is enabled by umbilicals (Figure 20) which are a number of hoses and electrical cables, wound together inside a large hose-like structure. The large external hose protects the hydraulic and electrical flexible sub-units from external pressures while maintaining adequate flexibility to allow for platform movements.

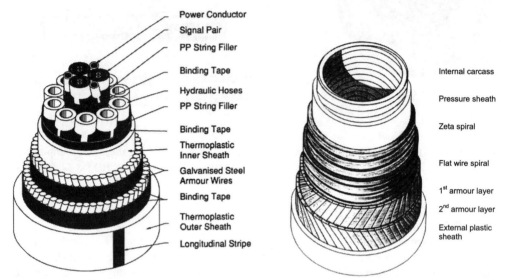

Figure 20: An example of an umbilical manufactured by Dunlop-Coflexip [33], and an example of a flexible pipe manufactured by Coflexip [34].

2.3.5 Production of hose spiral armouring

The application of armouring to a hose is very similar to the production of a spiral strand. In the case of hose, inner core bundle or tube is fed from a spool through the axis of the winder. The main difference in the application of the armouring will be that it is wound at a much greater lay angle, for reasons discussed in Section 1.8. The consequence of the steeper winding angle is that there will be proportionally many more wires in each layer than in the case of a rope. Hence hose spiral-winding machines have many more rotating bobbins of wires on each winding wheel, and do not incorporate epicyclic gearing to remove twist in the wire. However, the much steeper angle at which a layer of hose wire is wound means that introducing twist along the axis of the wire is not a problem.

2.4 Synthetic fibre ropes

The development of synthetic fibres as we know them today was largely due to the research effort from the early 1920's to World War II by Carothers and Staudinger. After WWII, nylon 6.6, a product of the work of Carothers at Du Pont in N. America (in the 1930's), became the first commercially available man-made fibre [35]. Polyester (polethylene terephthalate) fibres were first developed into commercial products by Winfield and Dickson in the 1940'/1950's.

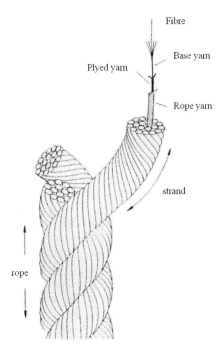

Figure 21: A three-stranded fibre rope from Leech [36], which is a five level repeating helical hierarchy.

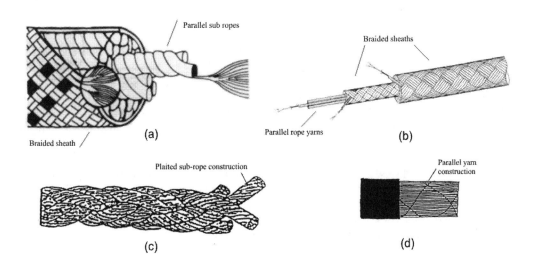

Figure 22: Four examples of rope constructions: (a) parallel sub-rope covered with a braided sheath [36]; (b) a double-braided fibre rope [36]; (c) a plaited rope [35]; and, (d) a parallel-yarn rope [35].

2.4.1 Types of fibre ropes

Polymeric filaments are either coarse mono-filament or fine multi-filament, which have diameters typically between 10 and 100 microns. (By way of reference, wire diameters are usually between 0.5 and 5 mm, some 20,000 times greater.) Yarns are formed of lightly twisted or discontinuously entangled bundles of 100 to 2000 filaments. In most rope constructions, a number of single yarns are twisted together into plied yarns, these being further combined to form rope yarns and strands. The strands are then used to produce a variety of constructions, some of them closely copying the wire rope type of constructions (e.g., compare Figure 21 with Figure 9a), or, owing to the high flexibility of the fibres, different type structures such as braided and plaited. Figure 22 shows examples of the range of fibre rope constructions in use.

2.4.2 Applications of fibre ropes

Fibre ropes have a number of properties that make them attractive alternatives to wire ropes. Currently the biggest growing application is in the use for offshore moorings. We will discuss the properties of fibre ropes with reference to the considerations for this application. Beneficial properties of polyester fibre ropes, such as are used offshore, include good strength-to-weight ratio, flexibility, ease of handling and near neutral buoyancy in seawater. Other materials such as aramid fibres, which owing to their high strength might initially seem suitable or even better as a material, would not be used for several reasons: it is too stiff, very expensive and not at all rugged. Thus it can be seen that as with wire ropes, each needs to be selected or designed with a full appreciation of the service for which the rope is required. Table 1 (which is not exhaustive) summarises some fibres and their key properties.

The near-neutral buoyancy of polyester fibre ropes in sea water is significant in that it makes possible the mooring of floating exploration and production oil platforms in the very deep waters (1000–3000 m) that are now being exploited (especially in the Gulf of Mexico and off the coast of West Africa). The benefit of the fibre rope is derived from its use in the taut moorings arrangements that are possible, such that the rope strength is used for station keeping rather than supporting the ropes self weight [35].

Fibre ropes tend not to be very resistant to crushing and abrasion, hence, where fibre ropes are used in deepwater moorings it is usual to employ a line that has a top section of chain or wire rope (usually six strand), and a bottom section to the anchor, of chain, spiral strand, or six-strand rope. The final choice of components is influenced by such factors as ease of handling, operation over a winch (top end) and abrasion / anchor embedment (at the sea bed). The use of multi-component mooring lines can lead to torsional problems as outlined in Section 1.7, but by careful design and installation these problems, for the most part, can be avoided.

Although fibre ropes are not affected by corrosion in the same way as wire ropes, they are susceptible to UV degradation. The UV degradation affects the exposed surface of the fibres, acting to reduce their strength. Hence it is more of a problem in some types of construction, such as plaited (Fig. 16c), and with smaller ropes compared with larger (where the exposed rope surface area is a greater proportion of the whole rope). Other design considerations in the selection of a fibre for an application are those of creep and elongation. Fibres such as polyamide (nylon) and polyester suffer from creep, and nylon displays considerable elongation under load. Aramid and LCP fibres on the other hand, are much stiffer and display negligible creep.

Thus it may be seen that the range and properties of the fibres used in synthetic fibre ropes varies considerably, and for any application there will a compromise between the properties and differing service requirements.

Table 1: Properties of fibre rope materials (compiled from [37]).

Fibre	Properties
Aramid (Kevlar®, Twaron®): A manufactured high-modulus fibre in which the fibre-forming substance is a long-chain synthetic aromatic polyamide of which at least 5% of the amide linkages are attached directly to aromatic rings	• Excellent strength-to-weight ratio • High resistance to heat (chars at 800°F) • Negligible creep • Poor abrasion resistance • Susceptible to axial-compression fatigue
Copolymer (Olyfin, polyester): The molecular combination of polyproylene/polyethelene fibres together with other fibres such as polyester	• Moderate strength/elongation • Low weight (floats) • Good UV resistance • Good abrasion resistance
HMPE (Plasma®, Spectra®, Dyneema®): High-modulus polyethylene fibres produced by gel-spinning ultra-high molecular weight polyethylene (UHMWPE)	• High strength-to-weight ratio • Very good abrasion resistance • Excellent dynamic toughness • Very low elongation (3–5%) • Good bend fatigue performance • Low resistance to heat • Susceptible to creep
LCP (Vectran®): High-modulus fibre produced by melt spinning from thermotropic liquid crystalline aromatic polyester	• Excellent strength-to-weight ratio • Zero creep • Excellent dynamic toughness • Excellent bend fatigue performance • Good abrasion resistance • High heat resistance (melts at 625°F)
Polyamide (Nylon): A manufactured fibre composed of linear macromolecules having in the chain recurring amide linkages, at least 85% of which are joined to aliphatic or cycloaliphatic units	• Good strength-to-weight ratio • Good shock-absorbing characteristics • High elongation (30–40%) • Good UV resistance
Polyester (Pet, Pen): Includes polymers composed of linear macromolecules having a chain at least 85% by mass of an ester of a diol and terephthalic acid	• Highest UV resistance of any fibre • Good abrasion resistance • Good strength-to-weight ratio • Moderate elongation (15–20%)
Polyolefin (PE, PP): A class of polymers in which the fibre-forming substance is any long-chain synthetic polymer composed of at least 85% by weight of ethene (ethylene), propane (propylene), or other olefin units	• Low weight • Low cost • Good general-purpose fibre

2.4.3 Production of man-made fibres

Traditional ropes are made from natural polymers such as hemp. Polymeric fibres used in rope making are mostly made from petrochemical feed stock. Table 1 gives more information on the composition of various commonly used fibres. In general, however, the process for producing polymers in the form of fibres is known as spinning and, although there are a number of different types of spinning, there are three generic processes:

(a) Preparation of a viscous dope;

(b) Extruding the dope through a spinneret to form a fibre; and,

(c) Solidifying the fibre by coagulation, evaporation or cooling.

Some spinning techniques involve the polymer being dissolved in chemicals (wet and dry spinning), but the preferred method of spinning (for example nylon and polyester) is melt spinning; this involves the use of molten polymer that is solidified after the spinning by cooling (Fig. 23).

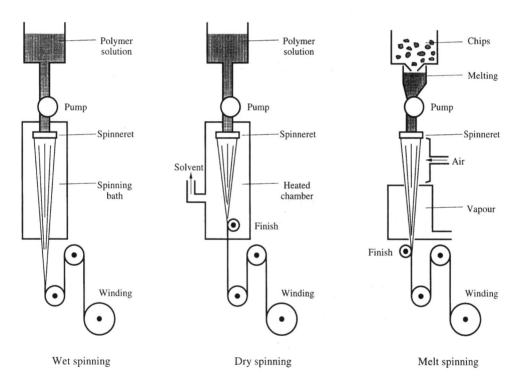

Figure 23: Three types of spinning commonly employed for fibre production [35].

Following spinning, the fibres have poor strength and stiffness since the molecules of the polymer are not preferentially oriented in the direction of the filament. Orientation is obtained by drawing. For fibre such as polyamide and polyester, typical drawing ratios are between 3:1 and 5:1 [38].

After production of the fibres, these are combined as mentioned above into strands and ropes. Some rope constructions (and hence production techniques) are similar to those used for wire ropes and will not be described again here. There are, however, two similar forms of production particular to fibre ropes: braiding and plaiting. Although both these techniques are fundamentally the same, in that they involve weaving of fibres, braiding may be seen as a technique to produce a cover (or series of concentric layers), whilst plaited ropes involve plaiting of the whole strands. Thus a rope made up of parallel strands may have a braided jacket (which may be of a different material with better UV tolerance) to allow it to be operated as a whole with the additional benefit of protection from UV light.

2.4.4 The braiding process

Braiding is a process that produces an interwoven tube of fibres with an equal number of fibres wound both left and right hand. The braiding process involves one group of fibres being wound in a sinusoidal path in one direction, the sinusoidal path thus allowing a second group of fibres to be interwoven in the opposite direction. In order to achieve this, a braiding machine has a number of key components [39]:

- Bobbins and carriers that hold the reels of fibres with a pre-determined tension.

- A deck plate that controls the movement of the carriers by means of two slots and also houses the horn gears

- Horn gears, a number of which are positioned around the centre of the machine, with four slots to hold the carriers. Adjacent horn gears rotate in opposite directions and drive two sets of fibres in their counter-woven path.

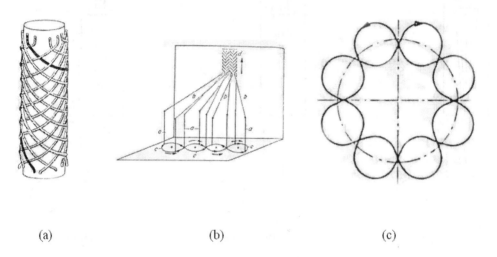

(a)   (b)   (c)

Figure 24: The braiding process, showing (a) a braided tube, (b) an example of the fibre path for a braided sheet and (c) the fibre path for a braided tube (from Matschoss [39]).

3 Description of biological rope-like structures

Tissues within an organism are tailored to their specific functional needs both by the properties of the constituent 'building blocks' and their structural organisation. There are many examples where a long helical (rope-like) structural organisation has been employed and this section gives some examples of this. Two broad groups of building blocks exist as polypeptides in mammalian structures (specifically collagen and elastin), and polysaccharides in plant structures and insects (cellulose and chitin).

As well as the fibrous building blocks of biological tissues, a number of other constituents exist that can be broadly termed as matrix materials, fillers and ground substances. These may have a critical role in the mechanical behaviour by either binding fibres together (in the case of hard tissues) or allowing free slippage between fibres (in the case of soft tissues). Some examples of these are globular proteins or glycoproteins and water, in un-calcified soft tissues; in hard tissues hydroxyapitite (in bone), and lignin in wood, are common examples.

A number of biological systems are discussed in terms of their structure-function relationships. Two building blocks have been chosen – collagen, a polypeptide, and cellulose, a polysaccharide. As mentioned above, there are other building blocks found in nature such as chitin, a polysaccharide, found in crustaceans and insects based on a helical molecule. Thus these examples should be seen as illustrative rather than exhaustive.

3.1 Polysaccharide structures

Plant structures are made up from elongated cells that have helical cellulose macro-fibres within their walls. The structure of these macro-fibres will be discussed and then their role within the organisation of a plant cell wall will be detailed.

3.1.1 Cellulose macro-fibres

The cellulose molecule is a polysaccharide with two glucose molecules rotated by 180° (known as polybiose) as its repeating disaccharide. This molecule is twisted into a microfibral [40], which is in turn twisted into a macrofibral along with pectin, glycoprotein and hemi-cellulose, which act as a gel-like lubricant or a glue depending on the stage of growth of the plant cell wall. Thus the cellulose macro-fibre has a hierarchy of helical elements, its place within the plant cell wall is discussed in the following.

3.1.2 Plant cell walls

Plants utilise two general mechanisms of structural support within their cell walls [41]. Flexible cell walls that rely on hydraulic 'turgor' pressure for bending stiffness and stiff cell walls that are bonded together with a stiff matrix and have stability even when dry. In the case of tree structures both types of structure exist within the development of the plant (Fig. 25). A brief description of these two systems is given.

The central living part of a plant cell (protoplast) synthesises layers of cellulose fibres within an amorphous matrix [42], which are gradually stacked one on another (i.e., the outermost wall being the first formed). The first layer formed (the primary layer) has a low fibre content, around 25%, and is embedded in a gel-like matrix, pectin, which gives a flexible wall structure. The inside of a cell at this stage is under hydrostatic pressure due to osmosis. The gel-like matrix also allows the cell to grow and elongate easily during this stage of development. The next stage of development involves the formation of secondary layers, generally referred to as S1, S2 and S3, which have a much higher fibre content than in the primary layers (gradually increasing to 80% by dry weight). The S1 layers consists of cross-helical fibres at around 80° to the axis, S2 and S3 are about 40° to the axis. At this stage both primary and secondary walls of the cell are impregnated with lignin, which is a complex organic polymer with a three-dimensional configuration [42] and bonds the whole structure, giving it bending stiffness without the need for hydrostatic support. Plant cross sections tend to be arrays of parallel cells each being helically wound tubes as described.

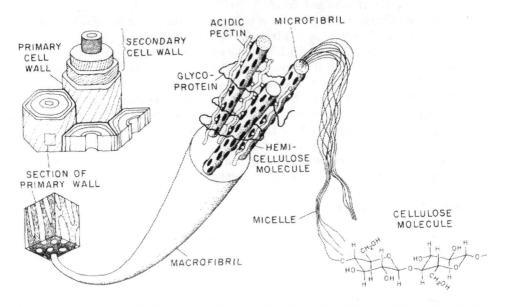

Figure 25:   The hierarchical structure of plant cell walls as found in wood, from Esau [41].

Wood structures are able to create pre-stress within their fibres to re-orient branches and trunks that are mechanically displaced from their original position. The same mechanism is employed by the aerial roots of the fig tree once it enters the ground in order to create a tension guy [41]. This type of wood is known as 'reaction wood' and the pre-stresses can be tensile or compressive.

Wood has a mechanism of toughness that enables it to absorb large amounts of energy before failure by the pseudo-plastic behaviour caused by the realignment of fibres of the fibre-wound wood cells (known as tension buckling). It has been found experimentally to have maximum energy absorption when fibre angles are around 15°.

3.2 Polypeptide structures

3.2.1 The collagen fibril

Collagen is a collective name for a group of fibrous proteins with similar structures and properties [44] (see Fig. 26). The most abundant amino acids within the basic protein molecule are glycine, alanine, proline and hyroxyproline. These molecules tend to be helical in orientation (α-chain) and grouped in threes, twisted together in the form of a coiled coil (collagen molecule or tropo-collagen), according to the model proposed by Rich and Crick [45]. Between four and eight collagen molecules twist together to form a microfibral [46] and it has been shown that these microfibrals, in turn, twist together to form a collagen fibril. Thus a collagen fibril is a four-level helical hierarchy. The collagen fibre forms the basis for many biological structures such as tendon, arteries, bones and skin, the first two of which will be discussed below. Collagen fibres are often present in materials that exhibit viscoelastic behaviour. Recent work by Purslow et al. [47] on skin suggests that this behaviour cannot be attributed to re-alignments of the fibres within the matrix. It is suggested that it is more likely to be caused by viscoelastic behaviour of the fibre itself (possibly by realignments of micro-filaments at a lower level within the fibre).

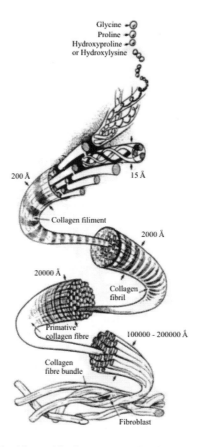

Figure 26: The hierarchical structure of collagen (from [43]).

3.2.2 Arteries

Arteries are relatively high-pressure, cylindrical, thick-walled vessels and the bulk of the load-bearing portion of arteries, the 'Tunica Media', is formed of alternating sheets of helically wound collagen fibres with elastin sheets. Two primary functions of the arteries are to bear the high pressures of the system and to smooth out the pulsatile flow caused by the beating heart. The smoothing of the pulsatile flow is achieved by the highly flexible properties of the arteries close to the exit of the heart. Otto Frank has made the analogy of the aorta being like a 'Windkessel' (air chamber) much as was used in hand-powered fire pumps to provide a uniform outflow with a pulsatile inflow [48]. The ascending aorta has a higher elastin content within the wall so that the vessel acts as an accumulator in this region, where the elastic recovery   is   98%

[49]. The elastin content of the ascending aorta is 30–40% and the collagen content is around 20%, then there is a gradual change in these ratios until around the abdominal aorta, where the collagen content is twice that of elastin. Roach and Burton [50] argue that elastin dominates at low tissue stress but collagen provides the strength. This does seem to be particularly true for the higher reaches of the aorta where E_o (initial, low-load elastic modulus) is 90 kPa at the ascending aorta and 10 kPa at the femoral bifurcation – in line with the elastin content.

Since thick-walled pressure vessels have a maximum tensile hoop stress on the inner radius that decreases on increasing radius (i.e., Lame's theory, (see [51] for example), optimum load bearing can be achieved by having a residual compressive stress on the inside of the tube. Work by Fung and co-workers [52, 53] has demonstrated that such a pre-stress exists within arteries and to varying levels at different locations in the system.

3.2.3 Tendon

Tendon transmits the forces developed by the muscle(s) of which they are an extension, to the peripheral bones so as to create moments about the intervening joints over which they course. Tendon is composed of between 70 and 80% collagen by dry weight [54], and has thus been the focus for considerable amounts of basic study on the properties of collagen, the main other components being polysaccharide ground substances (probably acting as a lubricant between fibres) and fibroblast cells for repair. The function of tendon is that of a load transmitter, with a minimum amount of hysteresis but with returnable energy storage with enough flexibility to go around joints. The collagen in tendon is arranged in parallel collagen fibrils. The fibrils tend to have a surface waveform that varies in different tendons from a helix in many tendons, (e.g., human palmaris longus to a planer crimp in rat-tail tendon [55]. It appears that this waveform serves the function of giving the tendon a high compliance at low loads (until it is straightened) and then a high stiffness beyond this point. Tendons also appear to twist to some extent on loading [54], and this is probably a secondary effect of the helical waveform.

3.2.4 Spider's silk

Silks are produced by the more than 30,000 known species of spiders [56]. There is a large variation in the properties of silk not only between species, but also that can be produced by an individual spider [57] Spider's silk is formed from protein and, like collagen, the majority of amino acid composition is made up of the small helix-forming amino acids glycene, alinine and proline [58]. Spider's silks vary in properties depending on the functional requirement. A typical araneid orb weaver has seven specialised glands, each producing different types of silk for wrapping, webs, hanging on, etc. [59]. Two common types of silk are dragline silk that the spider uses to hang on, which is stiff with some energy absorption at high loads, and viscid silk that is used within the web, and which must have a low stiffness and high hysteresis in order to absorb the impact of the captured fly.

One interesting property of spiders silk is that it contracts on exposure to water; this has the benefit of introducing a pre-stress into a web (it is also one reason why spiders silks are not used in manmade textiles). Recent microscopic work by Vollrath et al. [60] on the dragline silk of Nephila clavipes has led to the proposal of a structure for spiders silk as tube helically wound with microfibrils surrounding a less dense amorphous core. They have suggested that the mechanism of super contraction could be that of realignment of the helical fibres of the sheath caused by swelling of the core material.

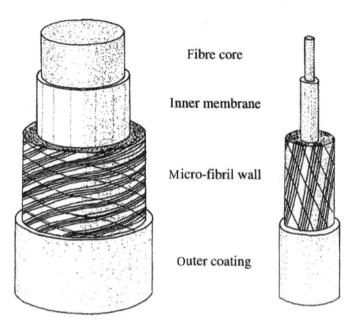

Fibre core

Inner membrane

Micro-fibril wall

Outer coating

Figure 27: A model for the structural organisation of spiders silk based on light microscope observations. The left-hand image is the state during swelling, the re-orientation of the fibres causing pre-tension in the silk [60].

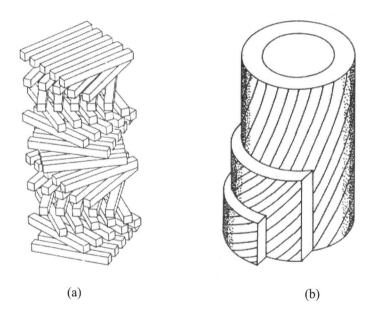

(a)

(b)

Figure 28: A cholesteric liquid crystal (also known as 'twisted nematic' or 'helicoidal'), (a) in planar form and (b) in cylindrical form, resulting in concentric helical fibres with varying angles, from Neville [61].

3.3 Nature's manufacturing techniques

Many of the molecules that make up compliant structures have a rope-like helical structure – for example the alpha helix, the triple helix and the DNA double-helix molecule. The formation of these helical molecules is by self-assembly: i.e., when the chain synthesises it preferentially forms a particular structure dictated by weak interactions, in particular the hydrogen bond and the interaction of the molecule with neighbouring water molecules.

The mechanism of forming biological 'materials' or structures from molecular subunits is an area of great interest. One school of thought is that biological materials go through a liquid-crystal phase during their formation. Neville [61] has put forward a strong argument for this in insect cuticle and plant cell walls. Wilcox et al. [62] have also put forward evidence for liquid-crystal structure within spider's silk. Fibres form into either a nematic (threadlike) or cholesteric (twisted nematic) conformation. Cholesteric liquid crystals tend to form in sheets of parallel fibres, each sheet being slightly twisted with respect to the previous (see Figure 28). A cholesteric liquid crystal forming on the surface of a cylinder will produce a helical construction with varying angles throughout the layers (as seen in a plantcell wall for example).

4 Discussion

The first man-made rope-like structures utilised biological materials such as hemp, cotton, silk, leather and rubber. It has only been in the last centuries that these materials have been gradually replaced by man-made equivalents. Now, ironically, with the science of 'biomimetics' there is a great interest in going back to the biological structures to see what man can learn from them. There seem to be many parallels between the structure of man-made and biological rope-like structures. Although there is very little evidence that man has copied nature in the past.

One rare example of copying was an attempt to model the structure of wood cell wall to imitate their 'tension buckling' characteristics in order to obtain good energy absorption [63], although this work was in the first instance to make an essentially planar composite material with corrugated layers rather than a helical structure.

We have seen that wire and fibre ropes are formed by combining with different levels of twist the basic elements of wires and fibre. The properties desired of the component may, to a certain extent be engineered by combining elements in multiple-helical sub-structures. Ropes may have excellent wear properties (e.g., locked-coil ropes), be very flexible (eight strands with fibre core), rotation resistant (multi-strand) or a combination of these. The manufacturing variables at the disposal of the engineer include material properties, size, shape, strand structure, direction of spinning, etc.

The helical or rope-like structures that we have discussed, and that are found in nature, share similar performance characteristics, although their scale and method of production is very different (especially in the case of wire ropes and armoured hoses).

One performance characteristic that we have touched upon in Section 1.7 is the effect of imposed twist in a helical structure – a stranded wire rope, particularly a six-strand rope that is torsionally very active. If the twisted rope, that is a rope with twist forced into it from an external source (e.g., see [8]), is unloaded, it will rid itself of some of the twist by forming what is termed a hockle (Figure 29a). If the rope is then re-loaded and the hockle pulled out, serious damage will occur. Compare this undesirable behaviour of the rope with that of the

DNA molecule (Figure 29b). The similarities in performance are obvious, although the scale and materials involved are completely different. Additionally, it should be noted that for the DNA molecule this type of behaviour is necessary for it to pass genetic code to the messenger RNA. Considerable work has been undertaken to model this phenomenon (see for example Thompson et al. [65]).

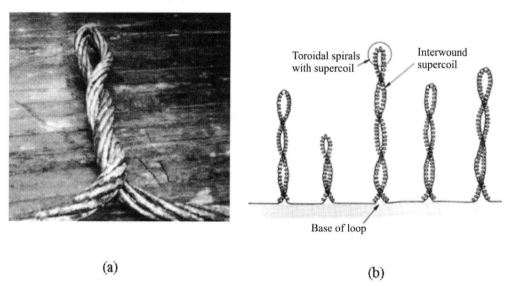

(a)   (b)

Figure 29: A comparison of hockling seen in a wire rope with a similar effect found in DNA molecules (DNA molecules from [64]).

Wood, arteries and spiders silk all share the ability to develop internal stresses within them in order to adapt or optimise. This idea of pre-stressing thick-walled tubes such as found in arteries has been used in man-made thick-walled pressure vessels (where the vessel is overloaded to cause the inner section to yield and therefore go into compression on unload) and is achieved by a technique known as autofrettage [66]. The mechanism that produces pre-stress in arteries is not fully understood but is unlikely to be caused by such a process. It is possibly more akin to the pre-stressing that is created in the helical armouring of a hose if the wires are spun with sufficient back tension on the bobbins.

Wainwright et al. [67] have suggested that the mechanism by which reaction wood is formed is by the swelling of the fibre-wound cells with fibres other than 55° causing a lengthening or shortening of the cylindrical wood cell (as described in Section 0). A similar explanation has been put forward for the pre-tension in spiders silk by Vollrath [60], involving the swelling of the internal core of the silk through water absorption (see Figure 27).

Some of the properties of silk produced by spiders seem to be analogous to the types of climbing rope in use: viscid silk to the types of ropes used for arresting a fall such as rock climbing and dragline silk to ropes such as those used for rappelling, which must be stiff to prevent too much bouncing. The climbing ropes achieve this variation in properties through helix-angle variations, but the mechanism by which the spider produce these properties in the silk still needs further investigation.

Acknowledgements

The authors would like to acknowledge and thank Professor J.H. Evans for many helpful comments and suggestions in this work. Thanks are also due to Dr. C.J.M. Del Vecchio for generously allowing the use of material from his thesis in the section describing synthetic fibre ropes.

References

[1]   Evans, J.J., *Aspects of the mechanical behaviour of helical wire structures relating to quasi static and fatigue properties*. PhD thesis. Imperial College, London, 242 pp. 1999.

[2]   Cook, J. & Gordon, J.E., A Mechanism for Control of Crack Propagation in All-Brittle Systems. *Proceedings of the Royal Society of London*, **A282**, pp. 508–20, 1964.

[3]   Hruska, F., Tangential forces in wire ropes. *Wire and Wire Products*, **28**, 455–60, 1953.

[4]   Gibson, P.T., Cress, H.A., Kaufman, W.J. & Gallant, W.E., Analysis of wire rope torque. *Wire and wire rope products*, November 1970.

[5]   Kollros, W., The relationship between torque, tensile force and twist in ropes. *Wire*, pp. 19–24, Jan./Feb., 1976.

[6]   Verreet, R., *The Rotation Characteristics of Steel Wire Ropes*, Casar Drahtseilwerk Saar GMBH, 1984.

[7]   Chaplin, C.R., Rebel, G. & Ridge, I.M.L., Tension/torsion interactions in multicomponent mooring lines. *33rd Annual Offshore Technology Conference*, Houston, Texas 2000.

[8]   Verreet, R. & Ridge, I.M.L., The use of swivels with steel wire ropes. *OIPEEC Round Table Conference on Rope Terminations and Fittings*, Bethlehem, USA, 2001.

[9]   Ridge, I.M.L., The development of rope. *OIPEEC Bulletin*, **65**, pp. 15–46 1993.

[10]   Newberry, P.E., *El Bersheh part 1 (the tomb of Tehuti-Hetep)*, Egyptian Exploration Fund.

[11]   Ridge, IML., *Bending Tension Fatigue of Wire Rope*, PhD Thesis, University of Reading, 321 pp., 1992.

[12]   Hipkins, W.E., *The Wire Rope and its Applications*, Issued by J. & E. Wright Ltd., printed D.F. Tayler & Co. Ltd.: Birmingham, 1896.

[13]   Smith, A., Communication. *The Mining Journal*, **422**, December 1844.

[14]   Hashagen, P., The Development of Fire Hose. *Firehouse Magazine*, 1998.

[15]   Buchholdt, H.A., *Introduction to Cable Roof Structures*, CUP, ISBN: 0 521 302633, 1985.

[16]   Anon. *Steel Wire Ropes and Fittings*, Bridon Ropes, 1992.

[17]   Costello, G.A., Analytical Investigation of Wire Rope. *Applied Mechanics Reviews*, **31**, pp. 897–900, 1978.

[18]   Rinehardt, H., *A Wire Rope Handbook and Catalog D*, Union Wire Rope Corporation, 1942.

[19]   Anon. *Wire Rope End Fittings Catalogue WR-48*, The Greening Wire Co. Ltd., 1948.

[20]   Anon. *Wire Ropes*, United Ropeworks, Rotterdam, Holland.

[21]   Seale, T., *USA Patent No. 315077*, 1885.

[22]   British Ropes. *Ropes for the Mining Industry*, Doncaster, 1970.

[23] Davies, T.H., Steel Wire Ropes Used in Mining Practice. *Proc. Wire Ropes in Mines*, Leamington Spa, Warwickshire, 1950.

[24] Lang, J., *Wire Ropes*, British Patent no. 138, 13th January 1879.

[25] Dohm, M., An evaluation of magnetic rope testing instrument defect detection capabilities, particularly in respect of low rotation, multi-layer rope constructions. *Proceedings of the OIPEEC Conference, The Non-Destructive Testing of Rope*, Krakow, Poland, 1999.

[26] Troitsky, M.S., *Cable-stayed Bridges: Theory and Design*, BSP Professional Books, Oxford, 2nd edition, ISBN: 0-632-02041-5, 1988.

[27] BS 302: pt 6, Stranded steel wire ropes: specification for ropes for mine hoisting, British Standards Institution, 1987.

[28] Franklin, J.R., Preston, R.P. & Allen, C., Heat Treatment and Alloying of Drawn Wires. *Wire Industry*, pp. 967–72, November 1980.

[29] Dickinson, H.W., A condensed history of rope-making. *Transactions of the Newcomen Society*, **23**, pp. 71–91, 1942.

[30] Cartwright, E., *British Patent No. 1876*, 1792.

[31] Evans, C.W., *Hose Technology*, 2nd edition, Kluwer Academic Publishers: Dordrecht 1979.

[32] Anon., *Polyflex High Pressure Hoses-Product Catalogue*, Polyflex Gmbh, Huttenfeld, Germany, 1992.

[33] Stratfold, M. & Legallais, L., Design of Umbilicals for Maximum Flex Fatigue Performance of Electrical Conductors. *Marinflex 92*, London, 1992.

[34] Estrier, P., Updated Method for the Determination of the Service Life of Flexible Risers. *Marinflex 92*, London, 1992.

[35] Del Vecchio, C., *Light weight materials for deepwater moorings*. PhD thesis. University of Reading, 1992.

[36] Leech, C.M., The modelling of friction in polymer fibre rope. *International Journal of Mechanical Sciences*, **44**, pp. 621–43 2002.

[37] Anon., *High performance ropes for heavy marine applications*, Puget Sound Rope, Cortland Cable Company Inc., USA.

[38] Davies, W. & Talbot, J.R., *Polyester Fibres Encyclopaedia of Polymer Science and Engineering*. ed. H.F. Mark, N.M. Bikales, C.G. Overberger & G. Menges, pp. 118–193 1985.

[39] Matschoss, C., Flecht- und Kloppelmaschinen. *Zeutschrift des Vereines Deutscher Ingenieure*, **70**, pp. 901–6, 1926.

[40] Viswanathan, A. & Shenouda, S., The helical structure of cellulose 1. *Journal of Applied Polymer Science*, **15**, pp. 519–35, 1971.

[41] Esau, K., *Anatomy of Seed Plants*. John Wiley: New York, 1977.

[42] Niklas, K., *Plant Biomechanics*: The University of Chicago Press, 607 pp. 1992.

[43] Rohrich, R.J. & Robinson, J.B., Wound Healing; Wound Closure; Abnormal Scars; Tattoos; Envenomation Injuries and Extravasation Injuries. *Selected Readings in Plastic Surgery*, **9**, pp. 1–40, 1999.

[44] Woodhead-Galloway, J., Collagen - the universal body builder. *New Scientist*, pp. 582–4, 1975.

[45] Rich, A. & Crick, F., Molecular structure of collagen. *Journal of Molecular Biology*, **3**, pp. 483–506, 1961.

[46] Lillie, J., MacCallum, D., Scaletta, L. & Occhino, J., Collagen structure: evidence for a helical organization of the collagen fibril. *Journal of Ultrastructural Research*, **58**, pp. 134–43, 1977.

[47] Purslow, P., Wess, T. & Hukins, D., Collagen orientation and molecular spacing during creep and stress relaxation in soft connective tissues. *The Journal of Experimental Biology*, **201**, pp. 135–42, 1998.

[48] Fung, Y., *Biodynamics: Circulation*. Springer-Verlag: New York, 404 pp., 1984.

[49] Burton, A., *Physiology and Biophysics of the Circulation*. Year Book Medical Publishers Incorporated: Chicago, 1972.

[50] Roach, M.R. & Burton, A.C., The reason for the shape of the distensibility curve of arteries, *Canadian Journal of Physiology*, **35**, pp. 681–690, 1957.

[51] Boresi, A.P., Sidebottom, O.M., Seely, F.B. & Smith, J.O., *Advanced Mechanics of Materials*, John Wiley, 1978.

[52] Chuong C. & Fung, Y., Residual stress in arteries Frontiers in Biomechanics. ed. G Schmid-Schonbein & S. Woo, Springer-Verlag, pp. 117–29, 1986.

[53] Fung, Y. & Liu, S., Change of residual stress in arteries due to hypertrophy caused by aortic constriction. *Circulation Research*, **65**, pp. 1340–9, 1989.

[54] Evans, J., Barbenel, J., Steel, T. & Ashby, A., Structure and mechanics of tendon. *The Mechanical Properties of Biological Materials*, Society of Experimental Biology: Leeds, pp. 465–9, 1980.

[55] Nicholls, S.P., Gathercole, L.J., Keller, A. & Shah, J.S., Crimping in Rat Tail Tendon Collagen: Morphology and Transverse Mechanical Anisotropy. *International Journal of Biological Macromolecules*, **5**, pp. 283–8, 1983.

[56] Kaplan, D., Adams, W.W., Farmer, B. & Viney, C., Silk - Biology, Structure, Properties, and Genetics. *Silk Polymers*, **544**, pp. 2–16, 1994.

[57] Madsen, B., Shao, Z.Z. & Vollrath, F., Variability in the mechanical properties of spider silks on three levels: interspecific, intraspecific and intraindividual. *International Journal of Biological Macromolecules*, **24**, pp. 301–6, 1999.

[58] Gosline, J.M., Guerette, P.A., Ortlepp, C.S. & Savage, K.N., The mechanical design of spider silks: From fibroin sequence to mechanical function. *Journal of Experimental Biology*, **202**, pp. 3295–303, 1999.

[59] Vollrath, F. & Knight, D.P., Liquid crystalline spinning of spider silk. *Nature*, **410**, pp. 541–8, 2001.

[60] Vollrath, F., Holtet, T., Thogersen, H.C. & Frische, S., Structural organization of spider silk. *Proceedings of the Royal Society of London Series B-biological Sciences*, **263**, pp. 147–51, 1996.

[61] Neville, A.C., *Biology of Fibrous Composites*, Cambridge University Press, 214 pp., 1993.

[62] Wilcox, P., Gido, S., Muller, W. & Kaplan, D., Evidence of a cholesteric liquid crystalline phase in natural silk spinning processes. *Macromolecules*, **29**, pp. 5106–10, 1996.

[63] Gordon, J. & Jeronimidis, G., Composites with a high work of fracture. *Philosophical Transactions of the Royal Society*, **A**, pp. 545–50, 1980.

[64] Calladine, C.R. & Drew, H.R., *Understanding DNA: The Molecule and How it Works*, Academic Press, 1992.

[65] Thompson, J.M.T., Van Der Heijden, H.H.M. & Neukirch, S., Supercoiling of DNA plasmids: the mechanics of the generalised ply. *Proceedings of the Royal Society*, **A**, pp. 959–85, 2002.

[66] Manning, W.R.D. & Labrow, S., *High Pressure Engineering*. Leonard Hill: London, 1974.

[67] Wainwright, A., Biggs, D., Currey, D. & Gosline, M., *Mechanical Design in Organisms*, Princeton University Press, 423 pp., 1976.

CHAPTER 8

Flexible-wing-based micro air vehicles

P.G. Ifju

Mechanical & Aerospace Engineering Department, University of Florida, USA.

Abstract

This chapter describes a unique flexible wing concept as applied to micro air vehicles. This flexible wing has numerous advantages over convention wing designs including passive gust rejection, improved aerodynamic efficiency, delayed stall, the ability to be reconfigured for storage and morphing, as well as improved durability. The materials and methods used to fabricate the flexible wings will be presented along with examples of the flight vehicles. A brief framework of the approach used to perform computational fluid dynamics modeling for fluid-structure interaction of flexible membranes will be provided. Results from flight tests, as well as wind-tunnel tests, will be provided to demonstrate the benefits of the flexible-wing concept.

1 Introduction

Micro air vehicles, or "MAVs", are a class of aircraft with a maximum size of about 6 inches and are capable of operating at speeds of 25 mph or less [1]. The concept is for a small, inexpensive and expendable platform that can be used for missions of surveillance and measurements in situations where larger vehicles are not practical. For example, they can be used for small unit battlefield surveillance, mapping out the extent of chemical/radiation spills or viral outbreaks, as well as more routine applications such as monitoring crops or wildlife distributions. Many potential uses involve launching of large numbers of MAVs to secure the necessary coverage with the intrinsically "close up" type of maneuvering allowed by a micro-sized aircraft. In some applications, MAVs could be used in swarms or sent to a pre-designated grid to collect and transmit data. Practical applications of MAVs are becoming more achievable with the ever-decreasing size and weight of the payload components that could include video cameras, chemical sensors, electronics, and communication devices. Only a few years ago, the thought of a 6-inch flying machine equipped with a functional video camera was science fiction. Today it is a demonstrated fact.

It is well known that in the Reynolds number range between 10,000 and 100,000, which corresponds to the MAV size range identified by DARPA, the aerodynamic performance of conventional airfoils is dramatically degraded. Figure 1 illustrates this phenomenon in a plot that describes the marked drop in the lift to drag performance as a function of Reynolds number for all smooth, rigid airfoils. This plot clearly illustrates that the design rules that have been adopted for large aircraft cannot be scaled down to the MAV scale. With smooth, rigid wings in this Reynolds number range, the laminar flow that prevails is easily separated, creating large separation bubbles, especially at higher angles of attack [2]. Flow separation leads to sudden increases in drag and loss of efficiency.

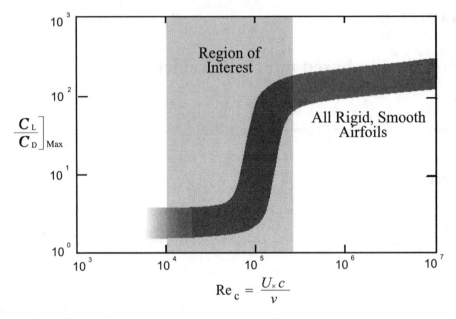

Figure 1: Coefficient of lift divided by coefficient of drag versus Reynolds number for all smooth air foils.

In nature, one can observe the relationship between Reynold's number and aerodynamic efficiency in birds, where large species soar for extended periods of time while small birds have to flap vigorously (high frequency) to remain airborne. The Reynold's numbers of the larger species are well above 100,000, whereas hummingbirds would fly at below 10,000 if they attempted to soar. Additionally, the wing loading for small birds is less than that for large birds.

Another major obstacle for flight at this small scale is the diminished stability and control characteristics that accompany the small mass moments of inertia of these tiny aircraft. Also, the velocity scale of the turbulence naturally exhibited by the atmosphere is comparable to the flight speed of these vehicles. Therefore, variations in airspeed over the wing can be large, and can even cause variations from one wing to the other, leading to difficulty in maintaining smooth flight. These factors make control of these diminutive aircraft difficult, both for a remote operator or an on-board autopilot. Other technical challenges associated with flight on the 6-inch scale include the need to provide reliable propulsion and miniaturization of components, including the electronics and actuators for the control surfaces.

In the quest to develop practical MAVs, two approaches have been employed so far. The first and most popular is to configure the airframe as a lifting body or flying wing using conventional propeller-driven thrust. In this approach, the emphasis is to increase the relative area of the lifting surface while decreasing drag, directly addressing the decrease in the aerodynamic efficiency, and ignoring issues of stability and control. In order for these designs to fly at all, active stability augmentation systems are usually required. In nature, the great optimizer, there are no examples of lifting bodies or flying wings. All birds and bats have well-defined wings and a fuselage. The second approach that has been explored on the MAV scale is the direct mimicry of birds [3–5]. By flapping, birds produce both lift and thrust. Researchers have demonstrated flapping mechanisms in the lab environment, but have yet to produce practical controlled flight vehicles. Complex control issues and high power consumption remain as formidable challenges for this type of MAV.

Conventional approaches have used optimized rigid wings and accepted the need for enhanced stabilization systems or supreme pilot skill to deal with the intrinsically unsteady behavior. Of all the examples of MAVs, the most successful to date is the Aerovironment's "Black Widow" [6], an electric 6-inch flying wing. Virtually every component on the aircraft is custom built, including a sophisticated gyro-assisted control system. Other successful examples of rigid wing designs include the "Trochoid" [7] developed by Steve Morris of MLB Company and Sander's "Microstar.' Both of these also have gyro-assisted stabilization systems. Without these enhancements, lifting bodies are difficult to control.

Previous studies, documented in Waszak [8], Shyy et al. [9–11], Smith and Shyy [12], and Jenkins et al. [13], indicate that an alternate approach, specifically letting the lifting surface move and deform, can lead to more favorable aerodynamic performance in a fluctuating low Reynolds number environment. These findings helped lead to the University of Florida's flexible-wing concept, which we have been applying to successful MAVs over the past four years [14–17]. Flight vehicles were developed that utilize conventional propeller driven thrust in combination with an adaptive-shape, flexible wing that adapts to flight conditions and also develops a stable limit-cycle oscillation during flight.

The wings were developed to produce smooth flight even in gusty wind conditions. In order to produce the best overall flight characteristics, one must first start with an airplane that is intrinsically stable. This is accomplished via the adaptive nature of the wing as well as its natural oscillation. These aircraft can be flown by novice to average RC pilots, without the aid of gyro enhanced stabilization. Merits of the flexible wing have been demonstrated at the International Micro Air Vehicle Competition by winning the event for the last four years in a row.

2 The flexible wing micro air vehicle

The development of the flexible wing utilizes a combination of biologically inspired design and the incorporation of modern composite materials. It is thin and undercambered, as are those of small birds and bats. In previous studies [13], it was shown that thin undercambered wings are more efficient than those with significant thickness. For birds and bats on the same scale as micro air vehicles, the wings have evolved towards the ideal thin undercambered shape as can be seen in Fig. 2. The wing of the micro air vehicle that was developed is constructed with a carbon-fiber skeleton (analogous to the bone structure of the bat) and thin membrane materials (analogous to the skin of the bat wing). The overall aircraft configuration is a departure from the traditional flying wing or lifting body design. It has a distinct fuselage and wing, more similar to that of birds and bats.

Figure 2: Small bats and birds have thin undercambered wings. Bats have a bone skeleton and a skin membrane.

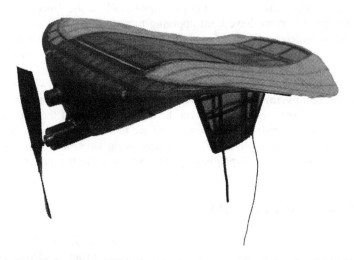

Figure 3: The University of Florida 6-inch wingspan flexible wing MAV is powered by an electric motor and has a color video camera on board.

The MAV shown in Fig. 3 is the product of more than three years of design iteration, using flight tests and pilot feedback as the primary method of evaluation. The planform of the wing allows for the maximum lifting surface while staying within a 6-inch diameter sphere. The 6 inch MAV weighs on the order of 65 grams and includes an electric motor, lithium polymer batteries that allow for 15 minute duration flights, two servos to control the elevator on the trailing edge of the wing, as well as the rudder on the vertical stabilizer, a FM receiver, an electronic speed controller, a color video camera, as well as a 2.4 GHz video transmitter. The aircraft has a range of about 1 mile and is typically flown using the video signal as the sole pilot feedback. The MAV can fly at speeds that range from 15 to 35 miles per hour.

2.1 Adaptive-wing design

The flexible nature of the wings can provide several non-obvious advantages over their conventional rigid counterparts. The wings that we have fabricated with a carbon-fiber skeleton and extensible latex rubber skin have the ability to adapt to the airflow to provide smoother flight. This is accomplished via the passive mechanism of adaptive washout. In sailing vessels, adaptive washout is produced through twist of the sail. This greatly extends the wind range of the sail and produces more constant thrust (lift), even in gusty wind conditions. In the wings that we have designed, the shape changes as a function of the airspeed and the angle of attack. The adaptive washout is produced through extension of the membrane and twisting of the framework, resulting in angle-of-attack changes along the length of the wing in response to air speed and overall angle of attack. For example, as the plane hits a head-on wind gust the airspeed suddenly increases. The increased airspeed causes a shape change in the wing that decreases the lifting efficiency, but because the airspeed in the gust is higher, the wing maintains nearly the same lift. Once the airspeed decreases, the wing recovers to the original configuration. If there is a decrease in the relative airspeed, the angle of attack increases and the wing becomes more efficient and near constant lift is restored. The net result is a wing that flies with exceptional smoothness, even in gusty wind conditions. The adaptive washout mechanism is subtle and must be tuned into the wings in order to work effectively. We have built hundreds of wing configurations and have been able to produce many wings with remarkably smooth flying characteristics. Figure 4 illustrates the flexible nature of the wing.

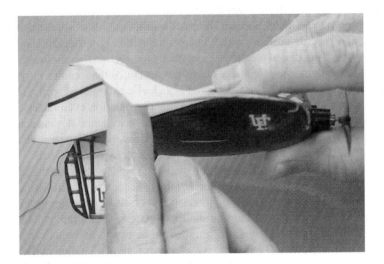

Figure 4: Due to the light wing loading during flight, it was necessary to incorporate an extensible membrane to achieve adaptive washout.

For aircraft with very small inertia, as in the case of MAVs, changes in wing loading can immediately affect the flight path. As the aircraft becomes smaller and lighter the need for suppressing the effects of wind gusts becomes more critical, especially if it is to be used as a camera platform. Additionally, as the airspeed of the vehicle decreases, wind gusts become a larger percentage of the mean airspeed of the vehicle. For example, our 6-inch aircraft flies between 15 and 35 mph. On a typical day, the wind speed can vary by more than 10 mph. For rigid wings, the lift can vary by 50% or more over the short period of time during the gust. To make matters more critical, gusts are not always head-on. Since control of these aircraft is one of the most important hurdles, it is critical to suppress unwanted and sudden changes in direction, elevation and orientation.

In nature, birds and bats display a similar form of adaptive washout. This passive mechanism can be observed on windy days by large soaring birds. The feathers at the wing tips flair to accommodate sudden changes in airspeed. To some extent, our design approach has been biologically inspired. We have observed both birds and bats and have designed our wings to have similar characteristics.

As mentioned earlier, the adaptive washout mechanism is subtle, therefore the location and stiffness of the carbon fiber skeleton members and thickness of the latex membrane are critical. In order to define the design space for our flexible wing, we built numerous prototypes to learn how the geometry of the carbon fiber skeleton affected flight performance. We also varied the relative stiffness of the different parts of the skeleton. Shown in Fig. 5 are 24 of the designs that were successfully flight-tested. We were able to make observations in the field in order to qualitatively rank their performance. Using this relatively crude trial and error process, we were able to down-select the configurations that provided the best performance. These designs were then tested using more rigorous means via additional flight tests and wind-tunnel tests.

3 Aircraft construction methods

In order to implement the flexible-wing concept on these small vehicles, traditional materials such as balsawood, foam and monocoat were not appropriate. Instead, the use of high specific strength and high specific stiffness materials in combination with flexible membrane materials was required [15]. For the skeleton, carbon fiber unidirectional and cloth prepreg materials were used. These are the same materials used for structures that require fully elastic behavior yet undergo large deflections. The fishing rod is a classic example of such a structure. For the membrane, extensible material was chosen to allow deformation even under very small loads, such as the case for lightly loaded wings. Latex rubber sheet material was used in this case.

During the development of the flexible-wing concept, and in the absence of mature computational capabilities, the effort was primarily driven by trial and error. This required an efficient and repeatable construction process that produced durable aircraft. Durability was extremely important since the aircraft were flight tested numerous times in the process of trimming them for level flight. Each flight ended in a crash landing during this process. If the aircraft structure was compromised during this process, trimming would be impossible. Additionally, even when the aircraft was trimmed properly and in the absence of landing gear, every flight ended in a crash. Our motto was "every crash is a landing and every landing is a crash". With the use of carbon fiber/latex rubber wings and a carbon-fiber fuselage, we were able to produce durable and yet lightweight aircraft that could survive multiple crashes without compromising flightworthiness. In retrospect, the construction methods that we developed were the enabling technology that allowed us to explore the flexible wing concept. Typically, the construction process requires only five man-hours to build an entire MAV.

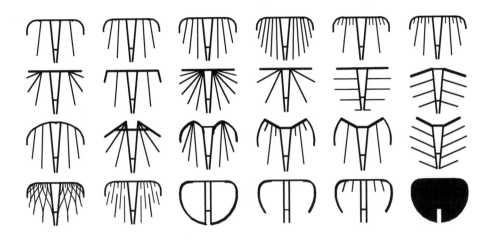

Figure 5: Numerous skeleton configurations were initially flight tested in order to narrow the design space.

Figure 6 illustrates the fabrication process. The first step in the fabrication process is drawing a wing-frame template that shows the location and thickness of each rib. This drawing is affixed to the wing tool, which is made from sheet metal and bent to the desired air-foil shape. Next, the wing is laid up on the wing tool using fine strips of unidirectional carbon-fiber prepreg (carbon fiber pre-impregnated with epoxy resin). Multiple layers are used where high stiffness or strength is required. The covering material for the access hatch and hinge material is integrated with the prepreg. The fuselage is made of a 0–90 bias carbon fiber cloth weighing 5.6 oz/yard^2. The cloth is wrapped around a hand-shaped foam male tool. It is then placed on the wing tool next to the wing so both parts mate perfectly when assembled. These parts are then vacuum bagged and subject to a five-hour cure cycle in the autoclave where they reach a temperature of 270° F.

After wet-sanding the fuselage with fine grit paper and removing sharp edges from the wing frame, the two are assembled with cyanoacrylate glue (CA). To prevent the glue joint from breaking, Kevlar thread is used to lash critical points. The motor and camera holes are then drilled and the vertical stabilizer is installed. Alignment of the stabilizer is critical, as on this scale even a misalignment of 1/16th of an inch can deteriorate flight performance. At this stage, the latex-wing skin is glued to the wing frame. First, a mist of spray adhesive is applied to the wing frame. Then the frame is pressed on a sheet of stretched latex. Finally, the latex is secured with a thin bead of low-viscosity CA along every rib. The final part of the assembly process involves installing the servos, motor, and control linkages. The servos are fixed to the fuselage with conventional servo tape and then lashed in place with Kevlar thread. The motor is glued in place with CA at a thrust angle of seven degrees from the mean chord line. The control horns are bent from brass rod, and the control rods are made from 1/64" piano wire. These control rods are supported by guide holes in the fuselage to prevent buckling.

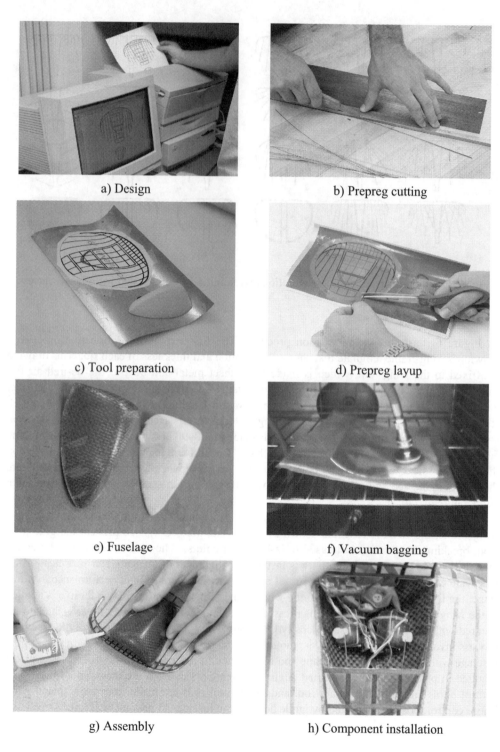

a) Design

b) Prepreg cutting

c) Tool preparation

d) Prepreg layup

e) Fuselage

f) Vacuum bagging

g) Assembly

h) Component installation

Figure 6: Steps to fabricate a 6-inch MAV.

4 Wind-tunnel tests

Wind-tunnel tests were conducted in the Basic Aerodynamics Research Tunnel (BART) at NASA Langley Research Center [14,16]. The purpose of the test was to collect a variety of data to aid in the study of the dynamics and control properties of the UFMAV concept. The data consist of aerodynamic force and moment measured with an external 6-component strain-gauge balance, static wing-deformation data from a projection moiré interferometry (PMI) system [18], and flow visualization using smoke. Figure 7 depicts an early version of the flexible-wing MAV mounted in the wind tunnel.

Figure 7: An earlier version of the 6-inch MAV in the NASA Langley wind tunnel.

Data was collected for a rigid wing and three different batten/membrane arrangements over a range of operating conditions determined by dynamic pressure, power setting, vehicle attitude, and control-surface deflection. The different batten arrangements are depicted in Fig. 8. More flexibility and larger membrane stretch characterize the one-batten design. The two-batten design is, by comparison, stiffer and exhibits less membrane stretch under aerodynamic load. Both wings were tested using a 4-mil latex membrane. The six-batten wing was covered with an inextensible monofilm membrane that further increased the stiffness of the wing and exhibited less membrane deformation and vibration. The rigid wing was constructed of a two-batten frame covered with a graphite sheet.

The static aerodynamic data were collected using a 6-component strain gauge balance and resolved into lift, drag, side force, pitching moment, rolling moment, and yawing moment. PMI was used to collect mean static deformation over a large fraction of the wing surface and the variance of the motions about the mean shape. Flow visualization was collected using digital video. Two methods were used: smoke flow and helium bubbles. The flow-visualization data provide insight into the underlying flow phenomena, and can be correlated with the aerodynamic and structural data.

4.1 Aerodynamic performance

Aerodynamic performance characterized by L/D is summarized in Fig. 9. These results represent L/D of the UFMAV with the propeller restrained from rotation (i.e., pinned) for several wings with varying levels of stiffness. The maximum L/D of approximately 3.0 is relatively independent of wing configuration. However, maximum L/D occurs at incidences of approximately 7.5 degrees for the rigid wing and roughly 10 degrees for the other wing configurations.

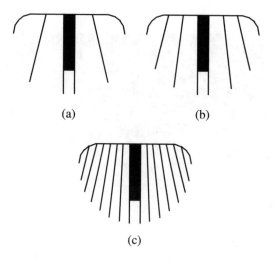

Figure 8: Three versions of the flexible wing were tested against a nominally rigid version. The rigidity of the wing increases from a) through c).

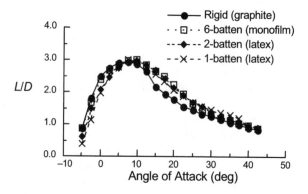

Figure 9: Lift divided by drag versus angle of attack for the four wings. The flexible wings show increased aerodynamic efficiency at high angles of attack.

Figure 10 depicts the lift curves for the various wing configurations. For small angles of attack, all the wings demonstrate similar lift characteristics with the stiffer wings having slightly higher lift coefficient. However, it is clear that the membrane wings stall at much higher angles of attack than the rigid wing. In fact, the most flexible wing configuration has double the stall angle of the rigid-wing configuration (35 degrees and 15 degrees, respectively). This could be a key factor in enhancing the range of operation and agility of micro aerial vehicles.

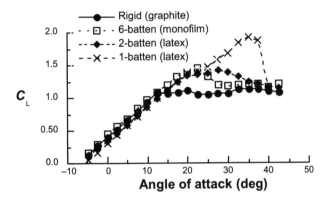

Figure 10: Coefficient of lift versus angle of attack shows that the rigid wing stalls at around 13 degrees, whereas the flexible wings stall at much higher angles of attack.

While these results are similar to the results for other low aspect ratio, low Reynolds number wings, there are important differences. At low angles of attack, the aeroelastic wings behave like rigid wings with similar aspect ratio. The lift curve slope for the UFMAV is approximately 2.9. The lift curve slopes of similar rigid wings at comparable Reynolds number and aspect ratio (Re=70,000, AR=2) are approximately 2.9 as well. However, these wings have stall angles between 12 and 15 degrees. The stall angles of the aeroelastic wings are between 30 and 45 degrees (i.e., stall angle of the vehicle plus the wing incidence angle) and are similar to that of much lower aspect ratio rigid wings (AR=0.5 to 1.0). However, the very low aspect wings exhibit lower lift curve slopes of 1.3 to 1.7. The aeroelastic wings appear to exhibit the stall behavior similar to rigid aspect ratio 0.5 to 1.0 wings and the lift-generating capability of rigid aspect ratio 2.0 wings.

4.2 Structural deformation of aeroelastic wing

It was shown previously that the flexible wing is able to operate over a wider range of angles of attack without stalling. Understanding how this is accomplished requires determining how the wing responds to changes in the flow conditions. PMI was used because it is noncontacting and requires no surface preparation. This is especially important for the small highly flexible wing of the UFMAV where it is difficult, if not impossible, to use typical sensors (e.g. accelerometers, strain gauges) without altering the dynamics of the wing.

PMI uses optical methods and digital image processing to create contour maps of the surface of an object [18]. The maps represent mean quasi-static deformation of the surface. In addition, it is possible to determine the variance of the deformation about the quasi-static shape. The measurement accuracy depends on the resolution of the digital image and the field of view. In this case, very fine details of the wing shape could be obtained. Analysis of the PMI data is ongoing but some preliminary results are presented here.

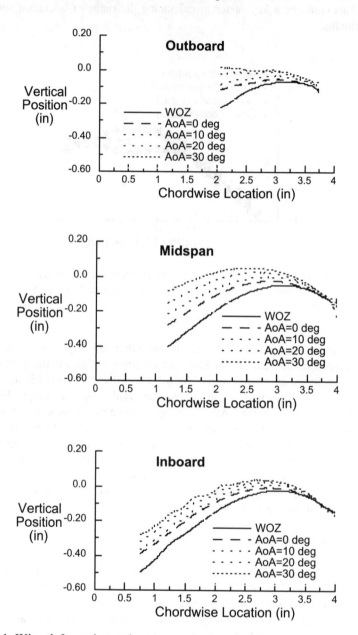

Figure 11: Wing deformation at three span-wise locations for various angles of attack.

Figure 11 shows the mean chordwise deformation of the wing at three spanwise locations, inboard, midspan and outboard. The results shown are for the two-batten latex configuration.

The wing leading edge is near a chordwise locaton of 4 inches. The chordwise deformation is presented relative to the wing at q=0 psf, i.e., wind-off zero (WOZ). The deformation data is determined at q=1.6 psf and trim power setting at four angles of attack: 0, 10, 20, and 30 degrees.

It is clear from these plots that the wing undergoes significant deformation. The maximum displacement of the membrane is approximately 0.25 inches at 30 degrees of vehicle incidence. The effect is to gradually reduce the camber of the wing as angle of attack increases. The degree to which the camber is reduced increases with span. Thus, though the vehicle may be at 30 degrees incidence, the wing sees a much smaller local angle of attack.

4.3 Flow visualization

Smoke and helium bubbles were used to perform simple flow visualization of the UFMAV for different wing configurations and flight conditions. Figure 12 shows a sample of the smoke-flow video. Several qualitative aspects of the aerodynamics of the vehicle were identified.

The wing-tip vortices appeared to be much weaker for the more flexible one-batten and two-batten latex membrane wings than for the more rigid wings. The latex membrane wings also exhibit a billowing of the membrane between the battens, especially at high angles of attack. It was also observed that the flow over the horizontal tail and elevons was very consistent across the entire range of angle of attack. The flow did not appear to separate from the upper surface of the tail, even at angles of attack near stall. This observation is consistent with the relatively linear behavior of the control effectiveness and insensitivity to changes in angle of attack.

Figure 12: Wing deformation and airflow visualization experiment using smoke.

4.4 Summary of wind-tunnel tests

The results indicate that the elastic membrane wing allows the vehicle to achieve higher angles of attack without stalling. This fact coincides with significant static deformation of the wing under load, particularly at higher angles of attack. It appears that the deformation allows the wing to see a smaller effective angle of attack at high vehicle attitudes. The deformation also appears to contribute to weaker wing-tip vortices. It is likely that there is some link between the vortex strength and structure, membrane billowing, and the stall resistance of the latex membrane wings. In addition, the static deformation is accompanied by extensive membrane vibration.

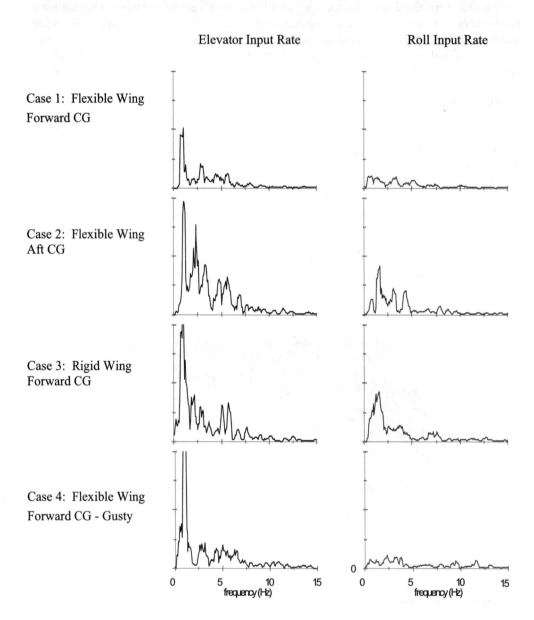

Figure 13: Frequency of pilot input illustrates that high-frequency input, associated with unstable aircraft, is minimized by the flexible wing.

5 Flight tests

The research effort to develop the flexible-wing-based micro air vehicle relied extensively on flight tests to determine the relative merits of various wing designs. For the most part our early conclusions were dominated by direct pilot feedback, which typically included qualitative language. Remarkably rich data on flight quality can be derived from such tests and thus this is an irreplaceable component in the design process. This method is very effective for getting planes to fly and trimming them out, however, it is not very scientific and lacks quantitative measure. Our challenge was to develop a quantitative method to assess flight quality. A method was developed to record pilot input on the two control axes, namely roll and pitch. From experience, we noted that when experienced pilots fly RC planes over a set course, the frequency of feedback is higher for poorly behaved aircraft. The converse is true for well-behaved or easy to fly aircraft. For unstable aircraft, high-frequency corrections to the flight path are required to maintain the course, making the pilot quite busy. By recording the input and plotting the results in the frequency domain, we could characterize how well an aircraft flew. High-frequency input was direct evidence of poor flight quality.

On a common fuselage, we tested four configurations to verify this method of assessing flight quality. A flexible wing was tested against a nominally rigid wing fabricated from a continuous sheet of carbon fiber with an undercambered configuration of the same shape as the flexible wing. The flexible wing was tested in three conditions; a forward center of gravity (CG) on a calm day, a forward CG on a windy day, and an aft CG on a calm day. Typically an aircraft with a forward CG will be stable and one with an aft CG will be erratic. The baseline, rigid wing was set to maximize its stability by setting the CG forward.

Figure 13 shows the spectral decomposition of the pilot input. It can be seen that the high-frequency pilot input was far less for the forward CG flexible wing on the calm and windy day than that for the other two configurations. This was the case for both the roll and pitch commands. This method confirms in a quantitative sense the qualities that our test pilots have been reporting about the flexible-wing concept. The flexible wing is easier to fly and more forgiving in windy conditions than nominally rigid versions.

6 Computational modeling

For a rigid wing, the pressure distribution is determined by the wing shape and free-stream flow properties. For a flexible wing, its shape changes under aerodynamic load, and consequently, the angle of attack and surface-pressure distribution will change along with the flight environment. In order to shed light on the aerodynamic characteristics of the flexible membrane wing, one needs to solve coupled fluid-solid dynamics to track both the shape change and the pressure distribution on the wing shape.

Even though the importance of the viscous effect on membrane-wing aerodynamics has been recognized for quite some time [19], little has been published that address the issue. To date, most of the work in membrane-wing aerodynamics is based on simplified fluid and structure models [20]. The first use of Navier–Stokes equations as the flow dynamics model in a membrane-wing theory appears to be the work of Smith and Shyy [21]. In their work a computational procedure is presented that models the interaction of a two-dimensional flexible membrane wing and laminar, high Reynolds number steady fluid flow. Results from the viscous-flow-based membrane-wing model were compared with a potential-flow-based membrane-wing theory. Unsteady laminar flow surrounding the membrane wing has been reported by Shyy and Smith [22], and a corresponding turbulent flow computation by Smith and Shyy [23]. Recently, Jackson reported an analysis to address the aerodynamics of high aspect ratio membrane wings of conical shape using the lifting-line and thin-airfoil theories. Aerodynamics and optimization of low Reynolds number flexible wing are reported in [9, 24–26]. In the following, we use the CFD simulations to highlight the aerodynamics of a representative wing.

The Navier–Stokes equations for incompressible fluids, written in three-dimensional curvilinear coordinates [27], are solved using a multi-grid-block, pressure-based, moving grid technique [11, 26]. To facilitate the solution of such moving boundary problems, we have implemented an automated regridding procedure to ensure that the grid system not only matches the geometric changes but also is smooth and not excessively skewed.

Obviously, the goal is not only to compute and analyze the dynamics of the coupled fluid and structure systems, but also to use the knowledge gained to improve the design capability. Accordingly, shape optimization has also been conducted based on the CFD solutions. To facilitate such an optimization task, we adopt a gradient-based search technique [28]. From the initial condition and the gradient information obtained in the course of computation, the shape is progressively modified toward the estimated optimal target. Such procedures require the generation of a series of new grid systems based on the new geometries. The present moving-grid technique can perform this task effectively because the remeshing process can be handled with exactly the same procedure as the moving-boundary problem, and with the same automation. The 3-D flexible wing aerodynamics and shape optimization efforts are ongoing.

From the analysis on the wing only, it was found that substantial three-dimensional pressure distributions on both sides of the wing are present. The distribution largely follows the geometric definition of the wing. It is well known [29, 30] that the rates of change of the lift and drag coefficients with angle of attack are strongly affected by the aspect ratio of the wing. Specifically, existing evidence, all based on high Reynolds number testing, indicates that the wings of various aspect ratios have about the same angle of attack at zero lift, but the slope of the lift curve increases progressively with increase of aspect ratio.

Streamlines at an angle of attack of 6° are shown in Fig. 14. Detailed flow structures including trailing vortex lines are clearly visible. The aerodynamic assessment has demonstrated that at the designated Reynolds number range, the lift is sufficient to support the current design. With the flexible-wing technology, the lift can be maintained with reduced influence from the unsteady flight environment.

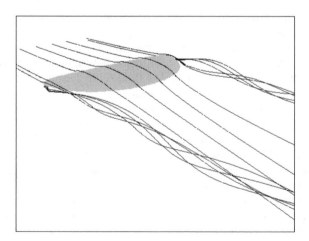

Figure 14: Streamline representation obtained from computational fluid dynamics model.

7 Reconfigurable and morphing wings

Flexibility can be used for purposes other than flight-quality improvement. These include shape manipulation and reconfiguration for both improved maneuvering and storage. Traditional control surfaces such as rudders, elevators, and ailerons have been used almost exclusively for flight control. This method has proven to be effective, albeit limiting, for very aggressive maneuvers, and for flight regimes where agility is required. By morphing or reshaping the wing using distributed actuation such as piezoelectric and shape-memory material, preferred wing shapes can be developed for specific flight regimes. Such reconfiguration, however, would required an inordinate amount of authority and thus energy if the wings were nominally rigid. The flexible nature of the wing allows for such distributed actuation with orders of magnitude less authority. For example, the individual battens on the wing can be made from shape-memory alloys or piezoelectric materials. Or traditional actuators such as servos can be used to pull, via thread, on various portions of the wing to affect the shape. This idea is as old as powered flight itself, with the first use of wing warping credited to the Wright Brothers. They used wing warping for directional control on their very first flights.

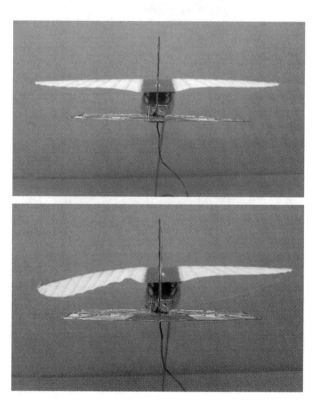

Figure 15. The flexible wing allows for wing warping to enhance vehicle agility.

At the University of Florida we have just begun to investigate using wing warping for control. Our initial work utilizes conventional servos and a string that "pulls" on various parts of the wing to affect the shape. Figure 15 shows one of our models with a thread connecting the wing tips to a servo in the fuselage of the airplane. As the thread is tightened on one side of the aircraft, the angle of attack of the wing increases, thus acting in a similar manner as an aileron. The roll rate developed by the actuation was considerably higher than that from the rudder. Additionally, it produced nearly pure roll with little yaw interaction.

An additional benefit of the flexible wing is the ability for it to be reconfigured for storage purposes. Figure 16 illustrates an 11-inch wingspan foldable wing MAV that can be stored in a 3"-diameter canister. In some military applications where a MAV is deployed from fast-moving larger manned or unmanned aircraft, the MAV must be packed into a small container. The container is deployed from the aircraft and parachutes towards the ground. It then opens and the MAV is released to perform the desired surveillance mission. This technology allows the MAV to be deployed for remote sensing and surveillance missions.

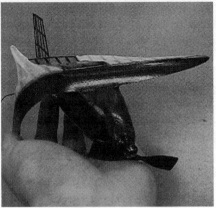

Figure 16: A foldable wing was developed in order to enhance MAV portability.

The wing utilizes a singly curved shell structural element on the leading edge. This allows for the wing to readily collapse downwards for storage yet maintain rigidity in the upwards direction to react the aerodynamic loads. The effect is similar to that of a common tape measure, where the curvature in the metallic tape is used to retain the shape after it has unspooled from the casing, yet it can be rolled back into the casing to accommodate the small-diameter spool. The curvature insures that the positive (straight) shape is developed after it is unwound from the case and can actually be cantilevered for some distance. The curvature of the leading edge of the wing acts as the curvature in the tape measure.

8 Summary

The flexible-wing concept developed at the University of Florida may be one of the enabling technologies that will lead to the mass deployment of flying machines known as micro air vehicles. Borrowing from nature, flexibility provides for smoother flight than conventional wings, especially in turbulent wind conditions. They also have the potential to achieve more aggressive maneuvers as a result of the delayed stall angle. A combination of flight tests, wind tunnel experiments and computational models has been used to document the physics behind the beneficial characteristics of the flexible wing. Further research into morphing technology, as well as increasing the sophistication of the computational model, is underway. This will lead to more advanced vehicles in the future.

Acknowledgement

The author would like to acknowledge Martin Waszak, David Rainey and Luther Jenkins from the NASA Langley Research Center for contributions including the wind tunnel results. Additionally, David Jenkins, Wei Shyy, Yongsheng Lian, Scott Ettinger, Mujahid Abdulrahim and Rick Lind from the University of Florida made significant contributions to the development, testing and analysis of the flexible wing concept.

References

[1]   Mueller, T.J. (ed.), *Proceedings of the Conference on Fixed, Flapping and Rotary Wing Vehicles at Very Low Reynolds Numbers.* Notre Dame University, Indiana, June 5–7, 2000.

[2]   Mueller, T.J., The Influence of Laminar Separation and Transition on Low Reynold's Number Airfoil Hysteresis. *J. Aircraft*, **22**, pp. 763–770, 1985.

[3]   Ellington, C.P., The Aerodynamics of Hovering Flight. *Philosophical Transactions of the Royal Society of London*, **305(1122)**, pp. 1–181, 1984.

[4]   Frampton, K.D., Goldfarb, M., Monopoli, D. & Cveticanin, D., Passive Aeroelastic Tailoring for Optimal Flapping Wings. *Proceeding of the Fixed, Flapping and Rotary Wing Vehicles at Very Low Reynolds Numbers*, pp.26–33, 2000.

[5]   Jones, K.D., Duggan, S.J. & Platzer, M.F., Flapping-Wing Propulsion for a Micro Air Vehicle. *AIAA Paper*, No. 2001–0126, 2001.

[6]   Grasmeyer, J.M. & Keennon, M.T., Development of the Black Widow Micro Air Vehicle. *AIAA Paper*, No. 2001–0127, 2001.

[7]   Morris, S., Holden, M., Design of Micro Air Vehicles and Flight Test Validation. *Proceeding of the Fixed, Flapping and Rotary Wing Vehicles at Very Low Reynolds Numbers*, pp. 153–176, 2000.

[8]   Waszak, M.R., Jenkins, L.N. & Ifju, P.G., Stability and Control Properties of an Aeroelastic Fixed Wing Micro Aerial Vehicle. AIAA 2001–4005.

[9]   Shyy, W., Berg, M. & Ljungqvist, D., Flapping and Flexible Wings for Biological and Micro Vehicles. *Process in Aerospace Sciences*, **35(5)**, pp. 455–506, 1999.

[10] Shyy, W., Thakur, S.S., Ouyang, H., Liu, J. & Blosch, E., *Computational Techniques for Complex Transport Phenomena*, Cambridge University Press: New York, 1997.

[11] Shyy, W., Udaykumar, H.S., Rao, M.M. & Smith, R.W., *Computational Fluid Dynamics with Moving Boundaries*, Taylor & Francis: Washington D.C., xviii + 285 pages, (1996, revised printing 1997 & 1998).

[12] Smith, R.W. & Shyy, W., Computational Model of Flexible Membrane Wings in Steady Laminar Flow. *AIAA Journal*, **33(10)**, pp. 1769–77, 1995.

[13] Jenkins D.A., Shyy, W., Sloan, J., Klevebring, F. & Nilsson, M., Airfoil Performance at Low Reynolds Numbers for Micro Air Vehicle Applications. *Thirteenth Bristol International RPV/UAV Conference*, University of Bristol, 1998.

[14] Ifju, P.G., Jenkins, D.A., Ettinger, S., Lian, Y., Shyy, W. & Waszak, M.R., Flexible-Wing-Based Micro Air Vehicles. AIAA Annual Conference, AIAA 2002–0705. Jan. 2002.

[15] Ifju, P.G., Ettinger, S., Jenkins, D.A. & Martinez, L., Composite Materials for Micro Air Vehicles. *Proceeding for the SAMPE Annual Conference*, Long Beach CA, May 6–10, 2001.

[16] Jenkins, D.A., Ifju, P.G., Abdulrahim, M. & Olipra, S., Assessment of the Controllability of Micro Air Vehicles. *Micro Air Vehicle Conference*, Bristol, England, April 2001.

[17] Ettinger, S.M., Nechyba, M.C., Ifju, P.G. & Waszak, M., Vision-Guided Flight Stability and Control for Micro Air Vehicles. *Proc. IEEE Int. Conf. on Intelligent Robots and Systems*, **3**, pp. 2134–40, 2002.

[18] Fleming, G.A. & Burner, A.W., Deformation Measurements of Smart Aerodynamic Surfaces. SPIE Paper No. 3783–25, 44th Annual SPIE International Symposium on Optical Science, Engineering, and Instrumentation - Optical Diagnostics for Fluids/Heat/Combustion and Photomechanics for Solids, Denver, CO, July 18–23, 1999.

[19] Nielsen, J.N., Theory of Flexible Aerodynamics Surfaces. *Journal of Applied Mechanics*, **30**, pp. 435–442, 1963.

[20] Jackson, P.S. & Christie, G.W., Numerical Analysis of Three-Dimensional Elastic Membrane Wings. *AIAA Journal*, **25(5)**, pp. 676–682, 1987.

[21] Smith, R.W. & Shyy, W., Computation of Unsteady Laminar Flow Over a Flexible Two-Dimensional Membrane Wing. *Physics of Fluids*, **7**, pp. 2175–2184, 1995.

[22] Shyy, W. & Smith, R.W., Computation of Laminar Flow and Flexible Structure Interaction. *Computational Fluid Dynamics Review*, ed. M. Hafez & K. Oshima, John Wiley & Sons, 1995.

[23] Smith, R.W. & Shyy, W., Computation of Aerodynamics Coefficients for a Flexible Membrane Airfoil in Turbulent Flow: A Comparison with Classical Theory. *Phys. Fluids*, **8(12)**, 1996.

[24] Shyy, W., Klevebring, F., Nilsson, M., Sloan, J., Carroll, B. & Fuentes, C., A Study of Rigid and Flexible Low Reynolds Number Airfoils. *Journal of Aircraft*, **36**, pp. 523–529, 1999.

[25] Levin, O. & Shyy, W., Optimization of a Flexible Low Reynolds Number Airfoil. *AIAA 39th Aerospace Sciences Meeting & Exhibit*, Paper No. 2001–0125, 2001.

[26] Lian, Y., Steen, J., Trygg-Wilander, M. & Shyy, W., Low Reynolds Number Turbulent Flows Around a Dynamically-Shaped Airfoil. *AIAA 31ˢᵗ Fluid Dynamics Conference*, Paper No. 2001–2723, 2001.

[27] Shyy, W., *Computational Modeling for Fluid Flow and Interfacial Transport*, Elsevier: Amsterdam, The Netherlands, xviii + 504 pages, (1994, revised printing 1997).

[28] Design Optimization Tools, Vanderplaats Research & Development, Inc., 1999.

[29] Prandtl, L. & Tietjens, O.G., *Applied hydro- and aero- mechanics*, 1934, Reissued by Dover, Now York, 1957

[30] Abbott, I.H. & Von Doenhoff, A.E., *Theory of Wing Sections*, New York, Dover, 1959.

CHAPTER 9

Compliant habitats

J. Kimpian & C. H. M. Jenkins
Compliant Structures Laboratory
Mechanical Engineering Department
South Dakota School of Mines and Technology
Rapid City, SD 57701

Abstract

This chapter provides a brief outline of the use of compliance in habitats, both natural and man-made.

1 Compliant habitats in nature

Early humans likely took ideas for design of their constructed habitats from nature. Several interesting examples are given below of the use of compliant habitats in nature (while other examples, such as spider webs, are given elsewhere in this volume). Examples such as these may have given early humans ideas for rapidly deployable and portable habitats.

1.1 Paper wasps [1]

Paper Wasp is the common name for medium to large size wasps that build nests from a paper-like substance. There are about two dozen species of Paper Wasps in North America and hundreds of species worldwide. A common North American species is the Golden Paper Wasp. The wasps are typically about 2 cm (0.75 inch) long with yellow markings on a brown, black, or reddish body. Nectar is the primary energy source for adults, while the larve feed on caterpillars.

The nests of most species look like an upside down umbrella suspended from a single stem or stalk (Figure 1). The nest consists of a few to several dozen brood cells (larval habitats). The Paper Wasp collects plant and wood fibers, which are then mixed with saliva and chewed into a papier-mâché like material and formed into the thin cells of the nest. Some nests are completely enclosed in a paper dome. Nests are constructed in protected areas such as under the eaves of buildings and in dense vegetation.

Figure 1. Paper Wasps attend to their nest.

1.2 Aquatic insects [2]

Many aquatic insects (e.g., Coleoptera and Hemiptera) carry air with them in the form of a bubble. Water bugs are members of the class Insecta and are good examples of insects that use compliant pneumatic habitats . The giant water bug belongs to the family Belostomatidae, one of 50 families in the order Hemiptera. There are approximately 100 species in the family Belostomatidae that live primarily in North America, South Africa and India. Giant water bugs are approximately 4 cm (1.5 inch) in length, with some species growing as long as 10 cm (4 inch) long. The body is brown, flat and oval, giving them an appearance similar to that of a cockroach.

The posterior end of a giant water bug has two retractable, semi-cylindrical appendages which, when held together, form a breathing tube. This tube is used for underwater breathing. Like terrestrial insects, air is exchanged through small openings of the respiratory system called spiracles.

When submerged for long periods of time, giant water bugs carry a temporary external air supply in the form of an air bubble. The bubble is in contact with the bug's spiracles located between their wings and their abdomen's upper surface. Patches of hairs or cavities under the wings hold the bubble against the insect's spiracles. As the insect consumes oxygen, the amount in the bubble decreases and more oxygen diffuses in from the water.

1.3 Labyrinth fish [3]

Labyrinth fish are very popular for home aquariums because of their beautiful colors and interesting behavior. In the wild, Labyrinth fish extend from China and Korea, all through southern Asia including the Philippines, to Africa. The single most distinguishing trait of the Labyrinth fish, which is unique among species, is the organ they possess that gives them their name. The labyrinth is located above the gills and consists of skin folds, called *lamelli*, which are filled with blood vessels and through which oxygen can be absorbed from the air. This feature allows the Labyrinth fish to survive in water with very low oxygen levels.

Many Labyrinth species build nest of small air bubbles. These nests are always built by the male, and their size, shape and position depends upon the species. The nest is made at the water surface among floating plants. Some fish incorporate plants into the nest and some are all bubbles. The male courts the female under the nest, where he curls around her and turns belly up. The eggs are extruded and fertilized from this position. They usually float up into the bubble nest and become almost invisible.

2 Compliant architecture

2.1 Indigenous compliant habitats

Indigenous peoples worldwide have made use of compliant habitats for centuries, whenever rapidly deployable shelter was needed. The tipis of the Native American (Indians) are typical examples. Constructed of animal skins supported by wood poles, the tipi provided a portable domicile (Figure 2).

Figure 2. View of a Native American Sioux tipi camp on the open prairie, Dakota Territory, showing a covered entry and timber piles with two figures in the distance (courtesy Western History/Genealogy Department, Denver Public Library)

2.2 Modern compliant architecture

Throughout the past millennium, inflatable structures have been at the frontier of scientific exploration wherever lightness, deployability, or structural economy was a prerequisite. From balloons to tires, from airships to spacesuits, pneumatic technology has helped realise some of the greatest visions of mankind. Harnessing the dynamic power of air, man escaped the constraints of gravity and friction; in challenging these constraints he furthermore discovered that huge structures could be deployed with a speed unknown to traditional types of construction.

Air-inflated structures came into their own during the Second World War when military imperatives sparked an unprecedented demand for deployable structures, like life rafts, escape slides, shelters and hangars that drove inflatable technology forward (Figure 3). In the 1950s, freed from the confines of military functionalism, these technological advances brought to light the great potential that instantaneous enclosures offered to architecture. Accordingly, air structures gained ground as a revolutionary construction technique, which would eliminate lengthy construction periods, be flexible and affordable, and functionally well integrated.

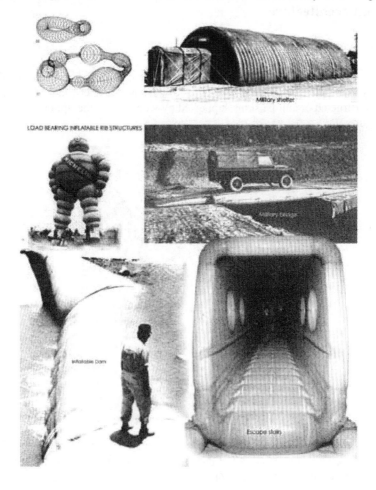

Figure 3. Examples of several inflatable terrestrial structures.

In the post-war era, freed from the confines of military functionalism, these technological advances brought to light the potential which 'instantaneous' inflatable enclosures offered to architecture. For the architects and designers of the time recent childhood memories of vast flying structures were a genuine source of inspiration that fuelled a utopian vision of the future in which multiform, adaptable and curved forms replaced the rigid and rectilinear architecture of the past. Inflatable form, which is organic in appearance and ephemeral by its very nature, offered the 1960s' generation liberation from architectural orthodoxy. Pneumatic structures also appealed to a whole generation of radical young engineers. Since no part of the pneumatic structures is in flexure or torsion, they are among the lightest forms of construction.

However, the optimistic hopes for flexible and affordable buildings, which culminated in the multitude of inflatable pavilions at the 1970 Osaka Expo, were short-lived. Inflatables fell victim to a series of technical and design problems (Figure 4). The difficulties inherent in designing and simulating curved form, manipulating dynamic structural behaviour, as well as inadequate materials and imprecise manufacturing led to poor designs and a decline of interest in pneumatic construction. Neither could simple membranes provide a universal solution that could satisfy the complex demands on a building skin. By the mid-1970s, the image of a glamorous architectural language, unbounded by material concerns and gravity, gave way to practical concerns over an awkward design process involving a perpetually vanishing building material (air), severe limitations in form and tectonic language, unpredictable structural performance, and a monolithic and uniform aesthetic. It was not until three decades later that science and technology caught up with the visions of the past and these problems could be re-assessed.

Figure 4. Inflatable tennis court enclosure at the University of New Mexico. Skin damage can be easily seen in the figure.

During the 1980s the emphasis shifted to canopy structures, which were used almost exclusively in roofing where they are less affected by membrane vulnerability and fire problems and still relatively inexpensive to "haul into place". Their success lay in the fact that rigidizing membranes through high tension conveniently eliminated unpredictable dynamics, unreliable pumps, and wrinkly, bulging forms (Figure 5). However tensile membranes also required a supporting structure, and detailing was more costly due to the higher stresses involved.

Figure 5. Tension fabric roof at the Denver (Colorado) International Airport

Transparency also remained a problematic area but since the mid-1990s. Foil cushions combined with rigid lightweight frames and cable net structures have begun to appear on the market (Figure 6). Their advantage over tensile membranes is that they provide much better thermal insulation and acoustic properties than conventional tensile membrane structures with substantially less supporting structure. These low-pressure transparent cushions have led a move back towards inflatable structures, albeit as forgiving cladding systems for curved buildings rather than genuine air-supported structures. The turn of the Millennium saw many of the 1960s' designs realised in this way, most famously the Eden Project by Nicholas Grimshaw and Partners, which strikes a strong resemblance to Buckminster Fuller's famous Pillowdome. Another notable example was Branson Coates' design for Powerhouse::UK, which highlighted a touring exhibition of British Design. Lighting effects dramatically enhanced the curves of four steel-framed silver cushion-clad drums, which were linked in the center by a tensile roof. The combination of concave (tensile) and convex (inflatable) membranes was reminiscent of Frei Otto's [4] and Antoine Stinco's similar proposals from the 1960s. However none of these structures used air for structural support or took advantage of its dynamic properties. Instead they are efficient tensile structures where lightweight air-inflated cushions act as 'solid' elements in a rigid structure.

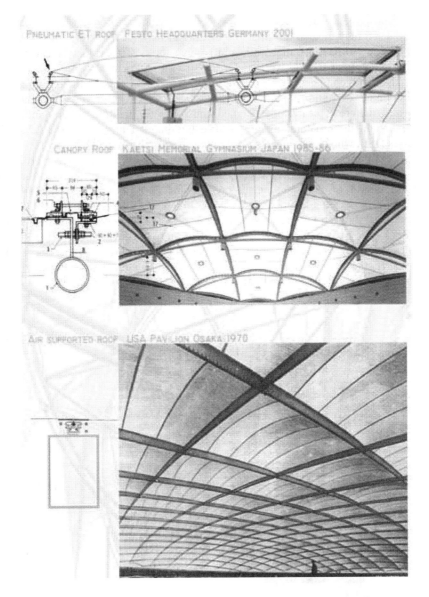

Figure 6. Examples of canopy and pneumatic cushion roofs.

During the mid-1990s, pneumatics began to experience a renaissance elsewhere. In 1992 Festo, a multinational engineering corporation specialising in the design and manufacture of pneumatic components for automation, decided to embark on a re-branding exercise. Led by the Director of Corporate Design, Professor Axel Thallemer, the company opted for an approach that would capitalize on the sensational image of pneumatic structures by marrying "fun" with high-tech. Festo had the financial muscle, as well as the motive, to adopt engineering feats from parallel industries to demonstrate new possibilities in pneumatic design. With each new endeavour they produced a major breakthrough for pneumatic structures.

Their initial project was a design for two hot-air balloons flying together, one of them inverted. In 1996 they erected an inflatable exhibition hall, 'Airtecture', which was the first pneumatic building to have parallel walls and a cubic form. The walls were made of spacer fabrics, with intermittent ET foil sections for transparency. Pneumatic roof beams, linked by depressurised fabric chambers, formed the roof structure. The building is flanked by pneumatic columns of minimal structural purpose but which define the articulation of the building. The structure is beautifully detailed and relies on pressure sensors and pneumatic pumps to maintain its structural integrity. The building's fabricators were inflatable boat manufacturers DSB, who were pioneers in adapting spacer fabrics for such use.

Festo's next project was 'Stingray', a pneumatic 'flying object' that was a cross between an airship and an aircraft. Its magnificent shape, sculpted by a succession of air chambers reminded the viewer of the giant manta ray (Figure 7). Two further inflatable aircrafts followed. Their most remarkable features were the wings, the shape of which could be gradually adjusted through the pressure regulation of the wing chambers. Unlike solid metal pneumatic/hydraulic parts, which have a motion lag, these pneumatic objects were the first to take advantage of progressive shape-change in compliant membranes. Professor Thallemer's group was the first to implement pneumatically controlled dynamic shape change in a saleable product. In the process they came up with a truly 'smart' membrane.

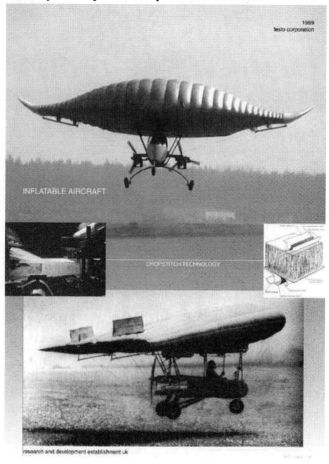

Figure 7. Inflatable aircraft.

A new wave of young designers is keen to explore new compliant design opportunities. Kimpian presented a design for a portable inflatable auditorium that demonstrates solutions for some of the obstacles that pneumatic architecture encountered in the past (Figure 8). Instead of suppressing the dynamic properties of air-inflated structures, the design took full advantage of them. Soft linkages allowed for the swaying of the beams in wind. Reconfiguration of the beams was achieved on the one hand by 'air film' technique, harnessing the power of 'expelled' air, and on the other, by 2D mechanisms. The sensors, the processing power and the programming mathematics necessary for the operation of such a structure are now readily available from the manufacturers of pneumatic systems. This form of tuneable geometric control of space and volume represents a new approach to construction and is particularly suited to the brief of the inflatable auditorium where the building can adapt to changing user requirements, and where the shape-change itself is part of the theatrical scene. The scheme also incorporated new membrane materials that are strong yet harmless to the environment. The structure's integrity was tested with software that had initially been developed for simulating parachute deployment.

Figure 8. Portable inflatable auditorium concept.

3 Conclusion

Since the earliest of times, nature has realized the efficacy of compliant habitats. Several examples have been given at the outset of the chapter. Humans are likely to gain inspiration from these natural designs. Over the last several decades, many examples can be shown of human-engineered membrane/inflatable habitats. Currently, experimentation, worldwide exhibitions, and a series of new publications suggest that the enthusiasm for pneumatic structures is far from exhausted. On the contrary, current technological advances suggest that we are getting closer to the source of fascination that inspired the visionary optimism of the post-war generation.

References

[1] www.everythingabout.net/articles/ biology/animals/arthropods/insects/wasps/paper_wasp/
[2] www.zoo.org/educate/fact_sheets/waterbug/waterbug.htm
[3] badmanstropicalfish.com/labyrinthfish.html
[4] Otto, Frei (editor), *Tensile Structures*, MIT Press, 1973

CHAPTER 10

Gossamer spacecraft

A. B. Chmielewski[1] & C. H. M. Jenkins[2]
[1]Jet Propulsion Laboratory, Pasadena, CA, USA.
[2]Compliant Structures Laboratory, Mechanical Engineering Department
South Dakota School of Mines and Technology, USA.

Abstract

Modern trends are driving spacecraft to the extremes of length scales. On the one hand, the ubiquitous trend toward miniaturization is pushing spacecraft ever smaller; one the other hand, many commercial, military, and science applications can only be done with very large systems. In either case, ultra-lightweight or *gossamer* technology will enable a future generation of spacecraft that have remarkable capability to accomplish missions beyond the reach of current systems. In this chapter we discuss the technology, and the challenges and opportunities, of gossamer spacecraft.

1 Technology background

1.1 Overview of gossamer spacecraft technology

Recent technological advancements in structural analysis materials, fabrication, and testing, have presented the space community with a low-cost, lightweight alternative to mechanically deployed space structures. These *gossamer spacecraft* have many benefits and advantages over current mechanical systems. They are low in mass and can be packaged into small volumes, which can potentially reduce the overall program cost by reducing the launch-vehicle size. Reduction in total system mass and deployment complexity can also increase system reliability. They are of particular advantage for mission architectures at the extreme ends of the size spectrum—from the very small to the very large.

To be clear, gossamer spacecraft are typically realized as *membrane* structures. We mean by *membrane* structures those structures (load-carrying artifacts or devices) comprised of highly flexible (*compliant*) plate or shell-like elements. This usually implies thin, low-modulus materials, such as polymer films. Membrane structures have very little inherent stiffness, and do not lend themselves well to carrying compressive loads. Thus, they are often found either in tensioned-planar or inflated-curved configurations. In what follows, we will use the terms *membrane, inflatable,* and *membrane/inflatable* interchangeably.

There is great interest in compliant structures by near-term space missions, and a possibility of enabling several breakthrough missions in the more distant future [1–20]. Membrane structures are envisioned for such applications as deep space antennas, earth radiometers, radars, concentrators, telescopes, sun shields, solar sails, solar arrays, and spacecraft booms. In 1997 NASA embarked on a technology development program to advance gossamer spacecraft technology and make it available to 21st century space missions. NASA has concentrated on such areas as deployment techniques, membrane and rigidizable materials, and analytical tool development. It is hoped this will accelerate technology development in the areas of large ultra-light apertures and solar sails, for example, which are among the most challenging applications of membrane structures.

The analytical simulation of mechanical performance of compliant space structures is absolutely essential to support the development of technology and projection of performance for this new class of space structures. There are a number of elements of this technology that must be understood analytically to develop and apply this technology. In addition to the modeling needed to characterize the structural dynamics of the on-orbit configurations, highly specialized approaches are needed to simulate other specific mechanical events and structural relationships. Such specialized capability should include simulation of a) specific control deployment techniques for structural members, b) generic spatially organized and controlled deployment processes, c) identification and application of scaling laws to enable the use of limited test results to project full-scale mechanical performance, and d) deflection characteristics of thin membranes under tension and loaded by differential pressure, among many others.

There are currently a number of different techniques for control of the deployment of gossamer structural elements. The most promising techniques currently under development have been simulated and will be verified experimentally with scaled hardware. New and unique techniques for spatially controlling deployment through the management of a number of discrete masses have been developed. The potential benefits of this process have been identified. Scaling laws for this new class of space structures have been developed. They have been applied to the test results of scaled hardware to show the relationship with full-scale structures. The basic equations have been developed to determine the deflection characteristics of a tensioned membrane under differential pressure loading. This characterization will be modified to include segmented membranes and the stiffness effects of their seams. This will enable the development of an error budget for precision inflatable reflector structures.

And what is the future of membrane structures in the new millennium? It can be summarized with just two words – *gossamer spacecraft.* "Technology to find it and then shake its hand" is a long-term vision. This somewhat humorous sounding motto appears even more outrageous when translated into scientific terms. NASA will develop technology to enable imaging of extra-solar planets to detect the ones that carry life. Once we find such planets, we will not be satisfied with "just" creating somewhat blurred pictures of these worlds or finding spectroscopic "smoking guns" of life's existence - we will want to travel there and take a closer look at our cosmic friends. We do not know how long this search will take; we do not know how successful we will be. One thing we do know is that, to make this vision more than just science fiction, we will need to develop radically different observatories and spacecraft.

A gossamer telescope, which will produce the first detailed image of an extrasolar planet, will bear little resemblance to any current space observatories. The gossamer telescope will be about 150 times lighter than the Hubble Space Telescope and its diameter will be 10–20 times greater. When such a telescope, or an interferometer consisting of an array of such telescopes, will finally produce an image of "the other world," there will be strong public summon to take an even closer look by means of interstellar travel.

In this day and age we envision three major ways that offer the possibility of interstellar travel. They are: matter–antimatter propulsion, nuclear propulsion, and solar sailing – the latter method recently getting much attention. The first-generation interstellar sail missions are envisioned to use gravitational boost from the sun in addition to the solar pressure. In the more distant future, lasers will propel the sails. Flexible structures will eventually make an interstellar sailing possible.

The "vision missions" for flexible space structures are the Interstellar Probe and the Extrasolar Planet Imager. Both of these missions can be considered the pinnacles of the technology-development roadmap. Before the technology is ready to enable either of these vision missions, there will be a series of technology-development products benefiting several types of space endeavors.

In general, gossamer spacecraft technology will enable very large, ultra-lightweight systems for bold missions of discovery such as:

- Very large telescopes for imaging extra-solar planets, studying formation of large-scale structure in the early universe, and continuously monitoring the Earth from distant vantage points.

- Large deployable and inflatable antennas for space-based radio astronomy, high-bandwidth communications from deep space, and Earth remote sensing with radar and radiometers.

- Solar sails for low-cost propulsion, station keeping in unstable orbits, and precursor interstellar exploration missions.

- Large solar power collection and transmission systems for human and robotic exploration missions, and for the commercial development of space.

The overarching goal of gossamer spacecraft technology development is to achieve breakthroughs in mission capability and cost, primarily through revolutionary advances in structures, materials, optics, and adaptive and multifunctional systems all described briefly in the following sections. (For a more complete discussion of these topics, the reader should refer to the monograph *Gossamer Spacecraft: Membrane/Inflatable Structure Technology for Space Applications* [11].)

1.2 History of gossamer aerospace structures

There has been interest in inflatable deployable space structures since the 1950s due to their potential for low-cost flight hardware, exceptionally high mechanical packaging efficiency, deployment reliability, and low weight. The earliest gossamer aerospace structures were the kite and the balloon.

A number of significant technology developments, focused on the demonstration of such potential, include the Good Year antennas in the early 1960s, the Echo Balloon series from the late 1950s to the early 1960s, the Contraves antennas and sun shades in the late 1970s to the mid-1980s, the L'Garde, Inc. inflatable decoys in the 1970s and mid 1980s, and their space-shuttle-launched Inflatable Antenna Experiment (IAE) in May 1996. The IAE was the most recent and the most significant demonstration of this technology. (Further details on the history of gossamer spacecraft can be found in [11].)

NASA's interest in demonstrating the potential of this relatively new class of space structure resulted in their sponsoring the IN-STEP Inflatable Antenna Experiment, which flew on STS-76 on May 29, 1996 (Fig. 1). L'Garde, Inc., who have been designing, manufacturing, and ground and flight-testing inflatable space structures for the past 30 years, developed the antenna concept used. The experimental objectives were to (a) verify that large inflatable space structures can be built at low cost, (b) demonstrate that large inflatable space structures have high mechanical packaging efficiency, (c) demonstrate that this new class of space structure has high deployment reliability, (d) demonstrate that large membrane reflectors can be manufactured with surface precision of a few millimeters and (e) measure the reflector surface precision on orbit.

Figure 1: L'Garde's Inflatable Antenna Experiment (IAE) during space flight.

The IAE inflatable structure was comprised of two basic elements, the inflatable reflector assembly and the torus/strut supporting structure. The reflector assembly formed a 14-meter off-axis parabolic aperture with an f/d of 0.5. The surface accuracy goal was 1.0 mm RMS as compared to a best-fit parabola. The reflector film, 13 µm (0.5 mil) aluminized Mylar, was stressed to approximately 8 MPa (1200 psi) by the inflation pressure of 2 Pa (0.0003 psi). This stress level was sufficiently high to assure a good reflective surface for the accuracy measurement system. The canopy was constructed from 62 gores of 13 µm (0.5 mil) Mylar, but was left transparent. The torus/strut structure are 610 and 457 mm (24 and 18 inch) in diameter, respectively, and are made with 305 µm (12 mil) thick Neoprene coated Kevlar. The function of the struts was to locate the reflector assembly at the effective center of curvature of the reflector parabola as required for operation of the Surface Accuracy Measurement Subsystem. The torus also provides the rim support for the reflector assembly without which the reflector assembly would take a spherical shape.

The experiment was flown on the recoverable Spartan Spacecraft and demonstrated the main objectives. New, unique, and low-cost space structures technology was demonstrated on orbit by (a) building a large inflatable space antenna structure on the order of about $1,000,000, (b) demonstrating extremely efficient mechanical packaging by stowing a 14 by 28 meter inflatable structure in a container the size of an office desk, (c) manufacturing an offset membrane reflector structure with a surface precision on the order of a few mm RMS, and (d) demonstrating the robustness of deployment for this new class of structure. The results of this experiment were used specifically to establish the technology database, and were the basis of a technology road map for the continued development of this type of space structure. The results of this experiment have been thoroughly documented by Freeland and co-workers.

2 Applications

2.1 Solar arrays

L'Garde Inc (Tustin, CA) developed for DARPA and Phillips Laboratory (now Air Force Research Laboratory) an inflatable solar array in 1993. The array supplied 274 W and weighed 2.94 kg (flight model). The array was 3.64 m long and 1.1 m wide. The support tubes were made from stressed aluminum laminate. Figure 2 shows the first controlled inflation of this large space system, deployed only by inflation in the supporting tubes. This system rigidized after inflation so that gas pressure need not be maintained. The array was successfully vibration tested at 12 G in all 3 axes and underwent five thermal cycles under this test program. Complete current - voltage tests were conducted before and after the deployment in vacuum at –90° C.

Future commercial and deep-space satellites will require solar arrays with higher specific power densities than the current state-of-the-art, which is on the order of ~40 W/kg, and lower costs to meet mission objectives. Planned communication, radar, DOD, and exploration satellites anticipate power requirements upwards of 30 kW. To meet these needs, revolutionary changes in solar array technology are required.

The advantages of using inflatable systems technology in designing a large solar array are reduced stowage volume and mass, increased specific power (greater than 100 W/kg), and reduced cost over current mechanically deployed solar arrays. The inflatable solar array is particularly attractive for missions that demand high power output with launch-vehicle size restrictions.

A good example of a solar array construction is the array originally designed under the auspices of the ST4 project in 1999 (Figure 3). The configuration of the ST4 solar array was a modular split blanket style with the deployment tube located on the array centerline. When stowed, the solar array modules were accordion-folded. Sharp's rigid, high-efficiency silicon photovoltaic assemblies were the basic building blocks for the modular blanket solar array. (Flexible thin-film solar cells using amorphous silicon (Si), copper indium gallium diselenide (GAS) or other materials hold great promise to provide even lower cost and lighter weight photovoltaic modules in similar arrays in the future.) Structural components included the inflatable beam, stowage panels, plume-offset panels, launch ties, and launch tie release mechanism. The inflatable beam could have been fabricated from any of the rigidization systems. However, the thermal heating method was utilized for the flight experiment design.

Figure 2: L'Garde's Inflatable Torus Solar Array Technology (ITSAT) deployed in a vacuum tank at the Air Force Research Laboratory (AFRL).

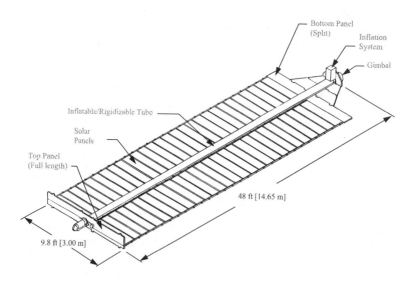

Figure 3: Champollion (ST4) Inflatable Solar Array developed by ILC Dover.

The purpose of the inflatable beam was to provide a deployment mechanism and support structure for the solar array. It is similar in function to the mechanical deployment truss masts currently utilized on spacecraft. The beam was located on the center of the split blanket and was stowed by rolling the tube.

The ST4 solar array design was reviewed for use in NASA's Space Solar Power (SSP) program. The SSP program requires array sizes on the order of 18 kW and a specific power of 250 W/kg. The ST4 solar arrays were designed to be 5.6 kW with a specific power of 102 W/kg.

The Teledesic program envisions a constellation of 288 satellites in low earth orbit to provide high data rate communication from anywhere on earth. Original concepts for the satellite included a pair of 6 kW solar arrays (see Fig. 4), with a cost target of $100/W in production. Inflatable technology was considered to be a leading candidate in meeting this goal and was therefore investigated by the Teledesic team.

Figure 4: Teledesic Satellite

ILC Dover, under contract to Boeing, designed an inflatable structure to support a 3-meter by 10 meter rectangular satellite solar array. A full-scale prototype demonstration unit was also fabricated and used in deployment trials (see Fig. 5).

NASA is developing several advanced rover vehicles for exploration of the Martian surface. Several concepts call for large deployable solar arrays to meet the power needs of the rover. One such concept utilizes 1.5-meter deployable wheels and an inflatable solar array to cover vast surface areas in rapid times (see Figure 6).

The Mars Rover Solar Array prototype, Figure 6, is a working, full-scale inflatable solar array for rover application. This prototype is a system to be packaged in a small volume for launch and deployed in situ to collect solar energy. The array is parasol shaped and consists of four main components: (1) the canopy, which is the membrane that carries the solar modules; (2) the inflatable torus; (3) the inflatable column; and (4) sixteen solar modules. The sixteen (16) Kapton gores (the individual segments of the canopy) of the solar array are tensioned by a 8.0 cm (tube) diameter by 150 cm (major) diameter, 16-sided inflatable torus, and supported by a 10.0 cm diameter inflatable column.

Figure 5: Teledesic Inflatable Solar Array deployed at ILC Dover.

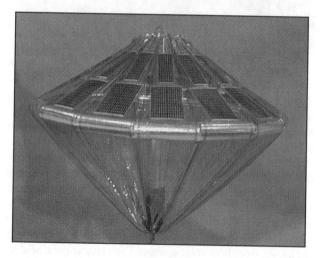

Figure 6: Inflatable Mars Rover Solar Array Prototype developed by JPL/ILC Dover.

Due to the requirement for multiple deployments, the torus of the prototype is constructed from a lightweight aluminized Mylar assembled by pressure-sensitive adhesive tape of the same material. The prototype inflatable column is fabricated from a laminate of Kapton and aluminized Mylar. The inflatable torus and column of the future flight unit will be constructed from thin-walled aluminum/Kapton laminates or UV cured laminates.

The Mars solar array prototype is capable of generating approximately 20 watts in a terrestrial environment or 12 watts in a Martian environment. Further optimization in cell population pattern, cell efficiency, and mass will further increase specific power to weight ratio.

A team consisting of ILC Dover, Aerospace Corporation, Lockheed Martin and NASA Glenn developed and tested a prototype of a so-called Power Sphere (Fig. 7). The Sphere is to be used to power small satellites needing 20–50 W. The size of the Spheres that would provide this power level is between 0.5 and 1 m in diameter. The main attribute of the design is insensitivity of the solar array to attitude, which lowers the overall system mass while reducing the necessity for solar array drives and attitude sensing.

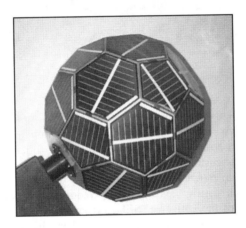

Figure 7: Prototype of the Power Sphere.

2.2 Communication systems

The National Aeronautics and Space Administration (NASA) and the Department of Defense (DOD) have been studying innovative concepts for large space antennas for several years. One concept has emerged out of these studies as an unequivocal leader - a segmented inflatable reflector based on the premise of seaming together flat-segmented gores of membrane material to form a highly accurate doubly curved surface (see Fig. 8). Inflatable space reflectors show tremendous promise for advancing all antenna parameters simultaneously. Their low mass, high deployment reliability, and small packaging volume reduce the mass, complexity, and cost of a host of missions and spacecraft. Studies estimate that for very large antennas, inflatables are approximately 10 times less expensive, 2–5 times lighter, and have 15–100 times smaller stowage volume than their mechanical counterparts. The low fabrication costs, as well as reduced launch vehicle size, could result in order-of-magnitude cost savings for missions requiring large apertures.

Figure 8: 3 m and 7 m lenticular antennas built by L'Garde Inc.

Large antennas and similar structures find a multitude of applications. Large antennas for space radio telescopes have been extensively described by Chmielewski and co-workers for the ARISE project [3]. Earth-observing antennas, such as for soil moisture and ocean salinity measurements, are primary customers for inflatable antenna technology in the near term. These new antennas will be characterized by: sizes exceeding 25 meters in diameter, fraction of a kilogram per square meter density, and operating frequencies between 1–100 GHz. NASA's Structure and Evolution of the Universe (SEU) theme needs large apertures for space radio frequency, microwave, and sub-millimeter telescopes. The SEU is also considering a mission to image luminescence created by extremely high-energy particles entering the Earth's atmosphere. Deep space applications will be developed for Solar System Exploration (SSE) and Sun Earth Connection (SEC), and high bandwidth communication systems for Human Exploration and Development of Space (HEDS).

2.3 Human habitats

Since the earliest of times, humans have desired shelter, and in many cases shelter that was rapidly deployable. One of the earliest forms of constructed shelter was undoubtedly the tent, formed, for example, from animal hides draped over branches. The tent made a significant impact on culture, because it now allowed people to be mobile, to leave their caves or other fixed shelters and migrate, following food and water. The tent exists throughout history, for example playing an essential role in military activities, even today. Modern architectural tension fabric structures are highly sophisticated versions of the ancient tent that are used to span large open spaces. The first air-supported roofs sprang up after the Second World War, when dozens of radomes were constructed to cover radar installations during the intensification of the Cold War. Since that time, air supported roofs have found favor in applications where large clear spans are required, notably recreational facilities such as football stadiums and tennis courts.

Terrestrial aerospace applications of membrane/inflatable human habitats are for the most part associated with providing shelter for aerospace support personnel and equipment. Again, tents play a leading role. Recently, hybrid membrane/inflatables have been developed to provide large, clear span space for aerospace vehicle maintenance, particularly for helicopter repair in the field. Curved beams of cylindrical cross-section are fabricated from coated fabric, and inflated on site. The beams span the space to be covered, supporting the membrane skin of the shelter.

A number of intriguing uses of membrane/inflatables are planned for human habitats in space (see Fig. 9). Nearest to earth, inflatables could provide efficient shelter for lunar habitation. Efficient for packaging and lightweight for launch, modules could be inflated on the lunar surface, and then covered with regolith to provide radiation protection for occupants. Inflatable modules have been proposed for space travel as well, for example as modules on planetary rovers or for the International Space Station.

ISS TransHAB   *Internal Configuration*

ISS TransHAB

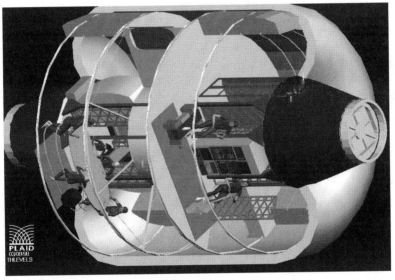

Figure 9: Transhab module designed by NASA.

2.4 Planetary surface exploration

All present planetary rovers are based on the standard Pathfinder Sojourner concept of a four or six-wheeled vehicle that must generally travel around most obstacles. To give a specific example, during a month of operation after its July 1997 landing on Mars, the 35-cm tall Sojourner rover only traveled a total of about 100 meters, and never more than 7 meters a day. The Mars Exploration Rovers (MER) launched in June 2003 are larger than Sojourner and can climb rocks up to 25 cm high. The rovers will move on the surface of Mars at a speed of 5 cm/s.

Membrane technology for surface exploration opens new parameter space. For example, an Inflatable Rover would travel tens of kilometers in a single day, with a range of hundreds of kilometers or more. The use of inflatables to increase speed and range is a critical enabling technology that will allow for robotic outpost development. Functions of inflatable rovers may include transporting other rovers to distant sites, transporting astronauts, and the long-distance transfer of heavy equipment or in situ resources, such as water ice from the Martian North Pole.

The Inflatable Rovers (see Fig. 10) would use novel, large inflatable wheels to climb over rocks, instead of traveling around them, thus enabling the rover to traverse quickly over 99% of the Martian surface. Preliminary tests using commercial nylon balloons as tires, a rigid metal chassis, and a simple joystick control, have shown great promise. Rugged, lightweight inflatable wheels and an inflatable-extendable chassis provide the ability to pack the rover into a small planetary entry capsule. An autonomous control system allows the rover to follow an astronaut or to uniquely climb over most obstacles to designated sites in a Mars-like terrain, while carrying smaller, conventional rovers in cooperative rover studies.

Figure 10: Jack Jones, JPL, with his Inflatable Rover and the artist's rendering of the rover deployment using a balloon.

The large, inflated spherical wheels allow the rover to basically "swallow" smaller rocks, while providing a large contact surface to climb up steep hills or over larger rocks, and to maintain excellent ground contact during windstorms. In fact, the present, simple 20 kg prototype, which uses commercial nylon balloons as tires (Fig. 10), has stood up well to 13 m/s

(30 mph) gusts, which is equivalent in force to 130 m/s gusts in the extremely thin Martian atmosphere (0.006 bar pressure). It requires very low power (18 W) to travel 2000 m/h and can climb steep hills.

In the near future, designs will also be initiated to allow the rover to carry much larger loads, such as two astronauts, several larger rovers, or heavy equipment and in situ resources, such as water ice from the Martian North Pole. A recent, preliminary design of a Mars astronaut transporter system is shown in Figure 11, which evolved from previous Lunar Apollo astronaut rovers. This design will likely be modified to include larger, more rugged inflatable wheels, and may include a removable habitat.

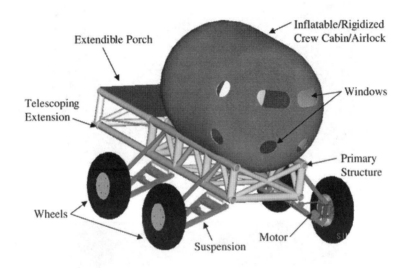

Figure 11: Inflatable Mars Rover trailer developed by a JPL team led by Jack Jones.

Inflatable technology is also critical and enabling in the area of Titan Robotics, since this type of rover is the only one thus far capable of operating on the liquid methane lakes anticipated on Titan. Numerous materials, such as Kevlar, Mylar, and PBO, are known to be capable of functioning well in cryogenic conditions, and the large tires can actually help insulate critical electronics from the frigid Titan surface. This insulating factor can also help prevent the rover from sublimating/melting into icy surfaces, such as on Europa, Callisto, and other moons, including the known polar ice crater on our own Earth's moon.

In the near future, inflatable rovers will also help in the successful long-distance transport of critical equipment and in-situ resources for astronauts, such as the transporting of Mars North Pole water ice, as well as the transportation of astronauts themselves on Mars. Control systems will also allow equipment rovers to follow walking astronauts or develop detached trains of equipment that follow in line.

Witold Sokolowski of the Jet Propulsion Laboratory, working with Mitsubishi Heavy Industries of Japan, also is developing a new alternative to space rigidizable material called the Cold Hibernated Elastic Memory (CHEM) structures (see Fig. 12). This material technology utilizes shape memory polymers in open cellular (foam) structures. The CHEM foams are self-deployable and are using the foam's elastic recovery plus their shape memory to erect structures.

JPL launched two rovers to Mars in 2003. The landers containing the rovers were designed to touch down on the surface of Mars cushioned by large air bags (see Fig. 13). The air bags are an evolutionary design from the Mars Pathfinder. The MER bags are designed for 40% increase in the payload delivery in comparison with the Pathfinder.

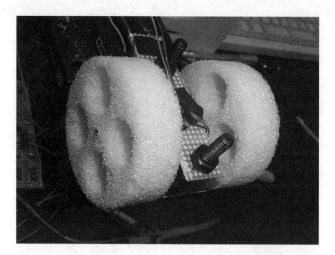

Figure 12: CHEM nano-rover wheels. Outside diameter is 6 cm.

Figure 13: Mars Exploration Rover air bags developed by ILC Dover.

A non-NASA commercial area studied by Federal Fabrics and Fibers is the use of an inflatable rover for land-mine traversing and detecting. With very light mass and a large contact area, the pressure on the ground is below the threshold for mine detonation. Outfitted with land-mine detectors, this rover could potentially help rid the world of the 100 million active, buried land mines.

In the more distant future, it is envisioned that there will be more lightweight, highly packageable equipment operating on surfaces of planets. Such a vision is portrayed in Figure 14, which shows inflatable rigidizable towers for cellular communications, inflatable solar power energy generation stations, in situ resource utilization tanks, rovers, and thin-film solar sails delivering cargo to the planet.

Figure 14: Artist's rendering of inflatable equipment on Mars.

2.5 Radar and reflectarrays

There is a critical need for enabling technologies that will reduce the mass, physical size, and cost of antennas. The inflatable SAR and Reflectarray described in this section represent advanced antenna technology that has the potential for providing an enhanced communication capability with relatively lower cost (1/10), smaller size (1/100 launch volume) and smaller mass (1/2) than current technologies.

A SAR program demonstrates the feasibility of a low-mass inflatable Synthetic Aperture Radar Array Antenna. Figure 15 shows the prototype system, including a flat, multiple-layered, metalized, thin-film micro strip array (a three-membrane assembly), tensioned and supported by an inflated frame that can be rigidized after deployment. The size of the full-scale array is 10 m × 3.3 m. The system was stowed in a rolled-up configuration on the spacecraft bus, and was deployed in a controlled manner via inflation gas. The objective of this program was to develop a functional subscale system that was less than 2 kg/m^2 of radiating area when projected to full scale. The depicted subscale prototype met the requirements and demonstrated the feasibility of the low mass SAR concept. The deployment method and supporting frame concept used in the SAR could also be used for a flexible blanket-type solar array in future developments. That is, the membrane assembly of the SAR could be replaced with a flexible thin-film solar-cell blanket and the system would then act as an inflatable solar array.

Figure 15: Inflatable Synthetic Aperture Radar (SAR) developed by Michael Lou (JPL) and ILC Dover.

The 3-m Ka-Band Reflectarray program is another recent development effort to demonstrate the feasibility of super low mass telecommunication and space-deployed SAR concepts. This 3-m prototype (see Fig. 16) consists of four major subassemblies: (1) the membrane assembly, (2) the rigid frame assembly, (3) the inflatable frame assembly, and (4) the suspension system.

Figure 16: JPL and ILC Dover 3-m Ka-Band Inflatable Micro Strip Reflectarray.

A horseshoe-shaped structure assembled from a straight rigid frame assembly and a U-shaped inflatable frame assembly suspends the reflectarray membrane. The rigid frame assembly is made from graphite epoxy with aluminum end caps. The inflatable frame assembly is fabricated from urethane-coated Kevlar to simulate a rigidizable material in the final application. The membrane support frame is 25 cm in diameter and the feed horn support torus is 7.5 cm in diameter. Three vertical struts grouped within 90 degrees of each other support the feed horn torus. The struts are tapered in diameter, from the larger diameter of the membrane support tube to the smaller diameter of the feed horn torus, to minimize material in the RF path, as well as in the system mass.

One of the critical requirements for reflectarrays is the flatness of the membrane. For this reason many packaging and deployment concepts are considered, with the current configuration being the best for this particular application. Again, similar to the rectangular frame used for the SAR array, the horseshoe frame concept could also be used for solar array deployment.

The main beam of the micro-strip reflectarray, unlike that of a parabolic reflector, can be designed to point at a large fixed angle (up to 60 deg) from the broadside direction. With the reflectarray integrated with low-loss phase shifters, a very large space borne beam scanning array antenna is now feasible. By developing this novel phased reflectarray concept, the complicated beam forming network, high-cost phase shifters, and high-cost transmit/receive (T/R) modules of a conventional phased array are no longer needed. A reflectarray antenna can even be combined with a solar array. Such a system would allow launching very large high power, large-aperture spacecraft on small launch vehicles.

The reliability of such an array is very high. Since each element in the reflectarray is isolated from others, the failure of one element will have insignificant impact on the performance of the complete antenna with thousands of elements. If 1/10 of the total number of elements fails, the drop in antenna gain is only 0.5 dB. The inflatable reflectarray lends itself to very large sizes. A 20-m X-band antenna is feasible. Because it is much simpler to manufacture an inflatable structure, such a structure will be much less expensive and reliable to deploy than conventional mechanically deployed systems. An inflatable "light SAR" would provide new capabilities in target detection and monitoring, foliage penetration, and topographic mapping.

2.6 Solar concentrators

There has been interest in solar propulsion since Kraft Ehricke first presented the concept in 1956. Solar propulsion is an alternative to chemical, electrical, and nuclear propulsion for inter-orbital, lunar, and interplanetary transfer missions. Chemical rockets require both fuel and oxidizer that, while providing high thrust, are extremely heavy and inefficient. Conversely, electrical propulsion is extremely efficient but provides very low thrust values. Nuclear propulsion overcomes many of these shortfalls, but has serious issues associated with safe ground handling and launch.

Only a single propellant is required for solar propulsion, which can provide moderate thrusts and efficiencies, with minimal safety concerns. Solar energy is collected and focused onto a thruster. The single hydrogen gas working fluid is heated and expanded by solar-heated material in or surrounding the cavity. The expanding gas provides thrust without ignition or combustion. Laug and co-workers at the Air Force Research Laboratory, Edwards site, have developed concepts to use membrane/inflatables as the solar concentrators. Similar to a membrane/inflatable antenna, these large double-curved concentrators could be packaged into a small volume for launch, and then inflated on orbit (see Fig. 17).

Solar concentrators can also be used directly to improve solar-electric efficiency. Photovoltaic (PV) cells have a relatively low efficiency, and carrying more photocells is a trade with increased mass. Another approach is to concentrate more sunlight (photons) onto a smaller number of cells. The Naval Research Lab has worked on concepts for a deployable membrane PV concentrator. These planar sheets would be placed on either side of a photovoltaic panel, forming a trough for concentrating sunlight.

Figure 17: 5-m solar concentrator developed by SRS of Huntsville, Alabama.

2.7 Solar sails and sunshades

In the early part of the last century when physicists first began to gain a better understanding of the nature of light, it became apparent that electromagnetic waves could, in certain circumstances, demonstrate properties typical of particles. Photons, or quantized "particles of light", each have an associated momentum equal to h/λ, where h is Planck's constant, and λ is the wavelength. Solar sails operate by using solar photon momentum exchange to accelerate a spacecraft; at 1 AU, the applied force is about 9 N/km^2. As such, a solar sail has 'infinite' specific impulse because it requires no propellant.

Sunlight falling on a large lightweight surface is a highly efficient method of changing the orbital energy of spacecraft. There is no need to carry onboard propulsion or fuel, and thus the reduced mass allows greater payload capacity and much shorter trip times for high-energy missions. The constant low thrust counteracts gravity to enable unique non-Keplerian orbits and new vantage points for space-physics measurements. Eventually, sails that use laser energy beamed from Earth may enable rapid access to all parts of the solar system and beyond.

Solar sails represent one of the few propulsion technologies that can be developed rapidly within the next decade, and lead to dramatic improvements in space exploration capability and affordability. Using solar-photon pressure to accelerate a spacecraft, solar sails enable a large number of very propulsion-intensive missions, from non-Keplerian orbits, to solar polar missions at less than 1 AU, to fast trips to the edge of our solar system.

Advances in thin-film materials, novel high-temperature sail substrates, and light-weight booms, combined with the need for low total mission costs, make sails a high-payoff space-transportation technology. Significant technology development that addresses issues of sail storage, deployment, and control is needed. Developing sails for propulsion applications is synergistic with other work on large gossamer thin-film space structures, such as the James Webb Space Telescope Sunshade, and large inflatable concentrators and antennas. Furthermore, solar sails represent the first step in beamed energy propulsion technology, where reflected laser light or microwave radiation provides the momentum to propel sail craft on interstellar mission. Solar sails are a key to lowering the cost of accessing space beyond low-Earth orbit as well as enabling new science missions.

In the near term, the Team Encounter is planning an imaginative mission to use a sail built by L'Garde to deliver a capsule containing DNA and digital pictures of thousands of program participants beyond the solar system. NOAA is also studying a joint mission with Team Encounter to test the sail technology for "pole sitter" satellites. The NASA New Millennium Program is studying space validation of solar-sail technology for the ST9 mission.

Intermediate applications could see the use of solar sails for fast missions to the outer solar system, heliopause, and perhaps the first mission into the interstellar medium. In the far term, a light sail, which uses light from sources other than the sun to accelerate, may provide the first propulsion technique to start a man-made object on a journey to another star. Sail use has the potential to reduce trip times dramatically because of the very high mission velocities achievable through close solar perihelion trajectories; depending on the sail materials, payload, and configuration, this could be well in excess of 100 km/s for solar sails in the next decade. Similarly, propulsion system mass could see significant reductions as lower areal density materials and advanced support structures become available.

A primary performance parameter for solar sails is their areal density (g/m^2). This parameter is an important measure of sail performance because it determines the acceleration of the sail (i.e., solar pressure [N/km^2] divided by areal density [g/m^2] gives acceleration). Areal density is determined by the thickness and density of the sail material, and the mass of the supporting structure. The term "loaded areal density" refers to the entire sail craft mass, including payload, divided by sail area. Dimensions range from tens of meters for small spacecraft with fairly modest mission velocity increment requirements, to hundreds of meters for more ambitious missions to the outer solar system. Solar sail areal density requirements range from around 20 g/m^2 to perform near-term demonstration missions, to around 1 g/m^2 to accomplish fast missions to the heliopause.

Operating temperature is another figure of merit for solar sails, as it dictates minimum solar distance and therefore maximum achievable acceleration for a given sail areal density. Maximum operating temperature is governed by the sail material's reflectivity and emissivity.

Sail-craft survivability also merits serious consideration by mission planners. Understanding sail performance degradation over time due to space environmental effects – micrometeoroid impacts, radiation, and sail charging – will be critical for successfully completing sail missions.

Sails can carry a spacecraft inbound toward the sun by using the solar-photon pressure to slow down in the direction of orbital motion; the spacecraft then being accelerated inward by the sun's gravitational pull. Spacecraft can spiral outward from the sun by positioning the sail to increase heliocentric orbital velocity. Sails can also be used for inner planet rendezvous missions or for applications that would prohibit more conventional propulsion approaches such as planetary "pole sitters". At Earth, an initial sail deployment altitude of around 2000 km is needed so that atmospheric drag is significantly less than solar pressure. Nevertheless, sails can be used for planetary spiral-out and capture.

There are several solar-sail design concepts that mission planners have considered; square and heliogyro sails represent the designs examined in the Halley Comet Rendezvous and subsequent mission studies of the 1970s. The inflatable sail concept is a recent innovation derived from inflatable antenna and structures technology. Deployment of round, spin-stabilized sails has been demonstrated in space with the Russian Znamya sails deployed by Progress vehicles.

The square sail consists of a thin sheet of metalized plastic stretched over a supporting lightweight boom. Small vanes are located at the corners of the sail; they are rotated to produce differential light pressure for use in maneuvering the sail. Alternatively, the sail can be maneuvered by shifting the center of mass relative to the center of (light) pressure. The World Space Foundation, a non-profit organization that recently has been incorporated into the Planetary Society, built a prototype square sail 880 m^2 in area for demonstrating on-orbit deployment and maneuvering. However, the sail was never flown in space.

The second type of sail, the heliogyro, is spun like a helicopter blade; the thin-sheet sail material is unrolled and stabilized by centripetal acceleration. Maneuvering is accomplished by changing the pitch of the blades. The heliogyro sail is easier to deploy than the square sail, has a greater stability from random disturbances (due to its rotational inertia), but has a slower maneuvering rate due to the rotational inertia. Thus, the two types of sails have different strengths and weaknesses, although the square sail, with its faster maneuvering response, might be favored for missions involving extensive planetary escape and capture spiral orbits.

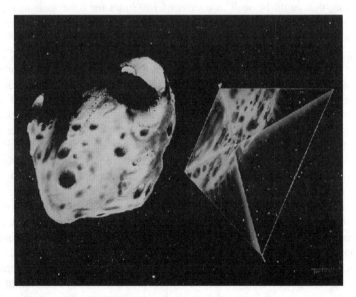

Figure 18: Artist's rendering of a sail rendezvous with an asteroid.

More generally, light sails provide spacecraft propulsion by using photon pressure from any light source; laser sails and microwave sails are two concepts that would require a source for beaming energy to a spacecraft. The source might be either ground- or space-based depending upon the mission requirements. Because of the infrastructure required for beamed-energy light sails, these concepts are longer term and merit lower Technology Readiness Level (TRL) ratings. Beamed energy sail concepts are among the few propulsion techniques that hold promise for interstellar missions; such applications would require kilometer-scale sails with areal densities on the order of 0.1 g/m^2.

Solar sails are being considered for several missions planned in the NASA Sun-Earth Connection (SEC) theme, including a Solar Polar Imager, and the first-generation Interstellar Probe launched to explore the outer reaches of the solar system. Several missions of the NASA Solar System Exploration (SSE) theme would also be greatly enhanced by the use of solar sails, such as missions to comets and the outer planets (see Fig. 18). This technology could also enable large sunshields needed to stabilize and protect large gossamer apertures and other cryogenic telescopes.

ILC Dover designed and manufactured several sail quadrants with deployment systems (see Figure 19). The average sail areal density was 6 g/m^2. The design included rip stops and deployment control systems. The material used for sail was 1 micron thick polyester film with Al/Cr coating. The finished assemblies were 7 m × 7 m × 10 m and 13 m × 13 m × 18 m. Multiple deployment tests were conducted at JPL and ILC.

Figure 19: Solar-sail quadrant developed by ILC Dover.

NASA is currently engaging in technology development for the James Webb Space Telescope (NGST) Mission scheduled to be flown in 2007. This mission, managed by GSFC, envisions a near infrared, 6-m aperture telescope to be positioned at L2 orbit for 5 to 10 years. In order to passively cool the telescope to below 60 K for maximum science return, a very large (up to 32 m by 14 m) sunshield with multiple-layers of thermal membranes was studied. The inflatable design offered several inherent advantages, including lighter weight and smaller launches volume, over its mechanically deployed counterpart. More importantly, an inflatable sunshield will be much less complex (e.g., at least one order of magnitude less number of parts) than a mechanically deployed sunshield. Less complexity leads to higher reliability, and cheaper fabrication and assembly costs.

ILC Dover worked with JPL and GSFC on the JWST sunshield program. The goal of that program was to demonstrate a 1/3-scale model of the JWST sunshield on a shuttle flight experiment named ISIS (Inflatable Sunshield In Space). A scale model was demonstrated in 1G; however, the ISIS program was cancelled and never tested in space (Fig. 20).

Figure 20: ISIS Deployed Configuration.

Figure 21: NGST half-scale sunshield.

The sunshield was a diamond shaped membrane structure that measured approximately 5 × 11 × 1 m when deployed. The system consisted of four layers of membranes that were deployed and supported by four inflatable beams, which later rigidized to provide a permanent structure. The membranes, when stowed, were accordion-folded or "Z" folded into a small packing volume around the bus structure. The roll-up method for controlled deployment and the heat-cured thermoset composite laminates were baselined for this demonstration.

The system shown in Figure 21 was a half-scale model deployed at ILC with a gravity-negation system attached to the sunshield. The booms were rolled and attached to the tips of the membranes and contain deployment control mechanisms. During deployment the booms unroll and dispense the membrane from the packing container in a controlled fashion. At full deployment of the membranes, the booms (aluminum laminates in this case) were inflated to a prescribed pressure to "rigidize" them, and then they were subsequently vented.

Solar sails are being considered for several missions planned in the Sun-Earth Connection (SEC) Division at NASA, including a Solar Polar Imager, and the first-generation Interstellar Probe launched to explore the outer reaches of the solar system. Several missions of the Solar System Exploration (SSE) theme would also be greatly enhanced by the use of solar sails, such as missions to comets and the outer planets. This technology could also enable large sunshields needed to stabilize and protect large gossamer apertures and other cryogenic telescopes, and block out unnecessary light (occulting) for imaging planets near stars (see Fig. 22).

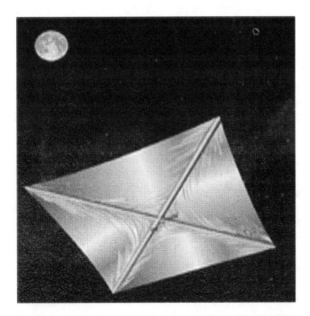

Figure 22: Sail occulter concept by Glenn Starkman, Case Western Reserve University.

2.8 Structural members

Membrane/inflatable structural members may take the form of rods, beams, rings, and the like. These members may find applications individually, in combinations with other structural members, or in conjunction with membrane structures. Research is underway to develop methods for rigidizing these members after inflation/deployment.

Inflatable rods of circular cross-section are fitted with end caps that allow them to be used as struts, or linked to form trusses. The recently launched Inflatable Antenna Experiment (IAE) used three pneumatic rods as struts to connect the antenna reflector to the feed. Prototypes for inflatable trusses go back at least to the 1950s and work at Goodyear on inflatable radar systems.

Besides providing axial resistance as struts, inflated cylinders also have bending rigidity and thus act as beams. An inflated cantilever cylinder can act as a boom for extending the reach of an astronaut. In an inflatable airplane, they can act as wing girders. Curved pneumatic beams were discussed above as being used for structural support in inflatable habitats. Curved beams, closed onto themselves, form pneumatic rings or tori. The IAE used a pneumatic ring to provide reaction for the inflated membrane reflector, and also as the attachment point for the pneumatic struts; other examples are given throughout this chapter as well.

Structures that respond to service loads primarily through membrane action do so typically because of a combination of small thickness and/or low modulus. For thin structures, bending resistance may be orders of magnitude smaller than membrane resistance, such that the former provides only a minor contribution to load resistance, if at all. An important by-product of thinness is that membrane structures are typically no-compression structures. A (possibly localized) buckling or wrinkling will occur upon subjecting a membrane structure to compressive loads, and this becomes a principal design driver. The literature on membrane/inflatable structures members is significant, and has been thoroughly reviewed by Jenkins and co-workers. Two works are of particular interest in the present context. An early interest in inflatable re-entry vehicles motivated a study by Leonard and co-workers in 1960. They reported on an inflatable cantilever cylinder, made simple "strength-of-materials' projections of maximum tip load before collapse, and provided some brief experimental evidence. Main and co-workers conducted a similar investigation on inflated fabric cantilever cylinders. Recent interest in inflatable boom technology has been significant.

Membrane structures rarely exist of and by themselves. They usually require some support structure, especially to carry compression. Examples include the already-mentioned hybrid membrane/inflatable tents and the IAE.

2.9 Telescopes and optics

Deployable space-based parabolic membrane optics is of current interest to NASA and DOD, and in particular to the Air Force Research Laboratory (AFRL). The interest is driven by the potential for large reduction in launch costs, through reduced structure mass and stowed cargo volume. In addition to large space-based optical quality membrane telescopes, this technology can be used for radio and radar antenna, as well as solar power and propulsion systems. Regardless of the use, one stringent requirement for the success of this project is the surface accuracy of the deployed optical membrane.

The surface precision required for optical quality mirrors is rigorous. A typical uncompensated '$\lambda/20$ specification' (i.e., $1/20^{th}$ the wavelength of interest) requires a mirror with a surface precision less than a micron rms. Precise grinding and polishing is essential in the production of conventional rigid optics in order to achieve such tolerances. For space-based applications, rigid optics is limited by both volume and mass, due to launch cargo capacity and thrust capacity. Therefore, in order to produce large space-based optics, a lightweight, deployable but precise structure is necessary to minimize both mass and volume, but maintain high performance.

However, rapid technology developments in wavefront reconstruction and adaptive optics provide an opportunity for the stringent precision requirements to be relaxed somewhat. In particular, holographic spatial light modulation techniques show promise to work in conjunction with membrane optics to achieve the desired performance levels.

When the AFRL began the research into developing deployable optics several years ago, the focus was on inflatable structures comprised of a membrane mirror and highly transparent canopy (lenticular configuration), along with the surrounding inflatable/rigidizeable support structure. The objective was to obtain a near-net parabolic shape by inflating either a plane monolithic circular membrane, or cutting and assembling flat gores such that the final shape was parabolic. Through this research it was determined that the requirements placed on both the transparent canopy and support structure were highly demanding. An alternative means of achieving and maintaining the desired figure needed to be found.

Spin casting of polymer film appears to be an ideal method for producing a near-net shape parabolic membrane that does not require an inflatable lenticular. Spinning mercury has proven effective in creating optically fast primary mirrors for telescopes. To produce the mold, this spinning method could be used with a hardening liquid that cures in a near-net parabolic shape. The solidifying substrate could then be produced atop the mold in the same spin-casting fashion. Finally, optical coatings can be applied such that the coating places tension on the substrate, thereby making it a "semi-rigid" structure capable of maintaining a near-net parabolic shape upon release from the mold. More details are given in *Gossamer Spacecraft: Membrane/Inflatable Structure Technology for Space Applications* [11].

NASA is studying future missions requiring very large space observatories. The long-range goal of the Astronomical Search for Origins and Planetary Systems (ASO) Division in the Space Science Enterprise is to detect and characterize planets in orbit around nearby stars. This grand challenge is a driver for gossamer technology development of large apertures (Fig. 23).

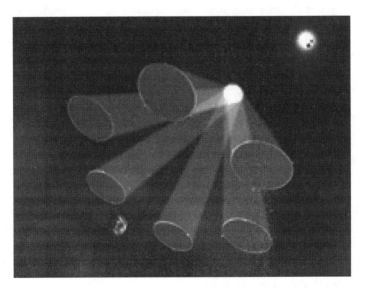

Figure 23: Gossamer telescope concept by Roger Angel and Neville Woolfe of University of Arizona.

Independent of any specific instrument concept, the basic detection physics sets minimum requirements for the optical apertures. Set against the benchmark of the largest ground-based telescopes and the 6-m James Webb Telescope (JWT), terrestrial planet spectroscopic characterization requires a ten-fold increase in aperture area, and low-resolution direct imaging requires an additional 25-fold increase in area. Such large collection area requirements most likely preclude implementing the missions with single telescopes. Rather, such missions are currently envisioned to utilize constellations of large telescopes flying in formation and operating as interferometers.

The basic building block for these systems is likely to be diffraction-limited optical collectors of 20–40-m diameter. One of the critical metrics for such systems is the areal density of the fully loaded primary mirror (optical surface, reaction structure, actuators, and wiring). An areal density of 100 kg/m^2 is typical for conventional telescopes. The JWT is striving to achieve areal densities between 10 and 15 kg/m^2. For future ASO missions, areal densities of 1 kg/m^2 or less are required to enable affordable system architectures. Ultimately, to achieve higher resolution imagery and spectroscopy, even more aggressive architectures with collecting areas equivalent to much larger (100s to 1000s of meters) aperture diameters and much lower areal densities (< 0.1 kg/m^2) will be required.

Large aperture technologies also have direct applicability to the needs of other NASA missions. Large apertures are needed for advanced X-ray, space radio frequency, microwave, and submillimeter telescopes. Large space radio telescopes and Earth-observing antennas, such as for soil-moisture and ocean-salinity measurements, will need great improvements in antenna technology in the near term. These new antennas will be characterized by sizes exceeding 25 m in diameter, fraction of a kilogram per square meter density, and operating frequencies between 1–100 GHz.

Researchers at Lawrence Livermore National Laboratory built and tested a 5-m Fresnel lens in 2002 as part of the Eyeglass project. This lens consists of 72 thin-glass (790 μm thick) panels, aligned and attached together in a foldable, origami-based, configuration. The $f/50$ lens has been optically tested, delivering tight focal spots at several visible laser wavelengths. While this lens demonstrates that large aperture, lightweight (1.7 kg/m^2) diffractive lenses can be made, it was primarily built as a prototype for much larger, space-based lenses; future lenses are expected to be built from thin polymer films, reaching 50–100-m sizes with specific masses of < 0.1 kg/m^2.

Mark Dragovan of JPL has presented a revolutionary design. Dragovan noted that a surface with zero Gaussian curvature is either flat or has the shape of a trough, so that one of the principal curvatures is always zero. Bending along only one axis can form such a surface. If the shape of the surface in the curved direction is a parabola, then a line focus results for an incident plane wave. To produce a point focus, a system of two trough-shaped reflectors properly oriented with respect to each other must be used (Fig. 24).

This layout takes advantage of a two-mirror reflector system where the individual reflectors are parabolic cylinders. The orientation and curvatures of the individual reflectors are chosen so that a point focus results for an incident plane wave. Tensioning a reflective foil over a frame, which has a parabolic contour along one axis and is rigid enough to support the tensioning, forms the parabolic-cylindrical surfaces.

Other applications that could benefit from large aperture technology include high-resolution imagers for land and tropospheric wind studies, radar for Earth and Space Science, deep-space communications, and large-scale solar power generation.

The Hubble Space Telescope (HST) represents the current state of the art in space apertures. The aperture size of the HST is 2.4-m diameter and the areal density of the aperture system is approximately 150 kg/m^2. Technological advances will be needed to archive 20–40-m aperture diameters and less than 1 kg/ m^2 densities. In the area of solar sails it is difficult to specify what the state of the art is, as no solar sail has ever flown. The cost of these systems will also have to be drastically reduced. No firm metrics for cost exist yet, but it is expected that the current level of funding per mission will not increase in the future. Even the most capable telescopes will have to stay within a cost cap of the currently planned telescopes such as JWST or Terrestrial Planet Finder (TPF).

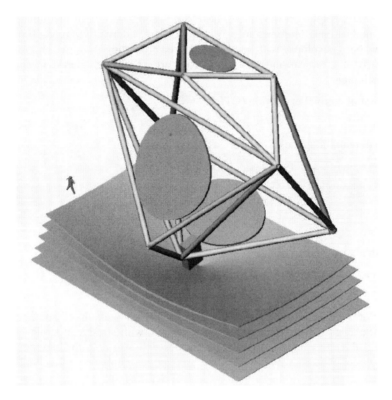

Figure 24: Artist's rendering of DART telescope and a ray trace showing the principle of a dual parabolic reflector.

3 Membrane materials

3.1 Materials for membrane/inflatables in space

Two characteristics are common to all membrane/inflatables: flexibility and lightweight. Both of these are achieved through some combination of low modulus and thinness of the material.

Stiffness scales with modulus and geometric dimension, while weight scales with density and geometric dimension. As an elementary example, consider the axial stiffness of a rod under tension P displacing an amount x, or $P = k_r x$. Here, the stiffness k can be shown to be equal to EA/L, where E is the modulus, A is the cross-sectional area, and L is the length. Note that making the rod thinner decreases the stiffness, as well as the weight. Similarly, the stiffness of a beam in bending is $k_b \sim EI/L^3$, where I is the area moment of inertia of the beam; again, decrease in thickness (decrease in I) decreases both stiffness and weight.

The stiffness of a membrane can be shown to be $k_m \sim Eh$, where h is the membrane thickness. Hence, the thinner the membrane, the more flexible (compliant) it becomes, and consequently the lighter in weight as well. Thus membrane/inflatable materials come typically either as thin polymer sheets or films, or thin-walled polymer tubes.

A number of candidate polymer films exist today. One of the earliest space-based films in use was Mylar, a polyester film usually coated with a thin layer of metal. Mylar was used to construct the Echo series of satellites, and is still used in high-altitude balloons and other space applications today. Kapton, a polyimide, has been a commonly used membrane material for recent space applications. More recently, several polyimide derivatives (e.g., TOR, COR, CP1, and CP2) have been developed with various improved properties.

A number of mechanical and other properties are of special interest in space gossamer spacecraft, including:

- Coefficient of thermal expansion (CTE)

- Modulus

- Low-temperature toughness

- Low-temperature ductility

- Dimensional stability

- Aging

- Surface smoothness

- Bend radius (esp. after coating)

- Potential to be "active" or to be integrated with active materials

- Potential to be "rigidized"

Strength is not included in the list. Although a nominal amount of strength is required, membrane/inflatables will in general be lightly loaded, with stress and strain levels at much less than their ultimate values. Low modulus values will also help to keep stress levels low, even though strain levels may be high. Failure by fracture or collapse is much more likely than tensile failure.

Other properties are also important for different applications. For example, optical properties are important in imaging applications. Electrical and thermal conductivity, and electromagnetic properties may be of interest across a number of applications. Environmental compatibility and survivability are important in nearly every application, and these issues are discussed in a separate section of this chapter.

3.2 Rigidization technology

For any long-term space application, an inflatable structure needs to be rigidized. This is because leaks will be developed through small holes in the walls of the inflatable, created by impacting micrometeoroids and space debris. If the structure is rigidized upon the completion of its inflation deployment, the need to carry a large amount of make-up gas to compensate for leaks can be eliminated.

Since the early 1960s, many researchers have engaged in finding the best rigidization methods for space inflatable structures. These include the development of a number of polymers that can be cured by space environments, such as vacuum, ultraviolet (UV) light, infrared (IR) energy, and low temperature. Several pioneering methods, e.g., solvent-loss systems, were part of these early efforts. In a solvent-loss system, a volatile plasticizer leaves the impregnated fabric that forms the wall of tubular inflatable structure, as soon as the structure is deployed in vacuum.

The desired features for space rigidization include:

- Easily adaptive to high-efficiency packaging
- Compatible with controlled deployment scheme
- No or low space power required
- No or low in-orbit out gassing or contamination
- Predictable post-rigidization configuration accuracy
- Adaptive to ground handling and testing

The space rigidization methods currently under favorable considerations and/or active development include:

- Stretched aluminum laminate
- Hydro-gel rigidization
- Open-cell foam
- Heat cured thermoset composite laminates (thermal heating)
- Thermoplastic composite laminates (passive cooling)
- UV curable composite laminates
- Foam injection
- Inflation gas reaction laminates

Bonding thin aluminum foils to polymer films, such as Kapton, makes sandwich laminates that can be rigidized. While the polymer films provide tear resistance and a gas seal, the aluminum foils are stretched by pressure just above the yield point to provide rigidity of the inflatable structure. Figure 25 illustrates the stretched aluminum laminate method.

To rigidize the cross-section, the structure is inflated to eliminate the wrinkles in the laminate and to a point of just yielding the aluminum. After yielding the aluminum, the Kapton/aluminum laminate is 'rigidized' and will maintain structural integrity. The inflation gas is then vented to space. A typical aluminum laminate cross-section consists of two multiple-layered components: (1) the multiple layer insulation (MLI) blanket, and (2) the support tube laminate. The MLI blanket is similar to that used for thermal-cured laminates, and it is tailored to mission environment and requirements. The support tube laminate is fabricated from layers of Kapton – adhesive – aluminum – adhesive – Kapton laminate. The thickness of each layer and the number of layers used can be tailored and designed to mission-specific requirements.

In addition to taking advantage of the inflation system that is already needed for deployment, this method also offers the following distinct advantages: (1) it can accommodate inflatable tubes that are either rolled up or z-folded; (2) it does not require power; and (3) it has a negligible level of out gassing. More importantly, both of the two component materials, aluminum and Kapton, of the stretched aluminum laminate have a long heritage of space applications. On the other hand, there remains a major shortcoming of the stretched aluminum laminate rigidization method that needs to be overcome. Since, due mainly to packaging constraints, only a very thin (no more than 0.005 inch) aluminum layer can be incorporated in the laminate, the inflatable/rigidizable tubes made of stretched aluminum laminates can only be used to carry relatively low axial loads. For the cases that involve high compression and/or significant bending loads, the thin-walled aluminum laminate tubes tend to fail by local crimping.

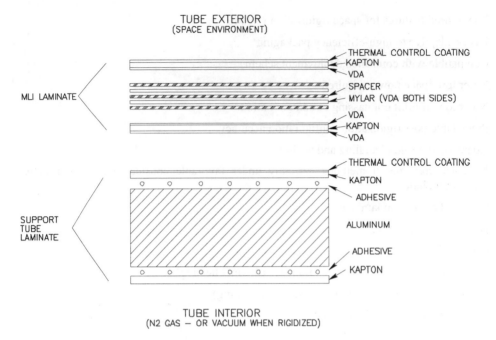

Figure 25: Aluminum laminate rigidization.

Figure 26: L'Garde truss assembly.

Hydro-gel rigidization is a rigidization method that has potential applications to certain classes of space inflatable structures. This method has been successfully applied by L'Garde to develop an inflatable/rigidizable space truss. The truss (see Fig. 26) is formed by tubular elements that are assembled together with complex metal joints. Each tubular element is basically a cylindrical tube that is made of woven graphite fabric and impregnated with a water-soluble resin (hydro-gel). Evaporation of the water content in the impregnated hydro-gel will occur after inflation deployment in vacuum and the dehydrated hydro-gel rigidizes to give structural stiffness to individual tubular elements. Like other solvent-loss systems, one major advantage of the hydro-gel method is that the rigidization process is completely reversible. That is, the rigidized inflatable structure can absorb water, get softened, and be re-rigidized repeatedly to facilitate ground testing and measurements of the flight inflatable structures.

Other on-going space rigidization development efforts include heat-cured composites (thermoplastic and thermoset) at ILC-Dover, cold rigidization at L'Garde, and UV-cured composites at Adherent Technologies. JPL, working with Mitsubishi Heavy Industries of Japan, is also developing a new type of space rigidizable material, called Cold Hibernated Elastic Memory (CHEM). CHEM is formulated by incorporating shape-memory polymers into open-cellular foam. This material has a maximum deployed/stowed volume ratio of 30 and is self-expanded when heated up above its glass transition temperature. This means that a space rigidizable structure made of CHEM does not need an inflation system to deploy.

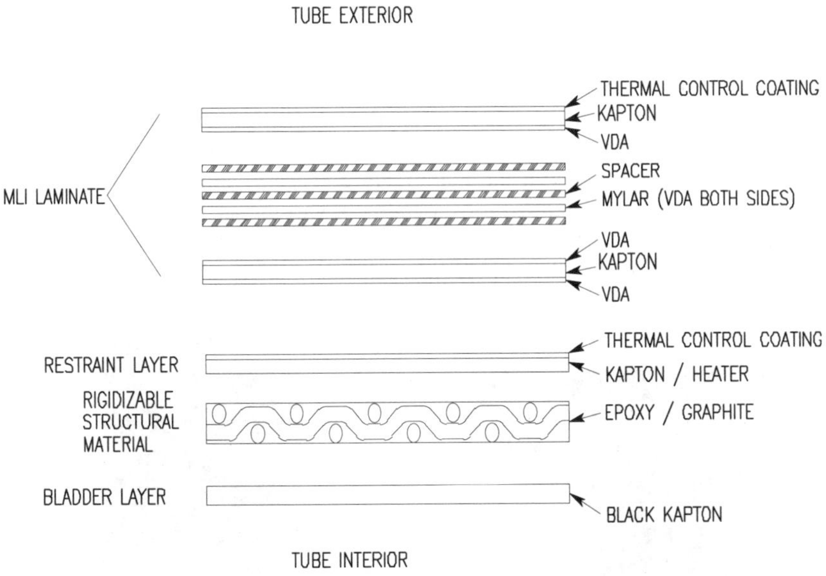

Figure 27: Composite laminate cross-section.

The Thermal Heating method has undergone further development at ILC Dover for potential flight experiments. The composite-laminate system, which consists of thermoset matrix resin and fiber reinforcement such as graphite, is cured or rigidized by heating. The thermoset resin hardens after being heated to a specified temperature and cure time. This rigidization method can be designed to cure from solar energy, or from the spacecraft power, or from a combination of both. The properties of the composite material are consistent with those used in today's spacecraft design. A typical composite laminate cross-section, as shown in Figure 27, consists of two multiple-layered components: (1) the MLI blanket, and (2) the support-tube laminate.

The MLI heating blanket is designed and fabricated from various layers of vapor-deposited aluminum (VDA) Kapton, VDA Mylar, and spacers. The purpose of the MLI blanket is to keep out the harsh space environment and at the same time maintain the required curing temperature inside. The design of the MLI blanket is tailored to the specific mission environment and requirements. The support-tube laminate typically consists of four separate layers: (1) the restraint layer that maintains the shape of the inflatable structure; (2) the heater assembly layer, which provides the proper temperature for deployment and curing (in some designs the restraint layer and the heater layer are combined to become one assembly); (3) the rigidizable composite laminate layer, fabricated from prepreg materials such as epoxy/graphite, is the support structure when cured; and (4) the bladder layer, manufactured from black Kapton, keeps and maintains inflation pressure during deployment. The thermoplastic composite laminates, which use passive cooling as the curing method, has a similar construction.

4 Flexible systems

4.1 Adaptive compensation

The ever-increasing need for higher antenna gains and efficiencies at ever-higher frequencies has led to the consideration of various types of inflatable precision apertures. Recent advances in reflector materials, design, analysis, predictive modeling and manufacturing are expected to yield accuracies almost an order of magnitude higher than present practice for surfaces of <1 mm RMS. However, one of the problems related to high-frequency performance of these inflatable reflectors is the surface distortion caused by thermal effects, in addition to the initial distortion caused by imperfections in the manufacture process, and long-term changes in the material properties. Both of these distortions are slowly varying as a function of time. There is also a problem with accurate pointing of the structure. There are several solutions to this problem, and some combination of technologies will likely prove to be most effective (Figure 28).

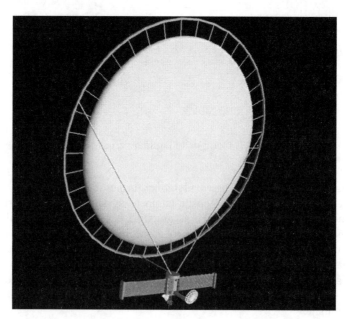

Figure 28: Elements of an aperture system designed for maximum antenna performance: the main reflector with torus, smart support structure, active secondary and electronic feed.

<u>Adaptive secondary reflectors</u> Combining the inflatable apertures with mechanically shaped secondary reflectors will further improve the aperture efficiency, as recently demonstrated on a 3.3-m secondary reflector by Composite Optics (Fig. 29) in a project for the National Radio Astronomy Observatory (NRAO.) The final wavefront correction can be accomplished using phased-array electronic compensation at the aperture focal region. This combined effect of improved primary, adaptive secondary, and phased-array compensation will improve the effective aperture surface accuracy by two orders of magnitude, and is expected to push the inflatable aperture performance into high radio frequencies and sub millimeter applications.

Figure 29: COI's 3.3-m adaptive reflector for 90–900 GHz applications.

<u>Holographic correction</u> One of the most promising methods for active compensation is a passive holographic technique utilized to allow existing reflector technology to be used in the optical spectrum, yielding apparent surface precision in the 1.0-micron range. Thin membrane inflatable reflectors utilizing this technology could be used for space projects requiring large apertures for optics.

<u>Boundary manipulation</u> It has been well proven analytically that manipulating the boundary of certain classes of inflatable reflectors can make significant improvements to their surface accuracy. Initial experimental studies have also verified this effect.

<u>Selective heating</u> It has been shown analytically that temperature gradients over the surface of a membrane/inflatable cut both ways: they may either distort or improve the surface accuracy. Selective heating may be considered as potential future shape control strategy.

<u>Array feed and deformable flat plate (DFP)</u> There have been many studies and experiments that use either array feeds or a DFP (investigated by William Imbriale of JPL) to compensate for reflector distortions. In many cases, especially for the DFP, it is assumed that the distortions are both stable and known, while for the array feed generally an adaptive system has been proposed. The disadvantage of the array approach is that the spread of the energy in the focal plane is quite extensive for modest distortions requiring a large number of feeds. The advantage of the combined approach is the reduction of the number of feeds required for

compensation. The DFP can focus all the energy into a small area in the focal plane. Also, by including a monopulse center feed, accurate pointing information can be obtained. Thus, such a system can provide almost compete restoration of the gain and also provide accurate pointing information to the active control system (ACS).

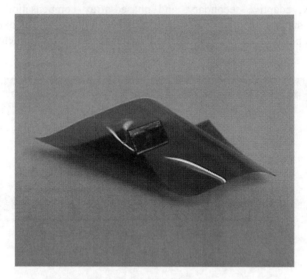

Figure 30: Thin electronics on a Kapton substrate.

4.2 Multifunctional membranes

Miniaturization, multifunctional, full-integration, low weight, and low cost are the major drivers for current and future space structures. Low cost, low launch volume, high-performance space structures may be developed by fully integrating technologies such as "system-on-chip" into the body of the deployable space membrane. In particular, polyimide films offer an outstanding opportunity for integration/packaging of multifunctional devices/chips on lightweight membranes. Today's thick silicon chips are relatively large multilayer polyimide systems. Mechanical integration and functional interfacing is of significant importance and is the foundation of many future space applications. The establishment of the related know-how and systematic study forms the basis of future research in this area. Currently, the technology has been established for reliable attachment of thin (25–35 micron) silicon chips, as well as thin chip-carrying polymer patches, to polyimide membrane (Fig. 30).

Technologies of specific interest in the upcoming years in the area of multifunctional membranes will be:

- Advanced materials and processes for integrating membranes, electronics, sensors, actuators, power sources, and their associated interconnect into a unified and adaptable structure.

- Methodology and modeling techniques needed to optimize materials and process selection for integrating MEMS devices with CMOS electronics.

- Lightweight, distributed power systems, and active or passive thermal-control systems integrated with membrane structures.

- Models will be needed which optimize power-storage and thermal-management designs.

- Materials with controllable surface properties that, when combined with integral control electronics, could adapt to changing environmental conditions or mission needs (e.g., changing optical properties to steer a solar sail).

- Concepts and components for active, adaptive wavefront control systems, including shape control of membrane mirrors, with correction to < 1 wavelength.

- Adaptive systems for measuring and correcting surface figure and wavefront errors, and for controlling structural geometry and dynamics.

- Thinning processes for substrates, and bonding processes for attachment to thin films and membranes.

4.3 Smart structures

One of the most important technology drivers for demonstration of the feasibility of ultra-lightweight inflatable structures is the requirement for reliably maintaining the surface precision during the mission's life. It is impractical, if not impossible, to qualify such large lightweight systems on the ground prior to committing to flight. A basic approach to assure confidence for maintaining the desired surface accuracy on orbit includes integrating actuators and sensors into the precision surface, as well as into the support structure of the inflatable system. The sensors will then be used to evaluate the surface accuracy in orbit and to make the required adjustments, using the actuators during the mission to achieve and maintain the required precision surface. This methodology will provide project managers confidence that requirements for the precision of the surface can be achieved before committing to launching an inflatable structure as part of a space mission.

The performance of inflatable optics and antennas critically depends on surface precision, which is difficult to pre-assure and is affected by service conditions. Emulating biological muscles allows control and reconfigurability of inflatable structures, while benefiting from packageability, low mass, and power. Embedding actuators in membranes addresses the critical need for shape control of inflatable structures.

Recent advances in materials technology have resulted in several possible new actuator and sensors that can be placed on thin membrane material with an actuation range of up to 5%. These new actuator/sensor materials are compatible with polymer membrane materials being considered in current inflatable structures and packaging approaches. Two of the potential materials are a long-stroke piezo-polymer and a thin-film shape-memory polymer.

5 Testing and deployment

5.1 Ground testing

Ground testing of any structural system may be required for the following reasons:

- Physical insight for mathematical model development

Physical testing and experience are often necessary to develop a sense of what parameters should be included in a model. For example, an impact model might require high-speed video of an impact to determine whether rebound of the target or projectile were significant parameters.

- Determination of model data
  Models that attempt to predict the response of real structures will require physical data about the structural system, such as material properties, loads, temperature, etc.

- Validation of mathematical models
  Every mathematical model needs a reality check. Model predictions must be compared where possible to actual physical response.

- Prediction beyond model capability
  Many physical phenomena will exist beyond the current capabilities of mathematical models, due to complexity, size, time, etc., and physical testing of actual or prototype systems is required.

Specific to membrane/inflatables, the following tests are of interest:

- Static loading
  Static-load tests range from determining mechanical material properties (strength, modulus, etc.) to structural component or system response to static loads (stress, strain, deflection). These tests may be time-independent (elastic) or time-dependent (e.g., viscoelastic). Loads may be mechanical forces or thermal loads.

- Vibration or modal
  Vibration or modal tests seek to determine "modal" parameters: natural frequencies, mode shapes, and damping properties. These tests may be at the component or system level. Due to the ultra low weight and flexibility of membrane/inflatables, vibrations tests must always be performed and often require use of a vacuum chamber to simulate the response in space.

- Surface precision
  Since a primary application of gossamer spacecraft is for antennas or mirrors, the characterization of their surface accuracy is important. Test methods include stereoscopic video topography for long-wavelength antennas with results given in mm rms. Optical reflector characterization may consist of Shack–Hartmann local slope measurement, with results given in waves of error.

- Deployment
  At the time of writing, deployment tests have been limited to slow deployment of structural members such as tube and struts, and planar membranes such as sunshields. Full ground deployment of a gossamer spacecraft remains elusive.

- Space environmental
  This testing is discussed further in the next section.

Especially challenging with gossamer spacecraft is the unique need to make test measurements via no contact methods. Due to their extreme low weight and flexibility, contact with the test article may intolerably disturb what is to be measured. For typical membrane materials:

- A strain gage will be much stiffer

- The smallest accelerometers will be orders of magnitude more massive

- Thermocouple leads will be more massive and stiffer

Alternatives to strain gages are optical extensometers for material testing, or optical methods such as moiré or electronic speckle interferometry for general strain measurements. Alternatives to accelerometers are laser Doppler velocimeters (laser vibrometers). Alternatives to thermocouples include infrared thermography. Jenkins and co-workers have demonstrated the use of both laser vibrometry and infrared thermography on gossamer spacecraft.

5.2 Micrometeoroid and debris testing

This testing is intended to provide data on micrometeoroid impact effects on spaced thin-film layers representative of long-life space missions. The James Webb Space Telescope (JWST) sunshield team proposed a comprehensive test plan for micrometeoroid and debris testing. A key issue with respect to the feasibility of the inflatable sunshield concept is the thermal-performance degradation caused by micrometeoroid impact effects. Micrometeoroid impacts can reduce sunshield thermal performance through the damage mechanisms.

Three basic types of tests should be conducted on any membrane structures in particular multilayer structures designed for long life in space:

- Gross-failure test: These tests are for the purpose of (1) providing data on the susceptibility of spaced thin films to gross failure and (2) on the number and size of holes generated throughout the multiple film layers in the sunshield from a single particle impact. Layer-to-layer spacing and impact particle size should be varied. Multiple shots should be made at a given layer-to-layer spacing and impact particle size, to provide data on various impact velocities and to increase the size of the statistical database. Tests should be conducted at a normal-impact angle and utilize multiple square film layers per test shot.

- Shallow-angle test: Shots should provide a check for the development of highly elongated holes that might tear under subsequent stressing. These shots should also measure any increase in the number of particles that impact the second layer.

- Thick-coating test: Shots should be made at normal angle at single film layers with a coating to check for cracking, delaminating, or other impact effects that could degrade performance.

5.3 Deployment/inflation methods

One of the great advantages of membrane/inflatables is their ability to be compactly packaged. That compactness is a double-edged sword, however, since it leads to additional challenges in going from the stowed to the deployed state.

Deployment can either proceed as sequential or parallel, in open or closed-loop control. In sequential deployment, one event is planned to occur at the conclusion of another. Parallel deployment consists of one or more events planned to occur simultaneously. Whether or not the events occur as planned depends on a number of factors, primarily on the adequacy of factors such as engineering, design, fabrication, etc. Here, however, we concentrate on the additional factor of deployment control.

Open-loop deployment control is non-feedback control. For example, in open-loop sequential control, a timer may be set to stage one event after the conclusion (with a possible delay) of another event. However, there is no feedback as to whether the previous event actually concluded, or in what state it left the system if it did conclude. The deployment of the IAE was an example of sequential open-loop control.

Closed-loop control seeks to minimize an error function, given some input, some reporting of the current state of the system (the feedback), and some desired system state. Continuing the example above, under closed-loop control, a new event would not begin until it was determined that the previous event had concluded, and had left the system in the desired state to begin execution of the new activity.

A technique for deployment of membrane/inflatable structural members, such as tubes and struts, is under development. Three techniques currently being investigated are:

- Rollout method

- Mandrel method

- Fan-fold method

In the rollout method, a tube is flattened and rolled out under pressure, analogous to the children's party favor. Judiciously placed Velcro tabs provide sequential open-loop control by supplying resistance for the tube to inflate against. In the mandrel method, a z-folded tube is extruded under pressure over a tapered mandrel. The mandrel provides passive directional control for the tube, as well as friction resistance to control deployment rate. The fan-fold method is similar to the mandrel, utilizing z-folded tubes, but the internal mandrel is replaced with an external framework.

Modeling of membrane/inflatable deployment is in its infancy. Modeling is hampered by the highly nonlinear deformations, displacements, and material properties encountered with membrane/inflatables. Moreover, although the initial and final deployment states may be well defined, it is likely that the intermediate states will be non-unique and non-repeatable.

6 Future directions

It is expected that the focus of future work in the area of flexible structures will be on technology development for solar sails and large apertures. For large apertures the areas of specific interest are:

- Very large, ultra-lightweight (areal density < 1 kg/m^2) optical systems for astronomical telescopes and Earth imagers observing in the sub-millimeter/far IR, IR, visible, UV, and X-ray spectral regions.

- Large deployable and/or inflatable antennas for use in space-based radio astronomy, microwave radiometry, radar, and communications.

Desirable performance characteristics for these systems, and in particular for near-term proof-of-concept technology and hardware development are:

- High packaging efficiency for small launch volume

- Rapid, low-cost manufacturing

- Design traceable to space-qualified materials

- Robust system response to re-pointing of aperture

- High surface reflectivity after repeated deployment

In the solar sail area, the main objective will be to rapidly advance the readiness of key technologies so that a solar sail space flight experiment could be conducted within the next 5-10 years. It is expected that both large apertures and solar sails will rely heavily on multifunctional and adaptive systems. The development of multifunctional and adaptive systems applicable to large, ultra-lightweight deployable or inflatable structures will be very important. To achieve breakthroughs in lowering the cost, launch volume, and mass of future missions, it will be necessary to develop highly integrated multifunctional membranes with embedded thin-film electronics, sensors, actuators, and power sources.

6.1 Material requirements

- A comprehensive membrane/inflatable material property data base, containing what we now know and how well we know it (test methods)

- Better interaction of material scientists with applied mechanicians, system designers, mission planners, etc.

- Multi-functional materials that integrate load carrying, electronics, thermal management, shielding, etc.

6.2 Analysis requirements

- The greatest challenge is to bridge length and time scales, from the nano- and micro-levels to structural-level response

- Better interaction of applied mechanicians with materials scientists, system designers, mission planners, etc.

- Environmental effects such as aging and degradation must be better linked to mechanical property changes, and all are incorporated into predictive models

- Thorough coupling of numerical and experimental analysis needs to occur

6.3 Testing and deployment requirements

- Deployment control
  Closed-loop control is essential, whether sequential or parallel. Passive techniques, such as Velcro, shape-memory materials, and friction resistance need further development. Sensors are required for state measurement. Active actuators and materials need development.

- Shape achievement
  The disadvantages with lenticular systems include the need for makeup inflatant when tears and micrometeoroid punctures occur, and the loss of information caused by the double-pass through the canopy. Non-lenticular methods for achieving service shape need to be developed, such as use of stress coatings on near-net shape membranes, and the use of precision rigidizable materials.

- Shape maintenance
  Sensors and systems to determine the current shape of large membrane/inflatables need to be developed. Considerable effort needs to be made in modeling the deployment dynamics, including employment of stochastic methods. Non-model-based algorithms, such as fuzzy-logic approaches, should be investigated. Integrated material/sensor/actuator systems are required.

- Damping control
  Since membrane/inflatables tend to have high inherent damping, we have not included a discussion of damping control here. However, configurations may exist for certain applications where damping is a significant driver, such as precision instrumentation positioned on the end of a long strut. Hence, some efforts need to be made to explore passive and active damping of such systems.

Acknowledgement

The authors wish to thank NASA for permission to use all of the figures in this chapter.

References

[1]   Basart, J.P., Mandayam, S.A. & Burns, J.O., An inflatable antenna for space-based low-frequency radio astronomy. *Proc Space '94: Engineering, Construction, and Operations in Space IV*, **2**, Albuquerque, NM, 1994

[2]   Cassapakis, C. & Thomas, M., Inflatable structures technology development overview. *AIAA* 95-3738, 1995.

[3]   Chmielewski, A.B. (ed.), *Arise Mission and Science Goals (2nd edn.)*, JPL 99-14, 1999.

[4]   Chmielewski, A.B., Moore, C. & Howard, R., The Gossamer Initiative. *IEEE*, 1999.

[5]   Chow, P.Y., Construction of pressurized, self-supporting membrane structure on the moon. *J. Aerospace Engineering*, **5**, pp. 274–281, 1992.

[6]   Freeland, R.E., Bilyeu, G.D., Veal, G.R., Steiner, M.D. & Carson, D.E., Large Inflatable Deployable Antenna Flight Experiment Results. IAF Paper 97-1.3.01, presented at the 48th Congress of the International Astronautical Federation, Turin, Italy, October 6–10, 1997.

[7]   Freeland, R.E. & Veal, G.R., Significance of the Inflatable Antenna Experiment Technology. presented at the 39th AIAA/ASME/ASCE/AHS/ASC Structures, Structural Dynamics and Materials Conference, AIAA/ASME/AHS Adaptive Structures Forum, April 20–23, Long Beach, California, 1998.

[8]   Grahne, M.S., Cadogan, D.P. & Lin, J.K., Inflatable Solar Arrays – Concept to Reality. *IAF-99*, 1999.

[9]   Grossman, G. & Williams, G., Inflatable concentrators for solar propulsion and dynamic space power. *J. Solar Energy Engineering*, **112**, pp. 229–236, 1990.

[10] Hedgepeth, J.M., Accuracy potentials for large space antenna reflectors with passive structures. *J. Spacecraft*, **19(3)**, pp. 211–217, 1982.

[11] Jenkins, C.H. (ed.), *Gossamer Spacecraft: Membrane/Inflatable Structure Technology for Space Applications*. AIAA Progress in Astronautics and Aeronautics Series, **191**, 2001.

[12] Jenkins, C.H. & Kalanovic, V.D., Issues in Control of Space Membrane/Inflatable Structures. *IEEE Aerospace Conference*, Big Sky, MT, 2000.

[13] Jenkins, C.H., Kalanovic, V.D., Padmanabhan, K. & Faisal, S.M., Intelligent Shape Control for Precision Membrane Antennae and Reflectors in Space. *Smart Matls. Struct.*, **8**, pp. 1–11, 1999.

[14] Jenkins, C.H. & Marker, D.K., Surface Precision of Inflatable Membrane Reflectors. *J. Solar Energy Eng.*, **120(4)**, pp. 298–305, 1998.

[15] Jenkins, C.H., Freeland, R.E., Bishop, J.A. & Sadeh, W.Z., An Up-to-date Review of Inflatable Structures Technology for Space-based Applications. *Space 98: 6th Int Conf & Expo on Engineering, Construction, and Operations in Space*, Albuquerque, NM, 1998.

[16] Leonard, R.W., Brooks, G.W. & McComb, H.G., Structural Considerations of Inflatable Reentry Vehicles. NASA Technical Note D-457, pp. 1–23, 1960.

[17] Rapp, D., Prospects and limitations of technical approaches for ultra lightweight space telescopes. JPL Report D-13975, 1996.

[18] Rogers, C.A., Stultzman, W.L., Campbell, T.G. & Hedgepeth, J.M., Technology assessment and development of large deployment antennas. *J. Aerospace Engineering*, **6(1)**, pp. 34–54, 1993.

[19] Sadeh, W.Z. & Criswell, M.E., A generic inflatable structure for a lunar/Martian base. Space IV, Proc Space '94, Albuquerque, ASCE, pp. 1146–1156, 1994.

[20] Jenkins, C.H., Shape Control of Precision Gossamer Apertures. In: *Electroactive Polymer Actuators*, ed. Y. Bar-Cohen, Chapter 20, SPIE, 2001.

Section V

Compliant Structure Design

CHAPTER 11

Design of compliant structures

C. H. M. Jenkins
Compliant Structures Laboratory, Mechanical Engineering Department
South Dakota School of Mines and Technology, Rapid City, USA

Abstract

Nature has embraced the compliant membrane structure as a central element in higher biological forms. Human-engineered structures have by and large followed the rule of "design with stiffness." This chapter first looks to nature for guidance in the design of compliant membrane structures. In particular, we are led to partition of structural function, structural hierarchy, and low material modulus. Then we examine how these and other issues, such as boundary design and seams, can be illuminated in the design of compliant membrane structures in engineering.

1 Introduction

Every structure is a material. Historically, the term "structure" has conjured up images of structural *form*, such as a truss or a bridge, with the structural *material* relegated to the background. The layperson immediately recognizes the structural form of a truss, regardless of whether it is made from wood or steel (Fig. 1). On the other hand, there are many modern structures, such as the high-altitude balloon shown in Figure 2, which, due to their high compliance, transcend easily compartmentalized topographical descriptions. It is surprising how much the material essence of the structure stands out in the figure.

Prior to the advent of *material engineering*, the structural engineering had little choice but to design the form of the structure, then search for an "off-the-shelf" material to use. Today, however, the ability to engineer the material at the same time as the structural form has changed the landscape of design. Pushing the performance demands of technology ever higher has led to new *material/structural systems* wherein the form and material become indistinguishable – this is indicative of approaching optimal design. Nowhere is this trend more evident than in compliant structures.

Figure 1: The structural form of a truss is unmistakable. The material from which the truss is constructed takes a background role. Is it steel, wood, or polymer?

Figure 2: Artist's rendition of a high-altitude long duration balloon (courtesy NASA). Is this structure or material?

Nature long ago embraced the compliant structure for the highest of biological artifacts. Among the many advantages of compliant structures, perhaps the most significant is the absolute essential need for compliance in the implementation of intelligence. *Of what use is intelligence to a rock?* Increased adaptability and controllability all require increased kinematic degrees of freedom, i.e., increased compliance. The human body is the grand testimony to compliant structural design in nature. Without the flexibility that our fingers, our toes – all of our articulated joints – give us, we would not be able to realize the results of our creative enterprise.

In this chapter we want to illuminate some of the principles behind compliant structure design. Before we do that, we first look to nature for clues regarding efficient structural design.

Figure 3: Stop sign and support. The support has a cross-sectional shape something like this: Π.

2 Cues from nature

2.1 Partition of structural function

In many human-engineered structures, a single component may be required to carry a number of different types of loading: axial tension, axial compression, bending, torsion, static, dynamic, thermal, etc. However, it is very difficult to optimize a material/structural system for a large spectrum of loading types; the fact that a brittle material such as concrete is significantly better in carrying compressive loads rather than tensile loads is an obvious example. Often, the "man for all seasons" design of structural components represents an intentional trade between performance and cost; in other cases, it represents unintentional low-order design.

Consider for example a simple wooden "2X4" used as a beam. Under typical conditions, half the beam cross-section is in tension while the other half is in compression. Strengths of wood are dependent on the loading direction relative to the micro-structural geometry. In the fiber direction (i.e., parallel to the wood grain), the compressive strength is only a fraction of the tensile strength; hence the flexural strength is governed by compression and the beam cannot be fully stressed. Furthermore, if the beam rests on supports, the reaction loads must be carried perpendicular to the grain. Strengths perpendicular to the grain in wood are only a few per cent of the strengths parallel to the grain. If the beam is now sized to carry these bearing loads safely, the structure is pushed even further from optimum.

As another simple example, consider a typical "stop sign support" (Figure 3).

The "open section" (the cross-section does not form a closed curve) of the support is a relatively inexpensive design that lends itself especially well to sign attachment. The support is always required to carry a small amount of static axial and flexural loads, and on a rare occasion must deal with a vehicle impact load (at what level of resistance is not a trivial question!). In some climates, the signs can be subjected to significant wind loads, which will more than likely be of the non-steady variety. Besides the nominal flexural loading due to the mean wind pressure, there is more often than not a torsional loading as well, due to both non-uniform pressure on the sign surface and flow-induced oscillations (*vortex shedding*). The open cross-section of the support in Figure 3 resists torsion poorly; hence it is not unusual to see such signs oscillating rapidly and wildly on windy days.

Figure 4. The wing configuration of the fruit bat is clearly evident.

Where designs require higher performance, such as in aerospace vehicles for example, separating the load-carrying functions to material/structure components most efficiently capable of carrying them is essential. This *partition of structural function* is widely seen in natural systems demanding high performance, such as in animal flight. The wing of a bat is a good example (Fig. 4). The aerodynamic loads on the wing are carried by a combination of tension and compression members. The wing covering is a flexible membrane-like skin that carries pressure loads essentially in tension. Compressive (and some flexural) loads are partitioned to the wing bones. In mammals, sinew and muscle carry tensile loads while bones carry compression. This makes for a highly efficient structure that can approach a fully stressed, minimum weight design. This is, by the way, how modern sailboats are designed (sail and guy wires taking tensile loads, while the mast carries compression and flexural loads). Cable-stayed bridges have been design in a similar way for decades. The micro-unmanned aerial vehicles discussed in this volume by Dr. Ifju rest on this same paradigm of partition of structural function.

2.2 Structural hierarchy

Human-engineered structures exhibit a "hierarchy" of design, that is, a gradation of structural functional. At one extreme, consider a concrete block wall (Fig. 5). Through the thickness of the wall, there is little variability in topology, material, or function, save for the occasional reinforcing rod, perhaps a thin decorative treatment on the inside, and a weather-resistant (and usually decorative) treatment on the outside. At the other extreme, the Eiffel Tower displays a surprising array of structural topology: trusses that themselves make up additional trusses, etc., in a self-similar way (Fig. 6).

Figure 5. Examples of concrete block walls in a building.

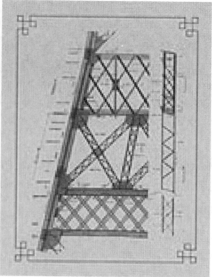

Figure 6: The Eiffel Tower. On the right, note the middle truss that itself is made up of trusses (from http://www.tour-eiffel.fr/teiffel/uk/)

Structural hierarchy is a hallmark of biological systems. Its importance is several fold. For one, structural hierarchy allows for variability in structural response at a much finer scale than would otherwise be possible. It allows for greater design freedom in layout, in reaching optimality. Optimizing a block wall is difficult because the smallest practical module, such as the block itself, is rather large on the scale of stress variation. The partition of structural function mentioned above is only possible when structural hierarchy is available.

2.1 Low elastic modulus

In many materials (at least in their elastic regime), whether natural or synthetic, stress and strain are related in such a way that if the strain increases so does the stress. However, the magnitude of the stress depends very much on the material's modulus or inherent stiffness. If the modulus is high, then even small increases in strain will result in high stress levels. Low-modulus materials can allow for large changes in strain while still keeping stress low. *Strength failures*, i.e., where the maximum stress in a structure exceeds a critical material strength, are less likely to occur in low elastic modulus materials.

Low elastic modulus materials usually allow for greater stress redistribution around stress concentrations, thus again reducing strength failures. Spider webs are an excellent example in nature. As load-carrying elements become damaged or scissioned, the low modulus of the threads allow a major shape readjustment of the web; this allows for reduced stress in any of the remaining threads and continuation of prey capture functions [1]. In human-engineered artifacts, pneumatic tires represent good examples. Due to their low elastic modulus, the tire deforms around an object, such as a rock, rather than trying to resist with stiffness and high stress (Fig. 7).

Figure 7: Tire testing using a machine (from www.mts.com).

Low internal stress also reduces demands on the boundary supports. For equilibrium, boundary forces must balance the net internal forces (nominally stress times area). Again, the spider web is a good example. Webs may readily be attached to tree leaves or blades of grass due to the low internal stress.

We now explore these and other issues as they relate to the design of compliant membrane structures.

3 Issues in the design of membrane structures

3.1 Form finding

Membrane structures deform largely to adjust to loading, so as to carry loads tangentially within the membrane "skin"; the deformation tends to minimize surface area as well. Fine examples exhibited in nature are bubbles (Fig. 8). It is well known that bubbles take forms that have minimum surface area [2], and they carry distributed pressure loads by surface tension. Form finding in nature generally has recently been addressed [3].

A planar membrane of circular boundary subjected to a central concentrated load normal to its surface tries to form a conical surface, a minimum surface with straight "fibers" in the meridional direction. Edge curvature in a plane membrane is possible with in-plane loading, due to Poisson contraction.

Form-finding algorithms in human-engineered membrane structures have been under development for many years [4]. An equilibrium solution is sought under possible large rigid body and elastic deformation. For these reasons, psuedo-dynamic techniques are often used, such as the method of dynamic relaxation. Often of interest is the "pattern cutting" problem, i.e., the determination of the flat pattern that, when cut and assembled, leads to the final complex form under a given initial loading. In this case, one essentially solves the "inverse" problem, going from the final configuration to the initial configuration.

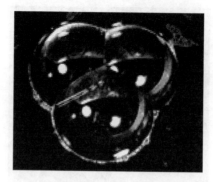

Figure 8: Three bubbles in contact. Each surface is a minimum surface.

3.2 Seams

A likely place for structures to fail is at an interface, i.e., at geometric or kinematic discontinuities. This is due to a number of factors, including generation of stress concentrations at the interface (e.g., abrupt change in load path and/or load-carrying area) and/or faulty manufacturing of the interface (poor adhesion, loss of bolt torque, etc.).

Seams in membranes, particularly large membranes, are often a necessary evil of fabrication. Fabrication of large monolithic membranes is extremely difficult. Examples of seam failures in compliant membrane structures are common – failure of seams in clothing is an obvious example (Fig. 9).

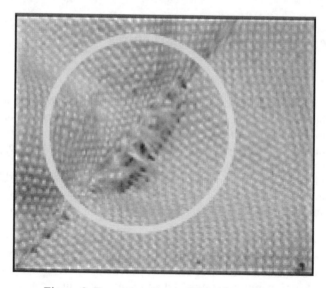

Figure 9: Example of seam failure in a fabric.

In an inflatable arena (Fig. 10), the seams represent a discontinuity in stiffness (the seam being stiffer than the parent *gore* material joined together at the seam) that may be of concern due to loss of prestress (see discussion under Wrinkling below); in a large gossamer space antenna (Fig. 11), the seams cause wrinkling that may lead to loss of performance.

Figure 10: Wrinkles are evident in between seams at the University of New Mexico inflatable tennis arena.

Figure 11: Left: ten-meter diameter inflatable antenna demonstrator at the Air Force Research Laboratory. Right: zoom of the reflector surface showing the wrinkling in the seam area in the right center of the picture.

Joint design has been well studied for decades [5]. Joint symmetry, particularly perpendicular to the loading plane is important to keep stresses low; e.g., single or symmetric doubler joints rather than single lap joints. Also important is to make gradual transitions into the joint and associated geometry changes; tapered joints are examples.

In principal, these design guidelines apply as well to seams in compliant membrane structures, but may be difficult to implement in practice, e.g., in tapering the joints. In precision membrane structures, active control integrated into the seams may be required [6 - 9].

3.3 Wrinkles

The lack of bending rigidity in compliant membrane structures, due to their extreme thinness and/or low elastic modulus, leads to an essentially under-constrained structure that has equilibrium configurations only for certain loading fields. Under other loading conditions, large rigid-body deformations can take place. In addition, these same characteristics lead to an inability to sustain compressive stress. All of this leads to the unique behavior of membrane wrinkling (see Chapter 3 in this volume and [10, 11] for a complete discussion).

Negative aspects of wrinkling include loss of stability, loss of prestress, loss of performance, and reduced aesthetics. For example, anyone who has ever attempted to tow another car with a rope knows that you do not want to accelerate the lead car when the rope is slack – very high dynamic forces result (leading to possible rope failure or bumper loss!). One typically prestresses the rope first before applying the full vehicle load.

Several design rules can be stated.

- Carry compression with compression elements: The sail and mast system mentioned earlier is a good example.

- Minimize shear loading: Any shear loading can always be resolved into a combination of tension and compression (the latter being unable to be accommodated by the membrane); one option is the use of a region surrounding the boundary with sufficient compliance to allow for shear strain mismatch (see Fig. 12).

Figure 12: Shear-compliant border in a plane-membrane concentrator developed by SRS Technologies for the Naval Research Laboratory. If the membrane had fixed boundaries and were subjected to thermal expansion or contraction, the shear-strain mismatch would result in a compressive stress. The shear-compliant boundary minimizes that issue.

- Minimize boundary motion: Movement of the boundary can lead to wrinkling; the shear loading discussed above is an example. An obvious example is the wrinkling seen in a Mylar party balloon (Fig. 13). In this case, the diameter of the originally plane shape decreases due to the boundary moving inward during inflation. This leads to compression in the membrane and the observed wrinkling.

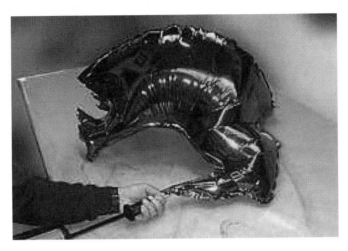

Figure 13: Boundary wrinkling in a common party balloon.

- Biaxial stress state to counteract Poisson contraction: A plane membrane pulled in tension may still exhibit wrinkling due to compression resulting from Poisson contraction (the inevitable reduction, for most materials, in dimension transverse to the extensional direction). A tensile load in the transverse direction must counteract this natural contraction, hence leading to a state of biaxial tension.

3.4 Boundaries

Some issues related to boundary effects were discussed in the previous section on wrinkling. Several additional issues are presented below.

- Low elastic modulus minimizes boundary requirements: Low elastic modulus was discussed previously, including the effects on boundary requirements. Suffice it to say that low membrane stress translates to low boundary force, with concomitant reduction in boundary mass (lower strength and/or stiffness requirements translate to less material required).

- Pre-shaping minimizes boundary requirements: Having to apply loads of any type, be they in-plane or transverse, to shape a membrane requires a corresponding reaction at the membrane boundary. Pre-shaping or *net-shaping* of the membrane has great potential to minimize those reactions and thus minimize boundary mass. Several methods are possible, including blow-forming, rigidization methods, and use of stress coating [12].

- Clamped vs. pinned: It is easy to show that for a true membrane, i.e., a material/structural system devoid of any bending rigidity, there is no difference between clamped and pinned boundary conditions. Even for thin elastic sheets that do exhibit some small bending rigidity (thin paper, for example), in many applications the difference between the two conditions can be ignored.

- Cable boundary: Cable boundaries (aka "catenary boundaries") have been used to support planar membranes without introducing shear. A flexible rope or cable runs in a pocket or sleeve in the membrane, the idea being to avoid shear at the interface. In practice, however, even small friction or misalignment between the membrane and cable can induce wrinkling in compliant membrane structures.

3.5 Active control

Good engineering demands that the first level of control be accomplished by passive measures: addition of intrinsic material damping is an example. However, in many applications, more aggressive measures must be taken, requiring external energy directed to the membrane, which is then converted to some membrane action (e.g., change of shape). Active control (other than the null case of "open-loop" control) requires both sensors and actuators. Incorporating sensors and actuators into compliant membrane structures is unlike what is encountered with more typical stiff structures, especially with regard to sensor/actuator "access" and "influence" [13].

For compliant membrane structures, *access* for sensors/actuator placement can be severely limited. Due to the extreme compliance of these structures, sensors/actuators can significantly disturb the surface figure merely by their placement on the membrane surface alone. The local stresses induced by the adhesive bonds, and the increased stiffness added by the sensor/actuator and adhesive, lead to local deformation in the vicinity of the sensor/actuator. This results in a phenomenon referred to as *print through*. For many applications, the local tilt deviation that can be tolerated in the surface may be on the order of a few tens of microradians, and print through is unaccepable.

In general, the effect on performance of discrete actuators contacting the surface of the membrane is undesirable (although not comprehensively quantified at this time). Hence the access for actuators distributed over the membrane surface is severely limited, if non-existent. Control methods that exploit the membrane boundaries or that act without contact at all are indicated.

The other issue to be considered alongside of sensor/actuator access is the *influence* of an actuator at a particular location. In the case of membranes, their extreme compliance can dramatically enhance the influence of a given actuator. The influence can be described by an *influence function* $\mathtt{I}$ that relates the spatial effectiveness of the actuator to the energy applied, time, and various other configurational and material parameters:

$$\mathtt{I} = \mathtt{I}(E, t; \boldsymbol{r}, \boldsymbol{x}(\partial), \boldsymbol{D}, h, a, \ldots) \tag{1}$$

where a and h are characteristic dimensions like aperture diameter and thickness, respectively, and

$\boldsymbol{D}$ material property tensor

E applied actuation energy

$\boldsymbol{r}$ position vector

t time

$\boldsymbol{x}(\partial)$ aperture response at the boundary

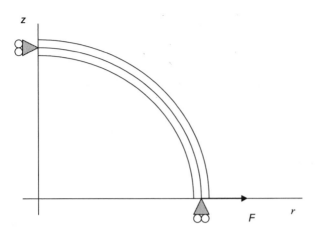

Figure 14a: Schematic of the cross-section of a doubly curved membrane under the influence of a boundary force *F*.

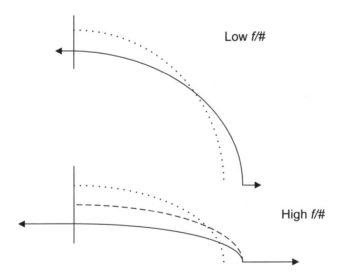

Figure 14b: For an equivalent boundary displacement, a reduced force is required as the f/# decreases, due to lower tangential force component. Moment equilibrium requires increased apex translation as boundary force increases. (The "*f/#*" or "*f*-number" is a measure of the membrane curvature – the higher the *f/#* the shallower the curvature.)

In a plate or shell structure, transverse discrete loads are resisted in a relatively localized fashion by the significant inherent bending stiffness provided. Hence the unit influence function for such structures is rather narrow, resulting from the rapid decay of the load response. On the other hand, in membrane structures, which cannot resist loads by localized bending resistance (since the bending stiffness is extremely low), greater global deformation of the structure is required for equilibrium. Hence the influence function of a membrane structure is relatively broader with much less rapid spatial decay [14].

There are two general choices for sensor/actuator placement: at the boundaries of the membrane or distributed over its surface. The boundaries are a natural choice, due to the need to interface the membrane with the support structure, and apply to flat or curved concepts alike. Curved membranes may require additional shaping afforded by surface actuation (e.g., electrostatic actuation).

The interface between the membrane reflector and structural support system is an ideal place to add active elements, since by definition there must be some physical connection between the two. Jenkins and co-workers have shown in numerous papers that boundary control can be an effective strategy to improve figure accuracy [15, 16].

Since a membrane cannot provide bending stiffness to resist boundary motions locally, the resulting *influence* of a given boundary action can be significantly greater over the surface of the membrane than for a shell structure. In fact, any locally applied couple must be enforced by global moment equilibrium, and resisted in part by global motion of the membrane (Fig. 14). In principal, the global motion could be quite large, but in practice it may be mitigated by such factors as pressure loads, circumferential (hoop) restraint, and some small bending rigidity.

4 Conclusion

Natural structures must be efficient structural designs: efficient in material usage, implementation of intelligence, and energy cost to build, maintain, and transport. It is clearly evident that nature has embraced the compliant membrane structure as critical to development of the higher biological systems. In this chapter we have examined several key factors of natural compliant design and then explored how these concepts may be used to guide human-engineered material/structural systems. Hopefully, future engineered systems will be improved by this knowledge.

References

[1]   Jenkins, C.H. & Alam, M.S., Use of Experimental Mechanics in Biomimetic Structural Design, *SEM Annual Conference*, Milwaukee, WI, 2002.
[2]   Otto, F. (ed.), *Tensile Structures*, MIT Press, 1973.
[3]   Bejan, A., *Shape and Structure from Engineering to Nature*, Cambridge University Press, 2000.
[4]   Leonard, J.W., *Tension Structures*, McGraw-Hill, 1988.
[5]   Hart-Smith, L.J., Design of adhesively bonded joint, *Joining Fibre-Reinforced Plastics*, ed. F.L. Matthews, Elsevier Applied Science: London & New York, 1987.
[6]   Jenkins, C.H., Kalanovic, V.D., Padmanabhan, K. & Faisal, S.M., Intelligent Shape Control for Precision Membrane Antennae and Reflectors in Space, *Smart Mater. Struct.*, **8**, 1-11, 1999.
[7]   Duvvuru, H. & Jenkins, C.H., Active Seam Control of Gossamer Apertures, *48th SPIE Int. Symp. Optical Science and Technology*, San Diego, CA, 2003.
[8]   Duvvuru, H., Hossain, A. & Jenkins, C.H., Modeling of an Active Seam Antenna, *4th Gossamer Spacecraft Forum, 44th AIAA/ASME/ASCE/AHS/ASC Structures, Structural Dynamics, and Materials Conference*, Norfolk, VA, 2003.

[9] Salama, M. & Jenkins, C.H., Intelligent Gossamer Structures: A Review of Recent Developments, *Gossamer Spacecraft Forum, 42nd AIAA/ASME/ASCE/AHS/ASC Structures, Structural Dynamics, and Materials Conference*, Seattle, WA, 2001.

[10] Jenkins, C.H. & Leonard, J.W., Nonlinear Dynamic Response of Membranes: State of the Art, *Appl. Mech. Rev.*, **44**, 319-328, 1991.

[11] Jenkins, C.H., Nonlinear Dynamic Response of Membranes: State of the Art -- Update, *Appl. Mech. Rev.*, **49(10)**, S41-S48, 1996.

[12] Jenkins, C.H. (ed.), *Gossamer Spacecraft: Membrane/Inflatable Structure Technology for Space Applications*, AIAA Progress in Astronautics and Aeronautics Series, **191**, 2001.

[13] Jenkins, C.H. Shape Control of Precision Gossamer Apertures. In: *Electroactive Polymer Actuators*, ed. Y. Bar-Cohen, SPIE, Chapter 20, 2001.

[14] Hossain, N.A., Jenkins, C.H. & Hill, L.R., Analysis of a Membrane-Modified Perimeter Truss Mesh Antenna, *48th SPIE Int. Symp. Optical Science and Technology*, San Diego, CA, 2003.

[15] Jenkins, C.H., Marker, D.K. & Wilkes, J.M., Improved Surface Accuracy of Precision Membrane Reflectors Through Adaptive Rim Control, *1998 AIAA Adaptive Structures Forum*, Long Beach, CA., 1998.

[16] Jenkins, C.H., Ash, J.A., Wilkes, J.M. & Marker, D.K., Mechanics of Membrane Mirrors, *IASS-ICAM 2000 Computational Methods for Shell and Spatial Structures*, Crete, Greece, 2000.

WIT PRESS

New Journal from WIT Press

Design & Nature
A Transdisciplinary Journal Relating Nature, Science and the Humanities

Editors: **C.A. BREBBIA**, *Wessex Institute of Technology, UK and* **S.C. BURGESS**, *University of Bristol, UK*

This journal will act as a forum for researchers studying nature and its significance to various aspects of modern scientific thought and design. Today, the huge increase in biological knowledge and developments in design engineering systems, together with the virtual revolution in computer power and simulation modelling, have all made possible more comprehensive studies of nature. Scientists and engineers now have at their disposal a vast array of relationships for materials, mechanisms and control.

Providing a channel of communication between all those working in this exciting new discipline, the **Design & Nature** journal will be published quarterly both online (ISSN: 1744-3679) and in paper format (ISSN: 1744-3687).

For further information please contact:
harnold@witpress.com.

Nature and Design

Editors: **M.W. COLLINS**, *London South Bank University, UK,* **J.A. BRYANT**, *University of Exeter, UK and* **M.A. ATHERTON**, *London South Bank University, UK*

This volume provides a comprehensive introduction to the common scientific laws of both the natural and engineered worlds. As well as straightforward engineering design and biology, it also features mathematics, physics, chemistry, thermodynamics, biomimetics, medical engineering and history of science. The individual chapters are intended to be personal 'flashes' of illumination, combining authority, inspiration and state-of-the-art knowledge.

Contents: What is Design?; Mathematics in the Natural World; The Laws of Thermodynamics – Cell Energy Transfer; Robustness and Complexity; D'Arcy Thompson – Nature and Design Through Growth and Form; Design in Plants; The Tree as an Engineering Structure; The Homeostatic Model as a Tool for the Design and Analysis of Shell Structures; Adaptive Growth; Optical Reflectors and Antireflectors in Animals; A Medical Engineering Project in the Field of Cardiac Assistance – A Lumped-Parameter Model of the Guldner Muscle-Powered Pump Trainer and its Use with a Ventricular Assist Device; Leonardo da Vinci; The Evolution of Land-Based Locomotion – The Relationship Between Forma and Aerodynamics for Animals and Vehicles with Particular Reference to Solar Powered Cars; Creativity and Nature.

Series: Design & Nature, Vol 1

ISBN: 1-85312-852-X   2005   360pp
£133.00/US$213.00/€199.50

WITPress
Ashurst Lodge, Ashurst, Southampton,
SO40 7AA, UK.
Tel: 44 (0) 238 029 3223
Fax: 44 (0) 238 029 2853
E-Mail: marketing@witpress.com

Flow Phenomena in Nature

A Challenge to Engineering Design

Editor: R. LIEBE, Siemens Power Generation, Mülheim, Germany

Do we have an adequate understanding of fluid dynamics phenomena in nature and evolution, and what physical models do we need? What can we learn from nature to stimulate innovations in thinking as well as in engineering applications? Concentrating on flight and propulsion, this unique and accessible book compares fluid dynamics solutions in nature with those in engineering. The respected international contributors present up-to-date research in an easy to understand manner, giving common viewpoints from fields such as zoology, engineering, biology, fluid mechanics and physics.

Contents: Introduction to Fluid Dynamics; Swimming and Flying in Nature; Generation of Forces in Fluids - Current Understanding; The Finite, Natural Vortex in Steady and Unsteady Fluid Dynamics - New Modelling; Applications in Engineering with Inspirations From Nature; Modern Experimental and Numerical Methods in Fluid Dynamics.

ISBN: 1-84564-001-2   2005   apx 800pp
apx £195.00/US$312.00/€292.50

Design and Information in Biology

From Molecules to Systems

Editors: M.W. COLLINS, London South Bank University, UK, J.A. BRYANT, University of Exeter, UK and M.A. ATHERTON, London South Bank University, UK

This book complements and extends the scope of **Nature and Design** (see previous page).
Partial Contents: Genomes, Genes and Proteins; The Human Genome Project; Green Grass, Red Blood, Blueprint; Flight; The Company as a Living System; Insect Observations and Hexapod Design.
Series: Design & Nature, Vol 2

ISBN: 1-85312-853-8   2005   apx 300pp
apx £99.00/US$158.00/€148.50

WIT eLibrary

Home of the Transactions of the Wessex Institute, the WIT electronic-library provides the international scientific community with immediate and permanent access to individual papers presented at WIT conferences. Visitors to the WIT eLibrary can freely browse and search abstracts of all papers in the collection before progressing to download their full text.

Visit the WIT eLibrary at
http://www.witpress.com

Optimisation Mechanics in Nature

Editors: **M.W. COLLINS, D.G. HUNT** and **M.A. ATHERTON**, *London South Bank University, UK*

This book comprises a study of the two great organic solids in Nature, namely wood and bone. The common scientific laws which act in parallel for both natural and man-made materials are detailed as wood and bone are studied in their natural structural environment as well as in the fields of engineering structural analysis and medical analysis. The relationship between them enables wood to be used in engineering structures and man-made materials to be used as scaffolding for tissue restoration in the human environment. The 'two-way traffic' relationship explored in this volume is termed biomimesis, a modern development of the ancient Greek concept of mimesis - the man-made imitation of nature.
Contents: Preface; Wood as an Engineering Material; Uniform Stress - A Design Rule For Biological Load Carriers; Nature and Shipbuilding; The Structural Efficiency of Trees; Application of the Homeostasis Principle to Expand Gaudí's Funicular Technique; Bones - The Need For Intrinsic Material and Architectural Design; Restoration of Biological and Mechanical Function in Orthopaedics - A Role For Biomimesis in Tissue Engineering; Design in Nature.

Series: Design & Nature, Vol 4

ISBN: 1-85312-946-1   2004   176pp
£70.00/US$112.00/€105.00

Design and Nature II

Comparing Design in Nature with Science and Engineering

Editors: **M.W. COLLINS**, *London South Bank University, UK and* **C.A. BREBBIA**, *Wessex Institute of Technology, UK*

Containing the proceedings of the Second International Conference on Design and Nature, this book brings together contributions from researchers working around the world on a variety of studies involving nature and its significance for modern scientific thought and design.
Over 55 papers are featured and these span the topics: Architectural Design and Structures; Architecture and Sustainability; Acoustics; Biology; Biomimetics; Design Philosophy and Methods; Human Biology and Medicine; Materials; Nature and Architectural Design; and Space.

Series: Design & Nature, Vol 6

ISBN: 1-85312-721-3   2004   648pp
£186.00/US$298.00/€279.00

Find us at
http://www.witpress.com

Save 10% when you order from our encrypted ordering service on the web using your credit card.

We are now able to supply you with details of new WIT Press titles via E-Mail. To subscribe to this free service, or for information on any of our titles, please contact the Marketing Department, WIT Press, Ashurst Lodge, Ashurst, Southampton, SO40 7AA, UK
Tel: +44 (0) 238 029 3223
Fax: +44 (0) 238 029 2853
E-mail: marketing@witpress.com

All prices correct at time of going to press but subject to change.
WIT Press books are available through your bookseller or direct from the publisher.